Introduction to Meteorology

INTRODUCTION TO

Meteorology

SVERRE PETTERSSEN, Ph.D.

Professor of Meteorology, the University of Chicago
Former Professor of Meteorology, Massachusetts Institute of Technology
Head of Upper-air Branch, British Meteorological Office
Chief of Norwegian Weather Forecasting Service
Director, Scientific Services, U.S. Air Force Weather Service

Second Edition   1958

McGRAW-HILL BOOK COMPANY, INC.

NEW YORK   TORONTO   LONDON

THE MAPLE PRESS COMPANY, YORK, PA.

Preface

The first edition was written seventeen years ago in response to a demand for an introductory text to serve in the wartime training programs. The long life which the book has enjoyed may, perhaps, be taken to indicate that it has met a wider need. In the meantime, meteorological research has made great strides, and knowledge of weather and climate has found applications in all walks of life. As a result, this second edition has been reoriented and completely revised.

The present text addresses itself to readers who wish to make a first acquaintance with the atmosphere. It is written for students who are considering meteorology as a profession and wish to know what the atmosphere has to offer in the way of interesting work and problems. It is written also for students in geography, agriculture, aviation, and various industries who seek to know the broad aspects of weather and climate and the manner in which they affect life and livelihood. The reader will find that the atmosphere does not just rest on the earth's surface but communicates freely with it. It is not going too far to say that the processes which determine weather and climate are intimately related to the composition and configuration of the earth's surface. Much space is devoted to the interactions between the earth and the atmosphere, the manner in which the distribution of oceans, continents, mountain ranges, etc., affects weather and climate, and how these, in turn, make their impressions upon our environment.

It has been my purpose to provide a general introductory text from which the instructor may choose to suit the purpose of his course. In a few places, simple mathematical expressions have been used to emphasize certain numerical relationships which are important for students who wish to go on to more advanced studies. However, readers who have developed "negative emotional responses" to symbols should not be too greatly concerned, for the messages that the formulas contain are also contained in the text and the diagrams.

Since meteorology covers a wide field, it has not been possible to discuss all its branches here. While a rainbow may be far more fascinating than the rain, and the sounds of the atmosphere may be more interesting than its gases, optical and acoustical phenomena have been left out altogether. The reason is that they are not of central interest and are better reserved for more specialized books. Weather forecasting, which is one of the major branches, has barely been touched upon, for this is a highly technical subject and belongs to advanced manuals and texts.

Since the book is on the elementary level, it does not contain references to the technical literature. Instead, I have added a list of recent books which I have found to be useful or entertaining. I have also added explanations of technical terms which are commonly used in meteorology.

In conclusion, I wish to express my thanks to Dr. C. H. B. Priestley for his help in reading several chapters in the manuscript stage and for supplying some of the material discussed in Chapter 6. My grateful thanks are due to the many colleagues who have allowed me to reproduce their diagrams.

Sverre Petterssen

Contents

1

The Atmosphere

That invisible and odorless something which we breathe, which sustains life and fire and produces an infinite variety of scenic nuances, is what we call air. We may say that natural air consists of dry air, water vapor, and various kinds of salts and dusts. It is convenient to discuss the dry air first.

Composition of Dry Air. In their speculative philosophy the Greek savants regarded air as one of the four elements (air, fire, water, and earth), and all other substances were explained as combinations of these elements. In our time it is well known that what we call air is a mechanical mixture of a variety of individual gases. This knowledge was gained through a series of discoveries, and each of these has marked a milestone in the progress of the physical sciences. While water vapor was recognized by Aristotle (384–322 B.C.) as being something different from ordinary air, it was only about 2,000 years later that it became evident that dry air was made up of component parts. The story begins with John Mayow (1643–1679), who conducted some experiments which led him to conclude that dry air consisted of two parts, one that sustains life and fire and one that does neither. The first of these he called "fire air," and although he did not collect it in pure form it can be identified with what we now call oxygen.

The first of the gases to be clearly identified was, strangely enough, carbon dioxide, which is present only in minute amounts. Joseph Black (1728–1799) found that by burning certain substances (which we now would call carbonates) a gas was given off. Again, by exposing the residue in the open exactly the same gas was taken up; the gas seemed to be fixed

1

in the substance from which it was obtained. In the language of his time, Black called it "fixed air," which is the same as what we now call carbon dioxide.

The amount of carbon dioxide in natural air is very small. When compared with the other gases at the same temperature and pressure, it accounts for about 0.03 per cent of the total volume.

The mass of carbon dioxide is not quite constant. It is continuously consumed by the vegetable world, and it is produced by the animal world, by the burning of fuels, by volcanic actions, and by various processes of decay in the soil. Although these processes are not always balanced, the oceans absorb carbon dioxide so readily that only a small portion remains in the air. In a manner of speaking, the carbon dioxide may be compared with an iceberg: only a small portion of it is present in the air.

The next gas to be discovered was nitrogen, which we now know makes up almost 80 per cent (by volume) of the total. Daniel Rutherford (1749–1819) carried out experiments with air in a closed container. By burning substances as long as possible and by removing what Black had called "fixed air," a residual gas was left. Rutherford showed that the gas differed from ordinary air in that it could support neither fire nor life. He therefore called it "mephitic air," which is the same as what we now call nitrogen.

Almost immediately after Rutherford's discovery, Joseph Priestley (1733–1804) and Carl William Scheele (1742–1786), working independently, discovered and isolated oxygen (or "fire air") and showed that it, alone, was able to support combustion far better than ordinary air.

In 1894 Lord Rayleigh and Sir William Ramsay announced their discovery of a fourth gas. By burning all the oxygen and removing any carbon dioxide that had formed, they found that the residual gas was slightly heavier than pure nitrogen. They succeeded in removing the nitrogen and thus isolated a new gas; since it was found to be chemically inert, it was called argon. Later measurements showed that argon makes up a little less than 1 per cent (by volume) of all air.

Thus, shortly before the turn of this century, the four major components of dry air were known. In later years their precise amounts have been measured with considerable accuracy (see Table 1).

Actually, the four principal gases account for about 99.997 per cent of the whole. The remainder is made up of minute traces of such gases as neon, krypton, hydrogen, xenon, ozone, radon, etc. Of these, only ozone is of any particular interest in meteorology.

Observation shows that, apart from small variations of the carbon dioxide, the composition of the dry atmosphere is constant all over the world up to about 15 miles (25 km) above sea level, indicating that the air

Table 1. The Four Principal Gases of the Dry Atmosphere below about 15 Miles (25 km)

Name	Symbol	Mole fraction (or volume per cent)
Nitrogen...............	N_2	78.09
Oxygen................	O_2	20.95
Argon	A	0.93
Carbon dioxide..........	CO_2	0.03
Total..............	Dry air	100.00 (approx.)

is perfectly mixed. At great heights chemical processes maintain a variable composition.

If the four gases shown in Table 1 were separated and brought to the same pressure and temperature, their volumes would compare as shown in Fig. 1. The volume occupied by the other gases would be represented by an almost invisible speck at the top of the triangle.

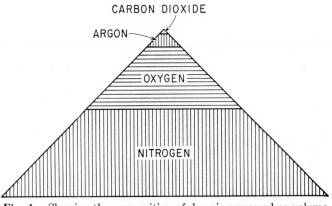

CARBON DIOXIDE

ARGON

OXYGEN

NITROGEN

Fig. 1.   Showing the composition of dry air expressed as volume percentage. Water vapor, which is present in variable amounts, is not included.

Three Forms of Oxygen. When we speak of oxygen as a part of natural air, we really mean diatomic oxygen (O_2), or molecules which are built up of two oxygen atoms. A very small part of the total oxygen, in fact a little less than 1 part in 400,000 by weight, is triatomic oxygen (O_3), or what is called ozone. Furthermore, on the outer fringe of the atmosphere we find oxygen in the form of single atoms (O), or what is called monatomic (or atomic) oxygen.

While everyone realizes that ordinary oxygen is necessary to sustain life, comparatively few recognize the useful function performed by ozone. In a manner of speaking, the layer of ozone in the upper air may be compared with an umbrella that prevents something from coming down to us. This something is extreme ultraviolet radiation from the sun.

Traces of ozone are sometimes formed by electric discharges in the lower atmosphere, but the bulk is formed (and destroyed) at great heights, such that a maximum concentration is maintained at about 12 to 20 miles (20 to 30 km) above the ground. The process of ozone formation and destruction may be visualized as taking place in four steps. An ordinary oxygen molecule (O_2) will dissociate completely into atomic oxygen (O) when it absorbs a quantum of energy whose energy corresponds to a free wavelength of less than about 0.240 micron.[1] We may symbolize this by writing (for the conditions mentioned)

$$O_2 + \text{energy} \rightarrow O + O$$

Now, when an oxygen atom (O) collides with an oxygen molecule (O_2) and any third neutral molecule (M), O_2 and O combine to form ozone (O_3). Thus

$$O_2 + O + M \text{ (in collision)} \rightarrow O_3 + M$$

A three-body collision is necessary since the energy and the momentum must remain unchanged.

Next, ozone is very unstable in the presence of sunlight, and when it absorbs energy at wavelengths less than about 1.1 microns, it reverts to diatomic and monatomic forms; thus, for the conditions mentioned,

$$O_3 + \text{energy} \rightarrow O_2 + O$$

and the atomic oxygen recombines with ozone such that

$$O_3 + O \rightarrow O_2 + O_2$$

The productive and destructive processes are going on all the time, mainly in the layer between 20 and 45 miles (30 to 75 km) above the ground, but the maximum concentration of ozone is found in the lower part of this layer.

The Mass of the Atmosphere. The total weight of the atmosphere is so enormous that even when we speak in terms of millions of tons, the figure is so large that it is difficult to form a clear picture of what it means. If we let M indicate a million and MM a million millions (that is, a U.S. trillion or a British billion), the total mass of the dry air would be a little over 5,600 MM tons. In the same units, the weight of the water vapor would be about 146 MM tons, and the weight of the ozone would be 3,300 M tons.

A clearer idea of the total mass of the atmosphere is obtained by

[1] A micron is one-thousandth part of a millimeter, or a little less than one twenty-five-thousandth part of an inch.

imagining that the weight of all the air is replaced by the same weight of ordinary water. This would amount to a layer of water about 34 ft (about 10 m) deep covering the whole globe. If all the water vapor in the air were condensed to rain and dropped evenly over the globe, a layer of water about 1 in. deep would form.

The Pump and the Barometer. Along with his many other interests, Galileo (1564–1642) was concerned with the workings of ordinary water pumps. This led to the invention of the barometer in 1643, only 3 years after he had invented the first thermometer. Thus, in the middle of the seventeenth century these two important instruments came into existence, and this may well be taken as the zero date in the development of the science of the atmosphere.

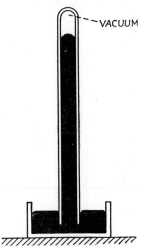

In Galileo's time suction pumps were commonly used to draw water from wells. In most cases the heights were small and no critical limits were reached. On one occasion it was brought to Galileo's notice that a perfectly good pump failed to lift water more than about 34 ft above the free water level in the well.

Aristotle's principle that nature *abhors* a vacuum was modified by Galileo, who spoke of *resistance against* vacuum, allowing some leeway. The failure of the lift pump to raise water more than 34 ft Galileo explained by saying that the water column broke of its own

Fig. 2. Illustrating Torricelli's experiment and the principle of the barometer.

weight, more or less like a long slender wire which is in suspension.

The true explanation of the failure of the pump, which came shortly after Galileo's death, is due to Torricelli, who not only invented the barometer but also discovered vacuum. Torricelli's experiment is readily explained by reference to Fig. 2. A glass tube about 3 ft long is sealed at one end and filled completely with mercury. The open end is closed tightly by a finger, the sealed end is turned upward, and the other end is dipped into a vessel containing mercury. If the finger is then removed with care, so that no air gets into the tube, the mercury in the tube sinks and comes to rest about 30 in. above the mercury in the open vessel. Obviously, the space above the mercury in the tube must be free of air; it is a vacuum, and there can be no atmospheric pressure acting on the top of the mercury column. Furthermore, since the atmosphere "rests on" the surface of the mercury in the vessel, the experiment shows that the pressure exerted by the atmosphere on the mercury in the vessel is equivalent to the weight of the mercury in the tube. Now, since mercury is about 13.6 times heavier than water, it is evident that the pressure of the atmosphere at the earth's surface is equivalent to the weight of a water column about 34 ft high; and this explains the failure of a suction pump to lift water above this height.

The Pressure of the Air. When Pascal heard of Torricelli's findings, he repeated the experiment and, in 1648, arranged for a barometer to be carried to the top of Puy-de-Dôme in France. As Pascal had expected, the length of the mercury column decreased when the barometer was carried to greater heights. Obviously, as the barometer is carried upward there is less and less air above it, and the balancing mercury column (Fig. 2) must decrease.

The law which these experiments revealed is called the *barometric law*, or the *law of hydrostatic equilibrium*. To formulate this law more precisely we must state what we mean by pressure. In the first place, pressure is defined as force per unit area. Next, a force is equal to the mass that it acts upon multiplied by the acceleration that it produces. Thus,

$$\text{Pressure} = \frac{\text{force}}{\text{area}} = \frac{\text{mass} \times \text{acceleration}}{\text{area}}$$

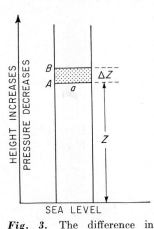

Fig. 3. The difference in pressure between two levels, A and B, is determined by the weight of the air between these levels.

Now, let us consider a vertical column of air as shown in Fig. 3. We divide the column into a number of thin slices, each having a depth Δz. Here, z means height and Δz a small increment[1] of height. If a is the cross-sectional area, the volume is $a\,\Delta z$, and if ρ is the density, the mass of a slice is $\rho a\,\Delta z$. Furthermore, if g is the acceleration of gravity, the gravitational force is $\rho g a\,\Delta z$, and the force per unit area is

$$\rho g\,\Delta z$$

This, then, is the pressure at the level A due to the mass within the slice between A and B. Now, if Δp is the pressure at the level B minus the pressure at the level A in Fig. 3, this pressure difference must be equal to the pressure due to the mass within the slice. Thus,

$$-\Delta p = \rho g\,\Delta z \qquad (1)$$

The minus sign indicates that the pressure decreases with increasing height.

Equation (1) is called the *hydrostatic equation*. Strictly speaking, it is

---

[1] In the following the symbol Δ will be used to indicate a small increment. For example, ΔT will denote a small increment of temperature.

correct only when the air is at rest. However, the effects of air motion are so small that the equation holds with a very high degree of accuracy.

Since the air density can be computed from observations of pressure and temperature, the hydrostatic equation may be used to compute heights. Normally, the pressure at any level will vary from one place to another, but the horizontal variations over any given distance are about 10,000 times smaller than the variations over an equal distance along the vertical. This being so, the height can be computed with good accuracy even when the observations are not made along a vertical line. For example, the height of Mount Washington can be computed from observations of temperature and pressure along its sides.

Pressure Units and Reductions. A word must now be said about pressure units and observations. The direct reading of the barometer gives the *length* of the mercury column. Since the mercury and the glass tube expand and contract as the temperature of the instrument increases and decreases, it is necessary to reduce the length to a standard temperature, such as 32°F (or 0°C). Next, the local gravity varies slightly from one place to another, and to obtain comparable values it is necessary to reduce the readings to some standard gravity; commonly used is $g = 980.665$ cm/sec². Finally, the pressure varies rapidly along the vertical, and to get comparable readings from different stations it is necessary to reduce the observations to some standard level, such as sea level. For example, on any day the pressure difference between the base and the top of the Empire State Building is larger than the maximum difference ever observed between New York City and Washington, D.C.

Up to about 1914, pressure was reported in units of length, in either inches or centimeters of mercury. In later years a new unit, called the millibar (mb), has come into general use. Normal pressure at sea level is 76 cm or about 30 in. Since the density of mercury is about 13.595 g/cm³, the mass of the column would be 1,033.22 g. Using the above-mentioned normal gravity at sea level, one obtains for the pressure in centimeter-gram-second (cgs) units

$$1{,}013{,}250 \text{ dynes/cm}^2$$

Since dynes per square centimeter is an exceedingly small unit, V. Bjerknes introduced the millibar, which is 1,000 times larger. The millibar is now used by all meteorological services, except that in the United States inches of mercury is used in press and radio reports to the general public.

A table for converting inches to millibars is given in Table I, Conversion Factors and Tables.

Water Vapor. In many respects water vapor is the most important constituent of the atmosphere. While the other constituents remain in the gaseous form, the vapor often condenses to liquid water, which sometimes freezes into snow and ice. This is due to the circumstance that condensation and freezing occur well within the range of atmospheric temperatures.

The amount of water vapor present in the air can be expressed as the pressure that the vapor exerts, and this is independent of the presence of other gases. This pressure is called the *vapor pressure;* it is usually denoted by e and expressed (like the atmospheric pressure) in millibars. The maximum amount of water vapor that can be present depends upon the temperature of the vapor. However, since the vapor in the atmosphere has the same temperature as the air, we may say that the maximum amount depends upon the air temperature; the higher the temperature the more vapor can the air hold.

The air is said to be saturated when the maximum is reached. If more vapor is added, or if the air is cooled below the saturation point, the superfluous vapor condenses. There are some minor exceptions to this rule, and they are discussed in a later section on clouds and rain.

Now, if E denotes the maximum, or the saturation, vapor pressure, the relative humidity U is defined as

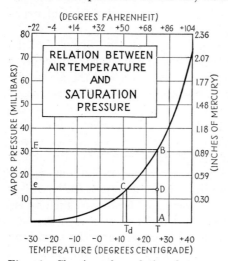

Fig. 4. Showing the relation between temperature and saturation vapor pressure, and the definition of dewpoint temperature.

$$U = 100 \frac{e}{E}$$

or as the actual vapor pressure expressed as a percentage of the maximum that can exist at a given temperature. The air is saturated with moisture when the relative humidity is 100 per cent.

The relation between temperature and saturation vapor pressure is shown in Fig. 4. For example, suppose that a parcel of air has a temperature T and a vapor pressure e. The plot in the diagram is then represented by D, and the corresponding saturation vapor pressure is indicated by B. The difference $E - e$ is called the *saturation deficit* and is indicated by the line BD. If more vapor were added at constant temperature, point D would move toward B, and the air would be saturated when B is reached.

Suppose next that the parcel at D is cooled at constant pressure and without addition of vapor. The point D would then move toward C, and the air would be saturated when C is reached. At this stage the air would have a temperature T_d, which is called the *dewpoint temperature.*

It will be seen from Fig. 4 that the saturation pressure is low at low temperatures and increases rapidly as the temperature increases. On a cold winter day in the arctic, the saturation vapor pressure may be as low as 0.02 mb, while on a hot day in a tropical jungle, it may be 50 mb or more. Life in the jungle is unpleasant not only because of the heat but also because of excessive perspiration. While the cold is severe in the arctic, an added factor of unpleasantness is the drying out of the skin exposed to the cold air. Newcomers to the arctic winter will do well to rub fat on their faces. It is interesting to observe that reindeer, after some exercise, surround themselves with an ice fog caused by evaporation of body liquids which condense and freeze in the bitterly cold air.

The contrasts between the jungle and the arctic, mentioned above, are not quite so severe as those which we should encounter if we ascended vertically through the atmosphere. If we ascended 8 miles along the vertical from, say, Miami, Fla., we might encounter temperatures as low as $-70°C$ ($-94°F$) and vapor pressures below about 0.01 mb. Thus, over these few miles we might experience a temperature difference of about $90°C$ ($162°F$), and, on occasions, the wind might increase from a light breeze to 150 knots or more. The variations along the vertical are tremendous in comparison to those along the horizontal. In fact, if we compare the vertical with the horizontal dimensions, the atmosphere may be thought of as being composed of a few extremely thin layers, or spheres.

The Spheres and the Fringe. The meteorological elements, such as temperature, pressure, humidity, etc., vary from one place to another, and they also vary with time. The time variations are relatively small oscillations around a steady mean state, and since the variations in the horizontal are very much smaller than those along the vertical, it is possible to make up a *standard atmosphere* which represents the essential features of the vertical structure, particularly in regard to temperature and pressure. Such a standard is useful for many purposes. For example, the customary altimeters used in aircraft show the height that corresponds to the pressure and temperature of the standard atmosphere. At any time and place the actual conditions may differ somewhat from the standard, but the effects of these deviations can be minimized by setting the altimeter according to recent observations.

The average conditions below about 15 miles (25 km) have been well explored by the aid of balloons and aircraft equipped with instruments. The upper layers are not so well known, and the conditions there may be more variable than in the lower layers. Some information from the upper regions has been obtained by rockets, but the bulk has come from studies of sound, radio waves, aurora borealis, meteors, etc. From the available information it is possible to outline the general structure at least up to 100 miles (160 km) above sea level. The salient features are shown in

Figs. 5 and 6. In the former the emphasis is on the lower regions and in the latter on the upper regions.

It will be seen that the pressure decreases rapidly in the lower layers (where the density is high) and very slowly in the upper layers (where the

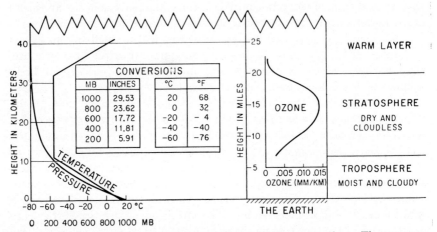

Fig. 5. Idealized structure of the troposphere and the stratosphere. The temperature and pressure curves represent the so-called "standard atmosphere."

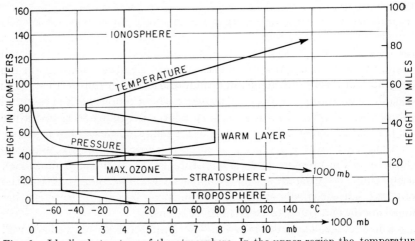

Fig. 6. Idealized structure of the atmosphere. In the upper region the temperature distribution represents a tentative standard.

density is low). This is in agreement with the barometric law stated by Eq. (1), for the pressure decrease per unit distance along the vertical is directly proportional to the air density. At 30 miles (50 km) above sea level the pressure has dropped to 1 mb, or $\frac{1}{1000}$ part of the pressure at sea level; at 60 miles, the pressure is about 1/1,000,000 part of the sea-level pressure.

The decrease in air density along the vertical closely follows the pressure curve. Some idea of the density variation is obtained by comparing the mean free path of the air molecules. At sea level the mean free path is about 1/3,000,000 in., at 40 miles it is about ½₀₀ in., at 60 miles it is a little over 1 in., and at 200 miles it is about 80 ft.

While the pressure and density decrease monotonically as the height increases, the temperature variation is altogether different. It will be seen from Fig. 6 that there is a strong tendency for the atmosphere to be divided into several concentric shells, and it has become customary to refer to them as spheres.

The Troposphere. This is the lowest layer, or the foot, of the atmosphere. On the whole, it makes up about 75 per cent of all the weight of the atmosphere and contains almost all the moisture and dust.

The top of the troposphere is called the *tropopause.* In the standard atmosphere (Fig. 5) it is placed at about 11 km (7 miles) above sea level. Under average conditions the height of the tropopause varies from about 5 miles at the poles to about 10 miles near the equator, but 7 miles is a good average for all latitudes. In individual cases the height of the tropopause may vary within wide limits. The higher the temperature of the lower layers, the higher is the tropopause. The height varies also with the pressure at sea level; the higher the sea-level pressure, the higher is the tropopause. A typical example is shown in Fig. 7.

The most striking feature of the troposphere is the steady decrease of temperature with increasing elevation. In individual cases, particularly during the cold season, a layer of cold air will be present near the ground, but Fig. 5 is meant to represent the average for the whole globe in all seasons. The rate of decrease of temperature over a unit distance along the vertical is called the *lapse rate* of temperature. In the troposphere the average lapse rate is about 3.6°F/1,000 ft, or 6.5°C/km.

The air in the troposphere is subject to frequent overturnings, and these occur on a variety of scales. At the lower end of the scale we meet with what is commonly called turbulence, or very small eddies which move up and down. The gusts and bumpiness experienced by aircraft in flight are due to rapid and irregular vertical motions of lumps of air which are a few hundred feet in diameter. The gusts are sharp and short-lived. The shower clouds and thunderstorms occur in connection with vertical motions over a horizontal stretch of a few miles; they may last 1 or 2 hr, and the vertical velocities in them are about 30 ft (10 m)/sec. At the other end of the scale we have the major storms (commonly called cyclones); their horizontal extent may be 2,000 miles or more; they may live several days and the vertical velocities are generally about 2 to 4 in. (5 to 10 cm)/

sec. Almost all phenomena which we call weather occur in the troposphere, and most of the remainder of this book will be concerned with this layer. But first we shall make a brief excursion into the higher spheres.

The Stratosphere. Until about 1900 it was generally believed that the temperature would continue to decrease upward through the atmosphere and approach absolute zero on the border of empty space. By about 1900 balloons had been developed which were capable of reaching considerable heights, and in 1902 Teisserenc de Bort found that the decrease was

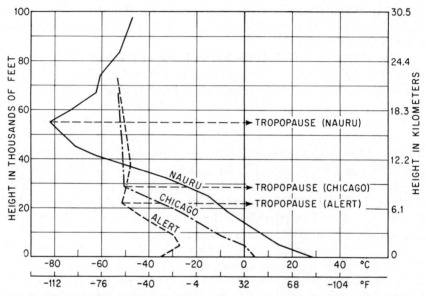

Fig. 7. Typical soundings through the troposphere and lower stratosphere. Nauru Island (26 miles from the equator), Apr. 13, 1951. Chicago, Illinois, Apr. 10, 1951. Alert, Ellesmere Island (450 miles from the North Pole), Apr. 8, 1951. Note that the temperature in the stratosphere decreases toward the equator.

limited to the lower layer, 7 miles or so, and that the temperature higher up was more or less uniform.

De Bort divided the atmosphere into two layers, the troposphere and the stratosphere. The word troposphere was chosen to indicate a sphere of relatively low stability, a layer within which overturnings occur frequently, and the word stratosphere was meant to indicate a layer with a highly stable stratification.

Broadly speaking, we may say that the tropopause is the upper limit of the overturnings that result from the yearly and daily heatings of the earth's surface and the air in contact with it. The stratosphere is, by and large, separated from these direct influences, and for this reason it contains very little moisture and dust, except such as may be brought to high levels by major volcanic eruptions.

Another characteristic of the stratosphere is that it contains most of the ozone, which was discussed briefly in a foregoing section. The amount of ozone varies considerably, and the distribution curve shown in Fig. 5 is meant to indicate only the general features.

The Warm Layer. The first indication of the existence of a warm layer (see Figs. 5 and 6) above the stratosphere came from studies of meteors. Once in a while a meteor is so large that it penetrates the atmosphere and hits the earth. The vast majority of meteors are, however, so small that they burn out and evaporate in the upper layers. Lindemann and Dobson (1923) found that the meteors disappeared most frequently either at about 50 miles or about 30 miles above the ground. This was remarkable for the following reason. The meteors move in from outer space with velocities of the order of 25 miles/sec. At such high speeds, the air on their forward sides is strongly compressed, and the compression causes the temperature to increase enormously, with the result that the meteors melt and evaporate. Now, if the air temperature were uniform, there would be only one level of maximum disappearance. The existence of two maxima could be explained only by assuming that there was a layer of very warm air somewhere between 25 and 40 miles above the ground. This inference soon found support in the works of Whipple, who analyzed the behavior of sound waves.

Our knowledge of the thermal structure of the uppermost atmosphere is derived partly from rocket observations and partly from indirect evidence obtained from observations of sound, meteors, and ozone. The temperatures thus obtained vary greatly from time to time, and there are large differences between the various methods. All that can be said with certainty is that there is a warm layer about 25 to 40 miles above the earth and that the maximum temperature there is higher than the temperature that prevails near the earth's surface. If the temperature in the warm layer did not exceed the temperature near the earth's surface, we could not explain the existence of the rings of sound and silence that have been observed in connection with large explosions.

It is now generally agreed that the warm layer is due to selective absorption of ultraviolet radiation by the ozone in the layer from 15 to 35 miles above the ground. Although the concentration of ozone is highest below 20 miles (see Fig. 6), the rate of production and destruction of ozone is highest in the layer above 20 miles.

While the terms troposphere and stratosphere have come to stay, there is no general agreement on the nomenclature for the highest layers. The warm layer is sometimes called the *mesosphere*, while some writers prefer the name *chemosphere*, to emphasize the chemical processes. The layer which contains the bulk of the ozone is often called the *ozonosphere*. Each sphere has an upper limit, which is called a *pause*. One may therefore speak of the tropopause, the stratopause, the mesopause, and so on. These pauses are sometimes indistinct, and the standard structure shown in Figs. 5 and 6 gives an exaggerated impression of their sharpness.

The Ionosphere. In 1902, the year in which de Bort discovered the stratosphere, Kennelly and Heaviside came independently to the conclusion that a highly ionized layer must exist at great heights, for without such a layer one could not explain certain aspects of radio transmissions over great distances.

At such low pressures as prevail in the uppermost atmosphere the ionization processes are lively, and this results in high concentrations of free electrons. With some simplification, the system earth-atmosphere may be compared with a closed d-c electric circuit, in which the earth's surface and the ionosphere play the parts of wires without resistance, or —what amounts to the same thing—surfaces with infinite conductivity. Now, a direct current can be thought of as being propagated by an electromagnetic wave of infinite length, and such a current would be perfectly reflected from the ionosphere.

On the other hand, we know that waves of light (which also are electromagnetic waves) go through the ionosphere with little reflection and absorption. If this were not so, our pictures of the stars, sun, and moon would be grossly distorted, and in the extreme case nothing outside the ionosphere would be seen from the earth.

Between these two extremes lie the ordinary radio waves, and both theory and observation show that we can neglect the influence of the ionosphere on light and microwaves, but for short radio waves and customary broadcast waves we cannot.

Between the ionosphere and the earth surface the radio waves are reflected repeatedly, and this accounts for the large distances over which radio transmissions can reach (see Fig. 8).

The electrical structure of the ionosphere is not uniform; normally several distinct layers are present. The lowest of these is the so-called D layer. Although it reflects low-frequency radio waves it strongly absorbs waves of medium and high frequency. It is present only during hours of sunlight, and it is particularly active during periods of strong solar flares. At times complete blackout of medium- and high-frequency transmissions may occur.

The E layer is found between 90 and 130 km (55 to 80 miles); it is usually well defined and reflects strongly. Above this layer are found several more or less distinct layers or regions, known as the sporadic E layer, the E_2 region, the F_1 and F_2 regions, and the G region. Best known is the F_2 region at the height of about 300 km (180 miles). It is of great importance in long-distance communication and for this reason has been studied intensively.

Perhaps the most spectacular manifestations of the interactions between the sun and the earth are the aurora borealis in high northern latitudes and the corresponding aurora australis in high southern latitudes (see Figs. 9 and 10). These are caused by bombardment of the upper atmosphere by showers of charged particles, or corpuscles, that have been thrown out from the sun. The auroras occur most frequently between 50 and 150 miles (80 to 250 km) above the earth, but on occasions they have

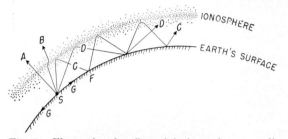

Fig. 8.   Illustrating the effect of the ionosphere on ordinary radio waves. The vertical beam *A* will escape without bending. The beam *B* will escape after double bending. The beam *C*, and all other beams with smaller elevation angle, will suffer multiple reflections between the ionosphere and the earth. These are the so-called "sky waves." The ground wave *G* weakens quickly, and the belt between *G* and *F* will receive neither ground nor sky waves; this is the skip zone, or the zone of silence.

been seen at heights of 600 miles, showing that atmospheric matter is present even at these elevations.

Conquest of the Vertical. As early as 1773, hot-air balloons were used, but the heights reached were small and the flights were few and far between. At the turn of this century balloons began to penetrate the tropopause, and since then bigger and better balloons have been developed, with the result that heights of about 15 miles are now reached routinely. After the famous flight of the Wright Brothers in 1903, aircraft have contributed to the exploration of the lower part of the atmosphere, but even the most modern jets are incapable of reaching great heights.

The revolution in the exploration of the uppermost atmosphere came at the end of the Second World War, when instrumented rockets were first used; already in 1951 heights in excess of 240 miles had been reached. In earlier years man was concerned with the concept of altitude; now he is concerned with the concept of distance from the earth and the possibility of visiting interplanetary space.

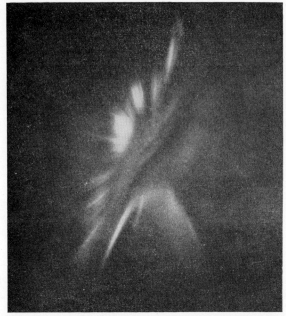

Fig. 9. A lively display of auroral corona photographed by Carl Störmer from Oslo, Mar. 22–23, 1920.

Fig. 10. A beautiful auroral curtain photographed by Carl Störmer from Bosekop (northern Norway), Oct. 13–14, 1916. Auroras may appear in many forms; they are of a greenish color sometimes mixed with red. They must be seen to be appreciated.

Suppose now we take off from Rocket City and ascend vertically. We are, of course, protected by a pressurized shell, but once in a while we shall imagine ourselves exposed to the atmospheric environment.

At sea level the atmospheric pressure is about 1,000 mb, and much of this is due to oxygen which we need to sustain life. The temperature in our lungs is about 98°F (37°C), and the air in them is almost saturated with water vapor, and contains a goodly amount of carbon dioxide. We cannot hold our breath very long, for we need to expel the water vapor and the carbon dioxide and inhale oxygen.

While we rise to about 13,000 ft everything is normal; we breathe with comfort, for the oxygen pressure is still high. It is in this lower part of the atmosphere that the drama of life normally unfolds. Since the word atmosphere was derived from the Greek word *atmos*, which means breath, we might say that it is only this lower part of the gaseous envelope that truly deserves to be called atmosphere. However, the air below about 13,000 ft is commonly called the *normoxid layer*, for oxygen is so plentiful that respiration is normal.

As we ascend higher the oxygen pressure drops off and gradually becomes so low that uncomfortable physiological and psychological effects set in, and we may speak of a *hypoxid layer*. Loss of consciousness begins within this zone as soon as the alveolar oxygen pressure drops below about 40 mb, or a little over 1 in. of mercury. At heights about 52,000 ft a zone of *anoxia* begins. The explanation for this may be sought in the composition of the alveolar air, for with normal body temperature all the available space in the lungs becomes filled with water vapor and carbon dioxide. Though some oxygen is present in the air, none will enter the lungs. In a manner of speaking we may say that a man exposed to the environment of the upper atmosphere will suffocate by drowning in his own water vapor.

In the troposphere (see Fig. 5) the relative humidity is generally high, and there is the abode of what is commonly called weather. As we ascend well into the stratosphere, the relative humidity decreases rapidly. Once in a rare while we see beautiful displays of mother-of-pearl clouds, but normally the sky is clear, the stratification is stable, and bumpiness almost unknown.

In the upper part of the stratosphere we pass through the ozone layer and lose its protection against harmful ultraviolet rays. At about 12 miles the pressure is so low that the body liquids begin to boil at ordinary blood temperature (37°C, or 98°F). Long before this height is reached nitrogen bubbles form in the tissues, causing pain.

As we ascend into the warm layer (see Fig. 6), the saturation vapor pressure becomes higher than the total pressure. The air must be extremely dry, and no condensation can possibly take place. In due course we enter the ionosphere. Toward the poles we see brilliant displays of auroras below as well as above our ship. The pressure has now sunk to a small fraction of a millibar; ionization processes are lively and produce useful layers which bend radio waves back to the earth.

On our way upward, from about 20 miles or so, we may watch for a large number of small meteors which come from outer space with speeds of the order of 90,000 mph. At such great speeds even the very thin air becomes strongly compressed and heated on the forward side of the meteors, and this causes them to melt and evaporate. The number of such bodies that enter the air in 1 day exceeds 1 million, and if our ship encountered one of them, the shell would be pierced; we should suffer complete anoxia and be unconscious within 15 sec.

Having passed through the ionosphere we enter the exosphere, or the outer fringe of the atmosphere. Here the molecules are widely separated. After a pair has collided the outer one travels into outer space but is dragged back by the pull of the earth's gravity. We sail further and leave the atmosphere behind. Gravity is still with us, but it weakens in proportion to the square of the distance from the earth's center. We sit lightly in our chairs. Eventually the chairs become useless, for weight has ceased to exist.

2

Instruments and Observations

It is not the purpose here to describe the engineering details of the multitude of meteorological instruments now in use but rather to acquaint the reader with the observational system, the most commonly used instruments, and the precautions which must be taken to obtain reliable observations.

Mercury Thermometers. The temperature of the air is commonly measured by a mercury thermometer of the type shown in Fig. 11. This consists of a glass tube with a small and uniform bore, expanded into a bulb at one end and sealed at the other. The bulb and part of the bore are filled with mercury, and the remainder is vacuum. As the temperature rises, the glass and the mercury expand, but the mercury expands much faster than the glass. A suitable scale engraved on the glass will, therefore, indicate the temperature.

Temperature Scales. There are several temperature scales in use. The clumsiest scale, and the one that is best known in the English-speaking world, was invented by the German physicist Fahrenheit in 1714. The zero point on this scale was marked at the top of the mercury column when the thermometer was placed in a mixture of equal parts of snow and sal ammoniac. The reason for this choice was that Fahrenheit thought that no lower temperature could be produced in a laboratory. On this scale the melting point of pure ice is at 32°F and the boiling point of water at 212°F. Thus, the spread between these points is 180°F. This spread is divided into 180 equal parts, and the grading is continued uniformly toward higher and lower temperatures. It is of some interest to note that while pure ice melts at 32°F, pure water may be cooled below this value before it freezes. A bucket partly filled with ordinary water and a generous number of ordinary ice cubes which are stirred together for some time will fix the melting point with good accuracy.

On his journey across the highlands of Asia, Marco Polo noticed that it took longer time to boil food in the "keen air" of the high mountains than in the denser air of the lowlands. It is now well known that the boiling point of water decreases slowly with the atmospheric pressure, and the boiling point referred to in connection with the thermometer scale is that which corresponds to pure water at normal sea-level pressure.

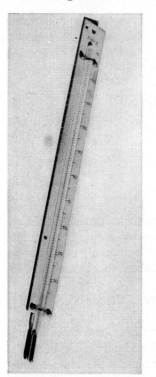

Fig. 11. A mercury thermometer. To obtain accurate reading, be sure to have the eyes level with the top of the mercury column. *(Friez Instrument Division, Bendix Aviation Corp.)*

The centigrade scale was invented in 1742 by the Swedish astronomer Celsius. On this scale the melting point of ice is marked 0°C and the boiling point of water 100°C. Thus, to a spread of 100°C corresponds a spread of 180°F, so that a difference of 1°C corresponds to $\frac{9}{5}$°F. And since the zero points differ by 32°F, the relation between the two scales may be written

$$°C = \tfrac{5}{9}(°F - 32) \qquad °F = \tfrac{9}{5}°C + 32$$

A table for converting °C to °F, and vice versa, is to be found in Table II, Conversion Factors and Tables.

A third scale was introduced by the French physicist Reaumur in 1731. On this scale the melting point of ice is at 0°R and the boiling point of water at 80°R. The Reaumur scale was much used in Central Europe until the beginning of this century but has since gone out of use.

Most scientists prefer a fourth scale, called the absolute (°A) or the Kelvin (°K) scale. This is similar to the centigrade scale except that the melting point of ice is placed at 273°A and the boiling point of water at 373°A. On this scale negative temperatures cannot occur; here zero means absolute zero. The constant difference of 273 comes into the scale in the following manner. If a gas in a container is heated while the pressure is kept constant, the volume of the gas is seen to expand. A certain increase in volume corresponds to each degree rise in temperature, and we may speak of a *volume-expansion coefficient*. This coefficient is very nearly equal to $\frac{1}{273}$ and is the same for all gases. Now if V_0 is the volume at 0°C and V_t is the volume at t°C, then

$$V_t = V_0(1 + \tfrac{1}{273}t)$$

Similarly, if a gas is heated while the volume is kept constant, one finds that the pressure varies according to a similar law, and we may speak of a *pressure-expansion coefficient*, which, like the volume coefficient, is $\frac{1}{273}$. Thus, for pressure

$$P_t = P_0\left(1 + \tfrac{1}{273}\,t\right) = P_0\,\frac{273 + t}{273}$$

We see then that if the temperature t sinks to -273°C the pressure drops to zero. According to the molecular theory of gases, this means that the molecules have ceased to move, and this point (-273°C) fixes the zero point on the absolute temperature scale. The relation between the centigrade and absolute (or Kelvin) temperature scale may be written very simply

$$°C = °A - 273 \qquad \text{or} \qquad °A = °C + 273$$

In the course of time the Reaumur scale emigrated from France and found a new home in Germany. The Fahrenheit scale left Germany and became the popular scale in the British Empire and the United States, where it is used in all reports from ordinary land and ship stations, while the centigrade scale is used for reporting the temperatures of the free atmosphere. The centigrade scale, which is often called the Celsius scale, spread from Sweden to all countries using the metric system of units.

Alcohol Thermometers. Since mercury freezes at -39°C, alcohol (which freezes at -130°C) is used as thermometer substance at low temperature.

Sensitivity and Accuracy. The size of the bulb in relation to the width of the bore of the thermometer (whether mercury or alcohol) is an important consideration. If the bulb is large, the thermometer will be sluggish; for the more mercury there is in the bulb, the longer it takes for the thermometer to adjust its temperature to the air temperature. Furthermore, if the bore is small the variations in the length of the mercury column will be large and, therefore, the readings accurate. On the other hand, if the bulb is small, the thermometer reacts quickly to temperature changes, but the variations in the length of the column will be small and the readings tend to become inaccurate. For meteorological purposes a certain amount of sluggishness is desirable, for it is preferable to obtain an average over a few minutes than to obtain a peak or a trough in the fine structure of the small and irregular variations. An important requirement is that the bore be uniform and the grading accurate. Amateurs should consult a Weather Bureau office or a reliable instrument firm before purchasing instruments.

Maximum and Minimum Thermometers. The highest and lowest temperatures reached during the daily cycle are of considerable importance, and these temperatures are measured by special thermometers.

The maximum thermometer (Fig. 12) is an ordinary mercury thermometer which has a restriction in the bore near the bulb. As the temperature rises, the mercury is forced past the restriction, and this continues until the maximum temperature is reached. However, when the bulb cools and the mercury contracts, the mercury already in the bore

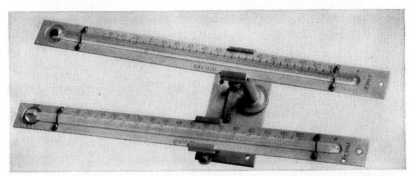

Fig. 12.   A maximum and minimum thermometer. (*Friez Instrument Division, Bendix Aviation Corp.*)

becomes trapped and leaves behind a record of what the highest temperature was. The principle is the same as that used in clinical thermometers, for the patient's temperature is the maximum temperature to which the thermometer has been exposed. After the maximum temperature has been noted, the nurse shakes her thermometer, and the meteorological observer spins his, until the mercury column has been united with the mercury in the bulb.

The minimum thermometer is an ordinary alcohol thermometer (see Fig. 12) which is mounted in a horizontal position. Inside the alcohol is a little rod, or an index, which rests on the floor of the bore and can be moved by tilting the instrument. When the temperature rises, the alcohol expands past the index, but when it contracts so much that the free end of the alcohol column touches the index, the surface tension of the meniscus drags the index with it. When the temperature again rises, the index is left behind as a record of the lowest point reached. About midday the observer tilts the thermometer and brings the index to the meniscus.

The Thermograph. A well-equipped station will have a thermograph, an instrument which records the temperature continuously. A typical thermograph consists of a substance which expands and contracts with the temperature variations, a clock which rotates a cylinder to which a sheet of paper is fixed, and amplifying levers with a pen that writes a curve on the paper. The record paper is called a thermogram; a typical example is shown in Fig. 13.

A commonly used thermograph is one which uses a bimetallic strip as reactor. Two thin, curved sheets of metal of widely different thermal

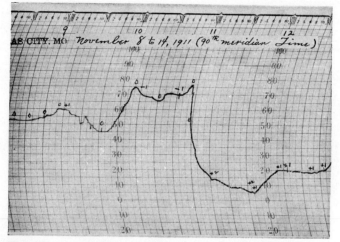

Fig. 13. An example of a thermogram, Kansas City, Nov. 11, 1911. The warm air was suddenly replaced by an invasion of arctic air. The temperature drop, from 76 to 10°F, is perhaps the largest one on record. (*U.S. Weather Bureau.*)

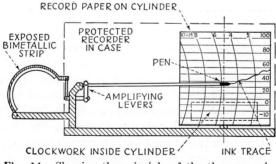

Fig. 14. Showing the principle of the thermograph.

expansion are welded together. When the temperature changes, the two metals will expand unequally, and the curvature of the strip will change. This change is transferred through levers to a pen that traces the temperature on the thermogram. The general structure of a thermograph is shown in Fig. 14, and a real instrument is shown in Fig. 15.

There are other types of standard thermographs, but the principle of construction is more or less the same for all. It is typical of all standard thermographs that they are not highly reliable for measuring absolute values, while they indicate the changes well. To obtain reliable values it is necessary to check the temperature trace against the reading of the thermometer and correct for the difference.

Fig. 15.   A thermograph (upper pen) and a hygrograph (lower pen). Note the bimetallic strip and the bundle of hair on the right. (*Friez Instrument Division, Bendix Aviation Corp.*)

Humidity Instruments.   As mentioned on page 8 the air contains a certain amount of water vapor, and it is this vapor (rather than cloud droplets, fog, and rain) which we refer to as humidity. There are several ways in which the humidity of the air can be expressed mathematically, and some of these will be discussed at the end of this section. Here, we are concerned only with ways and means of measuring the amount of moisture. The standard instrument used for this purpose is either the *hygrometer* or the *psychrometer*, and the quantities measured are (1) the relative humidity and (2) the temperature and the wet-bulb temperature of the air.

The Hygrometer. In the fifteenth century Cardinal de Cusa measured the moisture of the air by weighing large balls of wool; in damp weather the wool absorbed moisture and weighed more. Women have long known that their hair gets unruly in damp weather; in 1783 De Saussure used human hair to measure the moisture of the air and constructed the hair hygrometer, which, with later improvements, is still standard station equipment.

What this instrument actually measures is the relative humidity, which was defined on page 8. The principle may be illustrated as shown in Fig. 16. When the air is dry, the cells in the hair are close together; but when the air is humid, the space between the cells absorbs water vapor, and the hair thickens and lengthens. It is this lengthening that is used as a measure of the moisture.

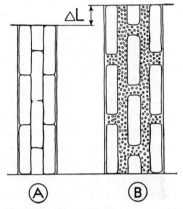

The instrument has a bundle of hairs, the upper end of which is fixed to a frame and the lower end to a weight. The weight is connected by amplifying levers to compensating cams which, in turn, are connected to a pointer which moves across a scale and indicates the relative humidity.

Fig. 16. The length of a human hair absorbs moisture and increases in length: (*a*) low relative humidity; (*b*) high relative humidity.

The hygrometer may be transformed into a self-recording instrument (see Fig. 17), and it is then called a hygrograph. Usually the hygrograph and the thermograph are built into one instrument (see Fig. 15).

The Psychrometer. This simple instrument consists of two thermometers mounted side by side. One of these is naked while the other has its bulb tightly dressed in fine muslin with a wick that draws pure water

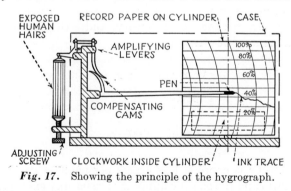

Fig. 17. Showing the principle of the hygrograph.

from a container, thus keeping the bulb wet. Now, when air is blown past the bulbs, the dry thermometer shows the temperature of the air, while water evaporates from the wet bulb. Since heat is required to evaporate water, the temperature of the wet-bulb thermometer sinks; it does so until a state of equilibrium is reached and then stays steady. The saturation vapor pressure (see page 8) at the wet bulb is then the same as that of the air, and no further evaporation takes place. The temperature shown by this thermometer is called the *wet-bulb temperature,* and we may say that this temperature is the lowest temperature to which the air can be cooled by evaporating water into it.

Now, if the air were saturated initially, no evaporation would occur, and the dry-bulb and the wet-bulb temperatures would be the same; the relative humidity would be 100 per cent, and the wet-bulb depression would be zero. The larger the saturation deficit, the more evaporation would be needed, and the larger would be the wet-bulb depression. Once the air temperature and the wet-bulb temperature have been observed, the relative humidity, and all other humidity measures, can be obtained from tables or graphs.

While the hair hygrometer is a convenient instrument, it is not an accurate one, for the quality of the hair is not constant. The psychrometer is accurate at high temperatures, but it is rather insensitive to moisture variations at such low temperatures as prevail in the upper atmosphere and over cold continents in winter. On the whole, there is no standard instrument that will measure the humidity accurately throughout the range of temperatures observed in the atmosphere.

In addition to the relative humidity, the vapor pressure, the dew-point, and the wet-bulb temperature, the humidity is often expressed in other ways. Thus, the *vapor density* is defined as the number of grams of water vapor contained in one cubic centimeter. This is sometimes called the *absolute humidity.* The *mixing ratio* is the number of grams of water vapor associated with one gram of dry air. Finally, the *specific humidity* is the number of grams of water vapor associated with one gram of moist air. Now, if ρ_v denotes the vapor density, and ρ the density of dry air, these definitions may be written

$$\text{Vapor density} = \rho_v$$

$$\text{Mixing ratio} = \frac{\rho_v}{\rho}$$

$$\text{Specific humidity} = \frac{\rho_v}{\rho + \rho_v}$$

The vapor density is expressed as grams per cubic centimeter (g/cm^3). The mixing ratio and the specific humidity are usually expressed as grams per kilogram, but in mathematical derivations one must express them as grams per gram. The choice between these measures is entirely a matter of convenience. In most theoretical discussions, the mixing ratio leads to the simplest formulas. Since ρ_v is very much smaller than ρ, the difference between mixing ratio and specific humidity is very small, and the two may be used interchangeably unless great accuracy is required.

The Instrument Shelter. While a sun bather may be interested in the temperature in a nook which is exposed to the sun and sheltered from the winds, the meteorologist has little use for such observations. What he wants are observations which, as far as possible, are representative of the conditions of the large air masses that move by. A thermometer which is exposed to sunshine, or to radiation or conduction of heat from buildings and the like, will give misleading values, and the same is true of the hygrometer. It is necessary, also, to protect the instruments against dew, rain, and snow, for if the thermometer gets wet, it will behave like a wet-bulb instrument. Heat exchange with the ground is harmful and must be screened out. Furthermore, the air in the immediate vicinity of the instruments must not be stagnant; it is necessary to provide for ventilation.

Fig. 18. The standard instrument shelter. (*Friez Instrument Division, Bendix Aviation Corp.*)

To obtain observations which, as far as possible, are representative of the moving masses of air, the thermometers, thermograph, hygrometer, and hygrograph are placed in an instrument shelter (Fig. 18). This is a wooden cage with a base of about 5 ft² and 3 ft high. The floor is nearly closed but permits some air movement through it. The walls are louvered to permit air to move freely through the shelter and, at the same time, screen out rain and sunshine. It has a slanting double roof through which air can move without much hindrance. The shelter is supported by four legs, so that the instruments are 5 to 6 ft above the ground. It should be mounted over grass and as far away from buildings as circumstances will permit. Free air movement past the shelter is essential.

The Mercury Barometer. The principle of this instrument was described on page 5. While the principle is simple, the construction of an accurate instrument is a task that requires great precision and skill. Also, the shipping, mounting, and calibration of mercury barometers require caution, and no amateur should attempt these tasks without having carefully studied the directions.

While it is difficult to obtain representative observations of the air temperature, it is quite easy to obtain reliable pressure observations. As explained on page 6, the pressure represents the weight of all the air

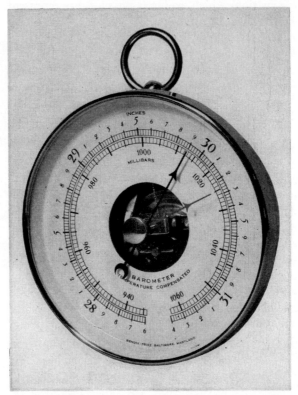

Fig. 19. The aneroid barometer. The pressure reading is 29.90 in. The hand on the right may be set on the reading. The difference between the two hands at any later time will indicate the change between readings. (*Friez Instrument Division, Bendix Aviation Corp.*)

above the barometer cistern, and is therefore not influenced by local conditions. Except in very strong winds the pressure in a room is the same as the pressure at the same level outside, and for this reason the barometer is mounted indoors.

The barometer is a relatively heavy instrument, and both the metal and the mercury adapt slowly to temperature changes. It is preferable, therefore, to mount the barometer in a room where the temperature is as constant as possible.

The direct reading of a barometer has but little meaning in itself; it acquires a meaning only when proper corrections, or reductions, have been applied. These reductions were explained in Chap. 1. Here it suffices to mention that the corrections for the temperature of the barometer and the reduction to standard gravity can be performed with great accuracy. When these reductions have been performed, one obtains the true pressure at the level of the barometer.

The major adjustment is the one that is applied to reduce all pressure readings to a common level such as sea level. As explained on page 7 the height difference between two points in the atmosphere, the one above

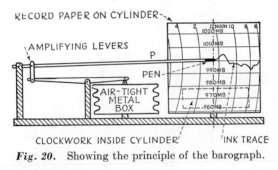

Fig. 20. Showing the principle of the barograph.

the other, can be computed from observations of temperature and pressure through the air column. However, when it is a question of reducing a pressure reading of a plateau station to sea level, there is no air column underneath, and the reduction is performed as if an air column were present. At normal temperatures the reduction gives fair accuracy, but with abnormal temperatures the reduction introduces large errors. In particular this is true over mountain plateaus in winter when cold stagnant air is present.

The Aneroid Barometer and the Barograph. A barometer which is cheap, robust, and handy for home use and travel is the aneroid (Fig. 19). Essentially it consists of an airtight metal box from which the air has been partly evacuated. When the atmospheric pressure increases the box will be slightly compressed, and when the pressure decreases the box will expand, and these motions are transferred through amplifying levers to a pointer which moves across a scale graduated in millibars or inches of mercury.

The aneroid barometer may be made to be self-recording so that a trace is drawn on a sheet of paper. The instrument is then called a barograph (Figs. 20 and 21), and the record paper is called a barogram. An example of a barogram is shown in Fig. 22.

The aneroid principle is used to construct the customary altimeters used in aircraft. In these instruments the pressure scale is replaced by a height scale that corresponds to the pressure and temperature of the standard atmosphere. A short table showing the relation between pressure, temperature, and height of the standard atmosphere is given in Table IV, Conversion Factors and Tables.

Wind Observations. When we read "the north wind doth blow we shall have snow," our thoughts are directed not so much to the direct

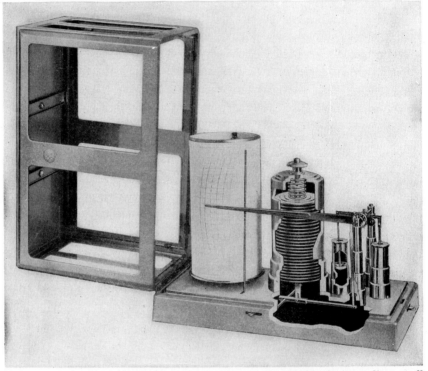

Fig. 21. A barograph with an open pressure scale, suitable for recording small variations. (*Friez Instrument Division, Bendix Aviation Corp.*)

effect of the wind as to the relation between air motion and weather. For example, when the wind blows over wet land, lakes, or oceans, evaporation will add to the moisture content of the air. If the air later ascends to greater heights, it will be cooled by expansion, and the water vapor may condense into rain-producing clouds. It is readily understood, therefore, that air motion is an important part of the weather processes, which we shall discuss in later chapters.

The direct effect of the wind is also important. It has been customary to refer to the horizontal components of air motion as *wind* and to mention separately the vertical currents. Furthermore, what is commonly called wind is the average air motion over a few minutes and not the instantane-

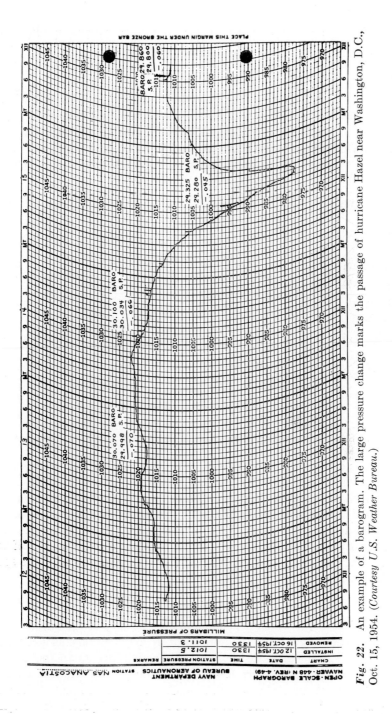

Fig. 22. An example of a barogram. The large pressure change marks the passage of hurricane Hazel near Washington, D.C., Oct. 15, 1954. (*Courtesy U.S. Weather Bureau.*)

ous gusts and lulls. The wind is therefore characterized by its direction, its speed, and its gustiness. The common observations include only direction and speed, and gustiness is reported only when there are squalls of appreciable strength.

The wind direction is taken to be the direction *from which* the wind is blowing. The zero point is true north; east, south, and west are 90, 180, and 270°, respectively, and these are commonly written as 09, 18, and 27. A north wind has direction 360° (36), and 0° is not used except in connection with a calm. In common parlance the wind directions are referred to

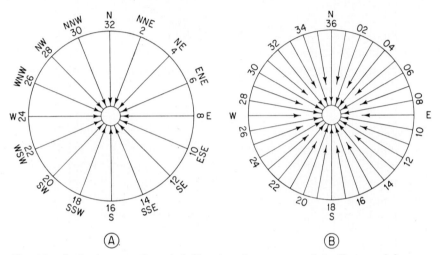

Fig. 23.   Scales for reporting wind direction. A, compass points; B, tens of degrees.

compass points, such as N, NNW, NW, etc., and in old records these directions are expressed by the numbers shown on the left in Fig. 23. In using such records it is necessary to ascertain whether the directions are expressed in compass points (00 to 32) or in tens of degrees (00 to 36).

The direct effect of wind on buildings and other obstacles is most directly expressed by the pressure that the wind exerts on a plate of unit area set at right angles to the wind. If P is the pressure and V the speed of the wind, the formula relating them is

$$P = KV^2$$

Here, K is a factor which depends upon the density of the air. Since the density varies but little in the horizontal, K may be taken as a constant. For example, if the pressure is expressed in pounds per square foot and the velocity in miles per hour, $K = 0.004$. Thus, if the wind speed were 10 mph, the pressure would be 0.4 lb/ft². On the other hand, if the wind were 100 mph, the pressure would be 40 lb/ft². Wind pressures as high as this would be ample to wreck ordinary buildings. Construction engineers are very much concerned with wind pressures, and particularly with the pressures during gusts and squalls.

Nowadays, the wind speed is commonly measured by instruments and expressed in terms of miles per hour (mph), knots, kilometers per hour (km/hr), or meters per second (m/sec). In earlier years the wind was mostly estimated by the aid of a scale invented by Admiral Beaufort in 1804. Originally this scale was developed for use in sailing ships, and the wind was graded according to the effect it had on the sails. Thus, Beaufort used his own ship as a wind-measuring instrument, and what he measured was the pressure of the wind over the sails. The Beaufort scale soon became standard throughout the world, and was modified for use on land stations, as shown in Table 2. Most old wind records, and many current ones outside the United States, are kept in Beaufort numbers.

While the Beaufort scale reflects the effect of the wind over a fairly large area surrounding the observer, a wind-measuring instrument gives only the spot wind, which may be much influenced by local conditions. To obtain reliable values it is necessary that the instrument be exposed freely, so that the air current is not obstructed by trees, buildings, and the like. On account of the frictional drag exerted by the earth's surface, the wind speed varies rapidly with height within the layer close to the ground. Exposures 20 to 30 ft above level ground, or well above the roof of a building, are preferable.

The most commonly used instrument for measuring wind speed is a revolving cup anemometer of the type shown in Fig. 24. Some of these instruments have four or more cups. The wind pressure on the concave side of the cup is greater than on the convex side, and this causes the cups to spin around the vertical axis. Friction is minimized by lubrication and ball bearings. The rate of rotation of the cups increases with the wind speed, the precise relation being determined either by calibration in a wind tunnel or by comparison with a standard instrument. The box (see Fig. 24) contains a mechanism which establishes a contact when the cups have rotated a certain number of times. These contacts close an electrical circuit, and the contacts are recorded on the paper of a drum which is rotated by a clock. An instrument which records in this manner is called an anemograph.

The wind direction is indicated by a vane of the type shown in Fig. 25. The variations in the direction may be transferred by a vertical rod or by electric contacts to a recording instrument. Often the vane and the cups are built into one instrument.

Another type of wind-measuring instrument is the pressure-tube anemograph. Here the wind vane carries a tube, with the nozzle facing the wind. The pressure exerted by the wind is transferred to a float partly

Table 2. The Beaufort Scale of Wind Force with Specifications and Velocity Equivalents

Beaufort number	General description	Specifications	Limits of velocity 20 ft above level ground			
			m/sec	km/hr	mph	Knots
0	Calm	Smoke rises vertically	Under 0.6	Under 1	Under 1	Under 1
1	Light air	Wind direction shown by smoke drift but not by vanes	0.6– 1.7	1– 6	1– 3	1– 3
2	Slight breeze	Wind felt on face; leaves rustle; ordinary vane moved by wind	1.8– 3.3	7– 12	4– 7	4– 6
3	Gentle breeze	Leaves and twigs in constant motion; wind extends light flag	3.4– 5.2	13– 18	8–11	7–10
4	Moderate breeze	Dust and loose paper; small branches are moved	5.3– 7.4	19– 26	12–16	10–14
5	Fresh breeze	Small trees in leaf begin to sway	7.5– 9.8	27– 35	17–22	15–19
6	Strong breeze	Large branches in motion; whistling in telegraph wires	9.9–12.4	36– 44	23–27	19–24
7	Moderate gale	Whole trees in motion	12.5–15.2	45– 55	28–34	24–30
8	Fresh gale	Twigs broken off trees; progress generally impeded	15.3–18.2	56– 66	35–41	30–35
9	Strong gale	Slight structural damage occurs; chimney pots removed	18.3–21.5	67– 77	42–48	36–42
10	Whole gale	Trees uprooted; considerable structural damage	21.6–25.4	78– 90	49–56	42–49
11	Storm	Very rarely experienced; widespread damage	25.5–29.0	91–104	57–67	49–56
12	Hurricane	....	Above 29.0	Above 104	Above 67	Above 56

Fig. 24. The cup anemometer. (*Friez Instrument Division, Bendix Aviation Corp.*)

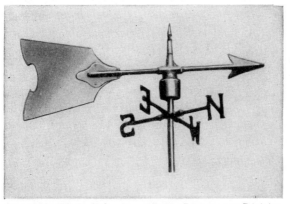

Fig. 25. The wind vane. (*Friez Instrument Division, Bendix Aviation Corp.*)

immersed in a liquid, and the movement of the float is recorded on a rotating drum carrying graph paper. The movement of the vane is transferred through rods and levers to a pen that traces the direction curve on the paper. The pressure-tube instrument is handy for obtaining the fine structure of the wind; it is often called a gust recorder.

Evaporation Measurements. The rate of evaporation from land and water surfaces depends on many factors; the most important ones are (1) the temperature of the liquid water as compared with the temperature of the air, (2) the relative humidity, or the saturation deficit, of the air, and (3) the wind speed.

The rate of evaporation is often measured by the use of a shallow circular pan about 8 ft in diameter and 1 ft deep. The pan is filled with water, and the loss of water is measured once a day. Such measurements are useful for local purposes, and particularly for assessing the evaporation from dams and reservoirs. These measurements, however, have but little bearing on the water budget of the atmosphere as a whole, for the pan observations are strongly influenced by the exposure. Furthermore, the water that evaporates from a pan is carried away with the wind, so that fresh air always sweeps over the pan. Over oceans and large water bodies, the air remains in contact with the water and gradually acquires some kind of equilibrium with the underlying surface, and this tends to reduce the evaporation. On the whole, the pan measurements tend to exaggerate the evaporation, and the water budget of the atmosphere as a whole must be obtained by indirect means.

Sunshine. While the sky is always blue above the clouds, it is often gray beneath. The Eskimo, the mid-latitudes farmer, and the desert dweller are equally interested in the intensity and the duration of the direct sunshine, although it affects them in different ways.

While modern instruments can record the intensity as well as the duration of sunshine, the ordinary station instrument records only the duration. For most purposes this is sufficient since the average intensity depends largely upon the elevation of the sun above the horizon.

A simple instrument for recording sunshine is a glass ball which focuses the sun's rays on a dialed paper, such that a charred trace is left of the sunny intervals. A more elaborate instrument is shown in Fig. 26. Essentially, this instrument consists of an inner and an outer glass tube between which the air has been exhausted so that the inner tube will not be affected by the air temperature. The bulb on the right is coated with lampblack so that it will absorb radiant energy more readily than the naked bulb. When the sun shines, a mercury column expands and closes an electric circuit, and this records the duration of direct sunshine. From such records the total duration each day is obtained and summarized for each month and the year. The duration of sunshine is expressed as a percentage of the total number of hours the sun could have shone if clouds had not been present.

Snow- and Rainfall. It is customary to refer to all the liquid and solid water that falls to the ground as precipitation, and the amount of precipitation is expressed as if it were melted to water. Thus, if 6 in. of fluffy snow fell, the amount of precipitation would be the depth of this snow after it had been melted to water, and this might not amount to more than 0.3 in. It is necessary, therefore, to distinguish between snow depth and amount of precipitation.

The simplest rain gage consists of a funnel-shaped collector mounted in a vertical position, with the wide end of the funnel upward. Below the mouth of the funnel is a long narrow tube with a cross-section area

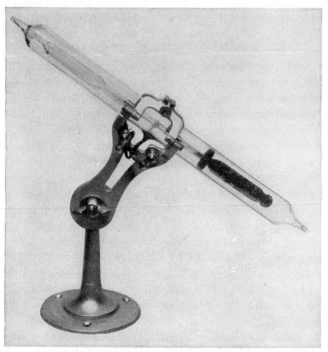

Fig. 26. The electric sunshine recorder. (*Friez Instrument Division, Bendix Aviation Corp.*)

exactly one-tenth of the collecting area. Thus, the rain will collect in the tube, and the length of the water column in it will be exactly 10 times longer than the depth of the water which fell. This amplification permits accurate readings even of small amounts. A finely graded rod is used for measuring.

The rain gage may be made as a self-recording instrument, and it is then called a pluviograph. Most commonly used is the tipping-bucket recorder. A bucket with two compartments is mounted at the mouth of the funnel such that the rain can enter only one of the compartments at a time. As one compartment fills, the bucket tips, empties itself, and presents the other compartment to the funnel. Each fill corresponds to a rainfall of 0.1 in. Every time the bucket tips, it closes an electric circuit which moves a pen on the record paper.

To obtain reliable values, the collecting area must not be too small, for turbulent air motion along the edge may carry some of the drops away from the funnel. A collecting area of 8 to 10 in. in diameter is preferable.

Accurate measurements of snowfall are difficult to obtain, for the lighter flakes drift readily with the wind, and turbulent motion around the snow gage will prevent some of the flakes from finding their way to the receptacle. The simplest snow gage is a cylindrical vessel of about 8 in. in diameter into which the snow falls. The water equivalent is determined by melting or weighing. To avoid evaporation during the melting operation, it is preferable not to apply heat in the customary manner, but to melt the snow by adding a known amount of warm water.

It is often difficult to find a suitable exposure for the rain and snow gages. They must not stand too close to buildings, trees, etc., and they should not be exposed to strong winds. The middle of a generous plot of level land surrounded by trees is preferable.

In addition to the water equivalent of the snowfall, the total snow depth is measured. Since the snow drifts and does not spread evenly over the ground, it is necessary to measure the depth in several representative places and to note the average.

Upper-air Observations. The first scientific balloon flights were made at the beginning of the nineteenth century (Paris, 1803), and a little more than a hundred years later aircraft equipped with instruments began to bring back data on temperature, pressure, and humidity. In the meantime the so-called "pilot balloon" had been widely used for measuring the winds aloft.

The pilot balloon is a small balloon made of rubber or synthetic materials. When appropriately filled with a light gas, for example, hydrogen, the balloon rises with an almost constant speed while it also drifts with the (horizontal) wind. The movement of the balloon is observed by a theodolite, and the azimuth and elevation angles noted at suitable intervals. Since the height is known from the time, the position in space of the balloon is obtained by simple trigonometry. The positions are plotted on a dial board, and from these the winds in the various layers are determined.

A major revolution in the upper air sounding system took place in 1928 when the Russian meteorologist Moltchanoff invented the radiosonde. Usually, the radiosonde consists of a small aneroid barometer, a bimetallic thermometer, and a hair hygrometer built into a cage which protects the instruments from rain and shine while letting the air stream through. The cage also contains a tiny radio transmitter with batteries supplying the power. The shelter and the instruments are attached to a balloon which rises while it also drifts with the wind. A little fan (resembling a cup anemometer) rotates a pointer which connects the instruments with the radio sender, and this sends signals to the ground, thus reporting the pressure, temperature, and humidity at frequent intervals.

Usually the balloon carries a reflector so that a radar set can determine its azimuth and elevation angle. The height of the balloon above the ground is obtained from the observed pressures and temperatures in the manner described on page 7. The winds at the various levels are then obtained as explained in connection with the pilot-balloon soundings.

3

Clouds and Precipitation

To the professional meteorologist the observations of the types of clouds and the forms of precipitation are as important as the readings of the thermometers and barometers. The ordinary observer, who is not a specialist, has simple classifications and descriptions to guide him in his observations. By the aid of such classifications and descriptions a skilled observer will be able to identify a number of different types of clouds and estimate their amounts and heights. He is also able to identify the more basic forms of precipitation, to distinguish between rain and drizzle, between granular and flaky snow, ice needles and plates, ice pellets and hail. The purpose of these distinctions is to enable the meteorologist to identify what the observer sees with the physical processes in the atmosphere.

Classification of Clouds. As seen from the earth's surface, the clouds may be divided into three main groups, according to their structure. These are (1) *cirrus*, or feathery streaks of clouds; (2) *stratus*, or layer clouds; and (3) *cumulus*, or heap-shaped clouds. These basic forms may be present simultaneously and in various combinations, such as layers of cirrus, layers of cumulus, and so on. Another important distinction is the height above the ground of the clouds. Thus, the cirrus clouds occur only in the upper part of the troposphere, and stratus occur only at low levels, while certain types of stratiform clouds are present only in the middle troposphere. On the other hand, the tops of the large cumulus clouds may reach up to the cirrus level, while their bases are only a few hundred feet above the ground.

Thus, depending on their height above the ground, their basic forms,

Table 3. Principal Types of Clouds

Name	Symbol	Height (approximate)
Cirrus...............	*Ci*	
Cirrostratus..........	*Cs*	High (20,000–40,000 ft)
Cirrocumulus.........	*Cc*	
Altostratus...........	*As*	
Altocumulus..........	*Ac*	Medium (8,000–20,000 ft)
Stratus..............	*St*	
Stratocumulus........	*Sc*	Low (below 8,000 ft)
Nimbostratus.........	*Ns*	
Cumulus.............	*Cu*	
Cumulonimbus........	*Cb*	Vertical development

and the more frequent combinations, the cloud forms may be divided into 10 principal types, as shown in Table 3. In addition there are many subtypes and combinations, but we shall not discuss them here.

Description of Cloud Types. The highest of all clouds are those belonging to the cirrus family. Their main characteristics are that they consist of fine ice crystals and that they have a fibrous structure and a delicate silky appearance. The *cirrus* clouds are sometimes arranged in

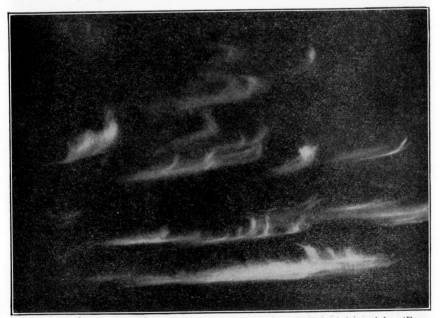

Fig. 27. White and silky streaks of cirrus drifting rapidly from left to right. (*From* "*International Atlas of Clouds.*")

streaks like skis or runners of a sledge (Fig. 27) and drift rapidly with the strong winds aloft. These clouds (*cirrus uncinus*) have detached themselves from the upper clouds of distant storms. Often the cirrus streaks merge upwind with a layer of cirrostratus; they are then usually the harbinger of bad weather. At other times the cirrus clouds are arranged irregularly in the sky as detached clouds without much drift; they are then called fair-weather cirrus. In thundery or squally weather a special kind of cirrus (*cirrus densus*) is frequently observed; it originates from the

Fig. 28.   A thin silky veil of cirrostratus with halo around the sun. Tops of cumulus clouds are seen far below the cirrus. (*From "International Atlas of Clouds."*)

anvils of thunderclouds and is often called false cirrus because it is denser and lower than ordinary cirrus.

Cirrostratus is a thin, whitish sheet of cloud, like a veil, sometimes covering the whole sky and merely giving it a milky appearance, at other times showing signs of a fibrous structure like a tangled web (Fig. 28).

Cirrocumulus (Fig. 29) consists of small, white flakes of cloud arranged in a pattern resembling lambs' wool or the skin of a mackerel. They are so thin that they show hardly any shadow even when the sun is behind them. The pattern is due to a single or double undulation of the cloud sheet.

Altostratus is a dense sheet of gray or bluish-gray color, frequently showing a fibrous structure (Fig. 30). Although the cloud sheet is dense

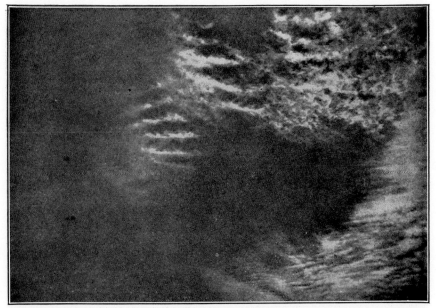

Fig. 29. A mackerel pattern of cirrocumulus. (*From "International Atlas of Clouds."*)

Fig. 30. A uniform sheet of altostratus through which the sun is barely seen. Below are fragments of low clouds, or scud. (*From "International Atlas of Clouds."*)

Fig. 31. Waves of altocumulus, merging with altostratus near the horizon. (*From "International Atlas of Clouds."*)

Fig. 32. Stratocumulus resembles altocumulus, but it is lower and grayer. (*From "International Atlas of Clouds."*)

the sun can usually be discerned through it. Increasing altostratus is usually followed by precipitation of a continuous and lasting type.

Altocumulus differs from cirrocumulus in that the cloud sheet is lower, and the flakes are larger and often show light shadows (Fig. 31). The typical altocumulus develops from dissolving altostratus. An important variety is called *altocumulus castellanus*. In appearance it resembles ordinary altocumulus; but it is more ragged and, in places, turreted tops

Fig. 33. Fair-weather cumulus (*cumulus humilis*) are rather flat and show no vertical growth. (*From "International Atlas of Clouds."*)

develop looking like miniature cumulus. Altocumulus castellatus usually indicates a change to a chaotic, thundery sky.

Stratocumulus is a low cloud layer consisting of large lumpy masses or rolls of dull gray color with brighter interstices (Fig. 32). The masses are often arranged in regular patterns and sometimes resemble altocumulus, except that they are lower and darker.

Nimbostratus is a dense, shapeless, and ragged layer of low clouds from which precipitation usually falls. It is often connected with altostratus that is present above the nimbus. Fragments of nimbus that drift under the cloud layer are called *fractonimbus*, or *scud*.

Cumulus is a thick cloud whose upper surface is dome-shaped, often of a cauliflower structure, and whose base is more or less horizontal. It is useful to distinguish between two types of cumulus. Flat cumulus clouds without towers or protuberances are called *cumulus humilis*, or fair-

Fig. 34.   Towering cumulus (*cumulus congestus*) with heads resembling cauliflower. (*From "International Atlas of Clouds."*)

Fig. 35.   Cumulonimbus without anvil. (*From "International Atlas of Clouds."*)

Fig. 36. Cumulonimbus with anvil. (*From "International Atlas of Clouds."*)

Fig. 37. A squall-line cumulonimbus. The dark roll of cloud may extend over a few hundreds of miles, and the more uniform cloud mass usually extends to great heights. (*From "International Atlas of Clouds."*)

weather cumulus (Fig. 33). Towering cumulus clouds which show internal motion and growth are called *cumulus congestus* (Fig. 34). They often develop into cumulonimbus.

Cumulonimbus, thunderclouds, or shower clouds are great masses of cloud rising like mountains, towers, or giant anvils and having a base that looks like a ragged mass of nimbostratus. The tops are often anvil-shaped or surrounded by false cirrus. Figure 35 shows a cloud without anvil, and

Fig. 38. A low stratus touching the hills. (*From "International Atlas of Clouds."*)

Fig. 36 shows one with anvil. The cumulonimbus clouds are accompanied by showers, squalls, or thunderstorms and sometimes hail.

The line-squall cloud is a variety of cumulonimbus that extends like a long line or arch across the sky (Fig. 37). It is usually accompanied by severe thunderstorms and squalls, and in pronounced cases tornadoes may occur.

Stratus is a uniform layer of low foglike cloud which does not touch the ground (Fig. 38). Seen from above, the stratus layers often show surges like a large swell on an ocean of cloud.

Fog is defined as a cloud that touches the ground and reduces the visibility to ⅝ mile (1 km) or less. If in similar circumstances the visibility is greater than ⅝ mile, the cloud is called a *mist*. It should be noted, however, that the word mist is popularly used in the United States to indicate a fine sprinkle of rain.

The heights of the various types of cloud vary within wide limits, and the figures in Table 3 indicate only the approximate ranges. The tops of the cumulonimbus clouds may reach up to 40,000 ft (13 km), while their bases may be only a few hundred feet above the ground.

Haze, Soot, and Dust. While the city housewife considers the dust in the air to be a nuisance (or worse), it is not generally realized that these impurities constitute a blessing in disguise; for if the air were perfectly pure life would be unbearable. The role that dust, soot, and salts play in

Fig. 39. The village of Manter, Kans., is about to become obscured in an April dust storm. In this area the Red Cross prepared to dustproof houses to prevent death and illness. (*Courtesy U.S. Weather Bureau.*)

the weather processes will be discussed in the following chapter; here we shall only mention the sources of impurities and their influence on the transparency of the air.

When the wind blows, dust, sand, pollen, etc., are lifted into the air. In extreme cases veritable sandstorms (Fig. 39) sweep over the deserts and steppes. The coarser material is, however, not carried very far, but the finer particles are kept aloft by the turbulent air motion. The deserts consist mainly of coarse material, and although sandstorms and drifting sand do occur occasionally, the air is, on the whole, quite clear, particularly during the night. The main source of dust in the air is the semiarid regions and the tilled land areas in the mid-latitudes.

The main source of salts is the ocean surface. When the wind is sufficiently strong, air is churned into the sea. The air bubbles rise to the surface and burst, shooting up minute drops, more or less like the fine spray which escapes from a bottle of Coca-Cola when the cap is removed.

The droplets evaporate and leave fine salt particles to float in the air. These particles are very small, their average diameter being less than about 1 micron. They are readily distributed through deep layers by mixing and can remain in the air for many days, unless they are washed out by rain or snow. But even after heavy precipitation, some remain in the air.

Forest fires, industrial plants, and dwellings produce large amounts of soot. When fuels burn at high temperatures, the hydrogen and oxygen combine to produce water vapor, and carbon and oxygen combine to produce carbon dioxide, and both of these are among the normal constituents of the atmosphere. However, when fuels burn at relatively low temperatures, the formation of carbon dioxide is hindered; much of the carbon is carried up with the rising currents and coagulates into soot. The soot trouble in industrial regions would be much reduced if fuels were burned at high temperatures.

Except in the case of sandstorms and drifting sand, the particles which make up the impurities are so small that they cannot be seen individually. However, their total effect on the visibility and on the coloring of distant objects is easily observed. The ensemble of dust in the air is called *haze*. When seen through a haze, distant dark objects, such as mountains, appear as if they were covered by a thin veil which subdues the colors and the details and lets the object stand out like a bluish silhouette against the sky. In the same circumstances, white objects, such as snow-covered mountains or clouds at the horizon, will acquire a yellowish tinge. The denser the haze, the shorter is the distance at which the details disappear. The combinations of clouds, shadows, impurities, and light account for the infinite variety of scenic nuances, which the great artists have represented so well.

Classification of Precipitation. The water cycle in the atmosphere consists of three distinct parts, namely, evaporation, condensation, and precipitation. While everyone realizes the difference between evaporation and condensation, the distinction between condensation and precipitation is less appreciated. Essentially, the condensation process consists in an accumulation of water-vapor molecules into exceedingly small droplets. On the other hand, the precipitation process is one in which a very large number of such droplets join to form drops (or aggregates of ice crystals) of the size that we call rain (or snow). An average raindrop has a radius of about 1,000 microns, while the average cloud droplet has a radius of rather less than 20 microns. Since the volume is proportional to the cube of the radius, it follows that an ordinary raindrop is made up of more than one million cloud droplets. These are rough figures, but they will serve to emphasize the difference between the products resulting from the condensation and precipitation processes.

The number of different forms of precipitation elements is quite large, and the description here will be limited to the more common forms.

Drizzle is a fine sprinkle of very small and rather uniform water drops, with diameter less than 0.02 in. (0.5 mm). The drops are so small that they seem to float in the air and follow the irregularities in the air motion. In a typical drizzle an umbrella is not very effective, for the drops dance about and some of them get under the umbrella. To qualify as a drizzle the drops must not only be small, but they must also be very numerous. The message that a drizzle report conveys to the meteorologist is about as follows: We (the drops) formed a short while ago in a low layer of rather deep stratus not far from the ground. Although the layer is deep, as far as stratus goes, it is quite shallow as compared with the depth of ordinary rain clouds, and for this reason we did not collide with many other drops while we fell. Hence, we came down as undersized individuals. This is a very useful message, and on the basis of it the meteorologist forms a picture of the structure of the lower layers of the atmosphere.

Rain is precipitation of liquid water in which the drops, as a rule, are larger than in drizzle. On occasion, the drops may be of drizzle size, but they are then few and far between, and this distinguishes them from drizzle. A sprinkle of such rain indicates that the drops formed in a cloud at considerable height and fell through a layer of relatively dry air so that some drops evaporated completely and the others shrank on the way down. It also suggests that the precipitation processes might not have been very active. Once in a while, rain is seen to fall out of clouds and evaporate completely before it reaches the ground. Such streaks of precipitation are called *virgae*. On the other hand, if the drops are large and numerous when they arrive at the ground, as they are in the downpour from a thundercloud, the inference is that the precipitation processes are very active, that the clouds are very deep, and that the air under them is relatively moist.

Snow is precipitation of solid water, mainly in the form of branched hexagonal crystals or stars. Even at temperatures well below freezing the crystals carry a thin coating of liquid water, and when they collide, they become matted together as large flakes. At very low temperatures the crystals are dry and large flakes are not seen. Again, the shape and size of the precipitation elements reflect the processes which led to their formation.

Sleet (British) is nothing but melting snow or a mixture of snow and rain. Much of the precipitation in high and mid-latitudes begins as snow in the upper layers, turns into sleet at and below the melting level, and comes down to the earth as rain. On the other hand, if rain from warm air aloft falls through a layer of cold air near the ground, it does not turn into snow. The falling raindrops will freeze into grains or pellets of ice. This is what is called *sleet* in North America.

Glaze, or freezing rain, is reported when rain falls into a cold layer of air and freezes when it strikes the ground, trees, power lines, etc. In pronounced cases this may result in veritable icing storms and cause much damage (see Fig. 40).

Fig. 40.   After an icing storm in New York, January, 1943. (*Courtesy U.S. Weather Bureau and Robideau Studios, Malone, N.Y.*)

Ice needles, or diamond dust, are thin shafts or small thin plates of ice which are so light that they seem to float in the air. They occur only at very low temperatures and are therefore rarely seen except in high mountains and in the polar regions.

Granular snow is opaque small grains falling from stratus clouds. It is the frozen counterpart of drizzle.

Hail. In reporting, distinction is made between three kinds of hail. *Soft hail* is round and opaque grains of snowlike structure with diameters from 0.08 to 0.2 in. (2 to 5 mm). The grains are crisp, and they rebound and disintegrate easily when they fall on a hard surface. *Small hail* is semitransparent, round grains of about the same size as soft hail. The grains have a core of soft hail surrounded by a crust of ice which gives it a glazed appearance. Small hail falls from cumulonimbus clouds together with rain. The word *hail* is used to indicate large balls or lumps of ice with average diameter from 0.2 to 2 in. or more. Such hail falls almost exclusively from violent thunderstorms in which the vertical currents are very strong. Often the hailstones show concentric layers of clear ice alternating with layers of snow. This structure indicates that the hailstones have been tossed up and down in the cloud while growing to such sizes that they could no longer be supported in the updraft.

Dew, frost, and rime. While drizzle, rain, snow, and hail form in the air and fall to the ground, dew and various kinds of rime form directly on the ground or on obstacles.

Dew forms directly by condensation on the ground, mainly during the night when the surface has been cooled by outgoing radiation. In rainy climates the dew is of but little importance for the vegetation. On the other hand, in dry climates the nightly dew may contribute substantially to plant growth. This is true particularly where dry steppes reach to the coast. Here the sea breeze brings in a shallow layer of moisture during the day which condenses to dew in the cool of the night.

Hoar frost consists of ice crystals in the form of scales, needles, feathers, and fans. It forms in the same manner as dew, except that the water vapor of the air is transformed directly into ice crystals.

Rime consists of white layers of ice crystals and forms when the droplets of undercooled clouds and fogs touch obstacles. In the high mountains and, also, over the polar fields of snow and ice, the amounts of rime deposit may be appreciable (see Fig. 41).

Genetical Classification. The classification of precipitation described in the foregoing section was based mainly upon the appearance of the precipitation elements. There is another, more genetical, classification which relates the precipitation more directly to the processes. The broad aspects of this classification may be summarized as follows:

1. *Intermittent or continuous precipitation,* such as rain or snow, falling more or less evenly from a continuous cover of altostratus and nimbostratus. This precipitation is due to widespread and slow upward movement of large masses of air. These are the migratory systems usually associated with fronts and cyclones.

2. *Showers* (squalls, flurries), or precipitation of short duration with fair intervals. This kind of precipitation comes from cumulonimbus clouds and indicates an unstable stratification in which rapid overturnings take place.

3. *Drizzle,* or small and numerous drops falling out of a fog or a low layer of stratus. This is an indication of stable stratification without any appreciable vertical motion. The small drops fall out rather because upward motion is absent.

Cloud Cover, Ceiling, and Visibility. The cloud cover is estimated by the observer and expressed on a scale ranging from 0 to 8. Here, 0 means clear sky, 4 means that one-half (or four-eighths) of the sky is covered, and 8 means overcast. The figure 9 is used to indicate that the sky is obscured, for example by smoke. Up to about 1948, the cloud cover was reported on a scale ranging from 0 to 10, and in using past records it is necessary to ascertain which scale was in use.

Fig. 41. Heavy rime deposits on east side of Mount Washington Observatory. (*Courtesy U.S. Weather Bureau.*)

The ceiling, or the height above the ground of the cloud cover, is of particular importance in aircraft operation. A ceiling is said to exist if the clouds below 10,000 ft cover more than one-half (⅝) of the sky. If the cloud cover is less, or the base higher, the ceiling is said to be unlimited. The height of the ceiling is measured by small balloons whose ascensional velocity is known. At night, it may be measured by attaching a light to the balloon. More commonly used is the "ceiling light," which is a vertical beam that throws a spot on the base of the cloud. The elevation angle of the spot is observed from a neighboring place and the height is obtained by simple trigonometry.

The visibility is the largest distance at which prominent objects, such as mountains, hills, buildings, towers, etc., can be seen and identified by the unaided eye. This distance depends upon the impurities in the air and upon the density of fog, mist, precipitation, and so forth. In a dense smog the visibility may be only a few feet, while in the pure air of the arctic winter, mountains may be seen at a distance of more than 100 miles.

Weather Symbols. The observer translates his observations into coded messages, and these are transmitted to the receiving centers. The code forms and specifications are determined by international agreement and published by the World Meteorological Organization and also by the national weather bureaus. Since the codes are changed from time to time to meet operational needs, reference must be made to current publications. Here, we shall reproduce only what is necessary to interpret the charts which will be included in the following sections.

1. *Instrumental Observations.* With few exceptions the instrumental observations are plotted as numbers. Since the atmospheric pressure, when reduced to sea level, is not far from 1,000 mb, the hundreds are not plotted and the decimal point is usually left out. Thus, 119 and 936 stand for 1,011.9 and 993.6 mb, respectively. The pressure change during the 3 hr preceding the observation is called the *barometric tendency.* It is plotted without decimal point, so that 25 stands for 2.5 mb. The sign and the general trend of the change are indicated by such symbols as

/   STEADY RISE

⌐\   RISE, FOLLOWED BY A LARGER FALL

ⁿ₂   IRREGULAR FALL

∨   FALL FOLLOWED BY A LESSER RISE

The wind direction and speed are indicated by an arrow such that the shaft shows the direction *from which* the wind blows, and the barbs give the speed in knots. For example, ⋰⋰⋱ would signify a wind from the west having a speed of 75 knots. The short barb indicates 5 knots, the long barb 10 knots, and the filled triangle 50 knots.

2. *Visual Observations.* Elements such as cloud forms, cloud cover, forms of precipitation, etc., are indicated by symbols which are intended to remind the reader of the phenomena to which they refer.

Cloud Cover. This is estimated by the observer and reported as the number of eighths of the sky covered by clouds. The station is identified by a circle, and the cloud cover is indicated by proportional filling:

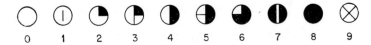

Here, 9 means that the sky is obscured so that the cloud cover cannot be determined.

Cloud Forms. The primary symbols corresponding to the classification given on page 41 are

⟋	CIRRUS	∿	STRATOCUMULUS
⟌	CIRROSTRATUS	⬱	NIMBOSTRATUS
⟋	CIRROCUMULUS	⌒	CUMULUS
�ᴜ	ALTOCUMULUS	⌂	CUMULUS CONGESTUS
∠	ALTOSTRATUS	⌂	CUMULONIMBUS
—	STRATUS	---	SCUD

These symbols may appear in combinations, such as cumulonimbus with scud, altocumulus with altostratus, cumulus and stratocumulus, etc.

Forms of Precipitation. The basic symbols are:

∞	HAZE	∿	FREEZING
=	MIST	✱	SNOW
≡	FOG	△	HAIL
⌢	SMOKE	▽	SHOWER
9	DRIZZLE	T₄	THUNDERSTORM
•	RAIN	⑀	DUSTSTORM OR SANDSTORM
⊹	DRIFTING SNOW		

x]	X ENDED DURING PRECEDING HOUR
|x	X HAS BECOME DENSER DURING PRECEDING HOUR
x|	X HAS BECOME LESS DENSE DURING PRECEDING HOUR

Coexistence of two phenomena is indicated by a vertical arrangement of the symbols. Thus, ∿ means freezing rain, and ⌂ᴛ means thunderstorm accompanied by hail.

Sequence of events is indicated by a horizontal arrangement of the symbols. For example, ≡] means that a fog existed but dissolved during the last hour.

Intensity is indicated by vertical repetition of the symbols. For example,

✱	LIGHT AND INTERMITTENT SNOW
✱ ✱	LIGHT AND CONTINUOUS SNOW
✱✱ (vertical)	MODERATE AND INTERMITTENT SNOW
✱✱✱	MODERATE AND CONTINUOUS SNOW
✱✱✱ (vertical)	HEAVY AND INTERMITTENT SNOW
✱✱✱	HEAVY AND CONTINUOUS SNOW

Similarly ⩟ would indicate a heavy thunderstorm with hail.

3. *The Plotting Model.* To facilitate the interpretation of the plots, each element occupies a fixed position relative to the station circle. The general arrangement is shown in Fig. 42. In the case shown there was a thunderstorm in the interval between the present and the foregoing observation; this was followed by a shower which ended during the hour preceding the observation; the amount of rainfall was 1.20 in.; cumulonimbus clouds were still present; six-eighths of the sky was covered by

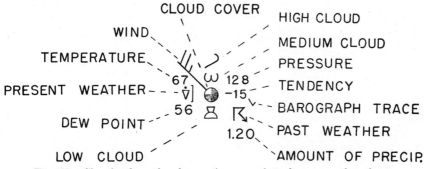

Fig. 42. Showing how the observations are plotted on a weather chart.

clouds; the wind was NW 25 knots; the barometer was 1,012.8 mb; the temperature was 67°F and the dewpoint 56°F.

Weather Charts. In the forecasting services, observations from land stations and ships are received every third hour, and these are plotted on weather charts, using the symbols summarized in the foregoing section. Upper-air observations of pressure, temperature, humidity, and winds are received at intervals of 12 hr, and these are plotted on other charts. It is customary to draw upper-air charts for the levels 850, 700, 500, and 300 mb. These are more or less standard levels. Additional levels are used to satisfy the needs of aviation. In particular where jet aircraft operate, the winds at 200 and 100 mb are charted.

An example of a plot of a sea-level weather chart is shown in Fig. 43. The reader is invited to examine the plots and translate the information into plain language, using the symbols in the foregoing section. Of some interest is the line, or zone, along which the wind and temperature change rapidly.

Figure 44 shows the analyzed sea-level chart for a much larger area but with much of the data omitted. The following features are of particular interest.

1. The center of an area where the pressure is low is marked L. The system of pressure and winds surrounding such a center is called a *cyclone*. The winds around such a center circulate in a counterclockwise direction

(in the Northern Hemisphere), and we say that the circulation is cyclonic. In the Southern Hemisphere the circulation would be clockwise, but this too is said to be cyclonic circulation. In a general manner we say that the circulation is cyclonic if it is in the same direction as the rotation of the earth's surface, and the isobars around a center of low pressure are said to be curved cyclonically.

2. The areas where the pressure is high are marked *H*. A high-pressure system is usually called an *anticyclone*. The circulation around

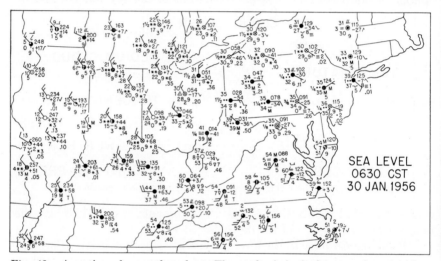

SEA LEVEL
0630 CST
30 JAN. 1956

Fig. 43. A section of a weather chart. The reader is invited to translate the plots into plain language, using the information given in the foregoing section.

such a system is said to be anticyclonic, and the same is said of the curvature of the isobars.

3. It will be seen from Fig. 44 that there is a line, or rather a narrow zone, running through the low-pressure center over Ohio, along which the winds shift abruptly. The same is true of the temperature and most of the other weather characteristics (see also Fig. 43). Such lines, or zones, are called *fronts*. They are the borders of air masses of different life histories. To the northeast of the low center, warm air replaces colder air, and the line of separation is called a *warm front*. On the southwestern side it is cold air that replaces warmer air, and such a front is called a *cold front*. On occasions, a cold front may overtake a warm one, and the combined front is then called an *occlusion*.

The fronts shown in Fig. 44 mark the intersection between a *frontal surface* and the surface of the earth. The frontal surface, or the layer of transition between the two air masses, has a gentle upward slope in the direction from the warm toward the cold side, so that the cold air forms a

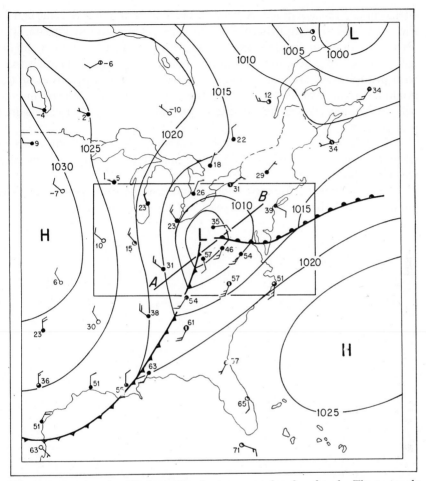

Fig. 44. This is a simplified weather chart on a much reduced scale. The rectangle indicates the area shown in Fig. 43, and the line *AB* refers to the cross section shown in Fig. 45. The full lines are isobars.

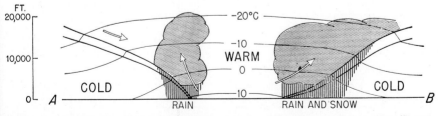

Fig. 45. Illustrating the meaning of the terms cold and warm fronts. Details are given in Chap. 13.

wedge under the warm air. A vertical cross section along the line *AB* in Fig. 44 would show a structure of the type represented in Fig. 45. The warm air will normally glide up over the warm-front surface; the warm air will cool by expansion, and this accounts for the fact that cloud systems with precipitation are often present in advance of the warm front at the ground. In the rear of the cyclone the cold air, on its forward march, will push under the warm air. Here, too, we normally find clouds and precipitation.

The slope of a frontal surface is normally very small. An average warm front has a slope of about $\frac{1}{100}$ to $\frac{1}{300}$, while cold fronts are usually steeper.

The air masses, fronts, cyclones, and anticyclones undergo typical life cycles, and these will be discussed in Chaps. 12 to 14.

4

Condensation and
Precipitation Processes

It is common experience that clouds may exist for days without releasing precipitation. On other occasions a heavy downpour may develop within an hour or two after the cloud has formed. We are thus led to consider not only the formation of cloud droplets but also the processes which release precipitation.

Condensation Nuclei. Observation as well as theory shows that condensation of water vapor into cloud droplets takes place on certain particles, or kernels, which have a high affinity to water vapor. Such particles are said to be *hygroscopic*, and they are called *condensation nuclei*. In effect, this means that the water-vapor molecules are incapable of joining into droplets except when they can begin to do so on a suitable nucleus. After this beginning, water vapor will condense on the liquid water which has already formed. The most active nuclei are either particles of sea salt or such products of combustion as contain sulfurous and nitrous acids. The salt nuclei vary in size from 0.1 to 1 micron, with a few giant nuclei as large as 5 microns. Their number is enormous and varies from 100 to 10,000 per in.^{3} (10 to 1,000 per cm^3). The combustion nuclei are generally smaller, and their number varies considerably with the industrial activity.

Formation and Growth of Cloud Droplets. In some of the foregoing sections we have used the term saturation and mentioned saturated air rather loosely. In order to understand how droplets form and begin to grow it is necessary to go into the details of the processes and to define our terms more precisely.

We say that *saturation* occurs when moist air has such a composition that it can exist in equilibrium with a *plane* surface of *pure* water which has the same temperature as the air. Here the term *equilibrium* means that there is no net transfer of water-vapor molecules from the air to the water surface or from the water surface to the air. This equilibrium then defines the saturation vapor pressure and 100 per cent relative humidity (see Fig. 4).

The qualifications that the water must be pure and that the surface must be plane are important, for if the water is not pure or if the surface is not plane, other equilibria will exist. We know, for example, that ordinary crude salt gets wet long before the relative humidity (as defined above) reaches 100 per cent. Therefore, if the droplet contains salt it can be in equilibrium with the surrounding air when the relative humidity is less than 100 per cent. The difference depends upon the strength of the solution, and we speak of this as the *solute effect*.

Let us now imagine that we introduce a salt nucleus in moist air which is not saturated. Condensation will then occur on the salt. However, as the droplet grows the solution weakens, and the growth of the droplet would be more or less as shown by curve *A* in Fig. 46. When the drop has grown so that its radius is about 2 microns it is so diluted that, for all practical purposes, it behaves as if it were pure water. Thus, the solute effect is important only at the very beginning of the process, but during this phase it is all-important, since droplets would not form if nuclei were absent.

The solute effect is counteracted by another effect, which is called the *curvature effect*. When the drops are very small the surface tension is appreciable. The "skin" of a droplet (like that of a soap bubble) behaves like a stretched membrane, and work must be done to stretch it further. In effect, this means that such a droplet will resist the advances of the vapor molecules in the air until the vapor pressure of the air is greater than the saturation vapor pressure corresponding to a plane water surface. In other words, a small droplet will not be in equilibrium with the surrounding air until the relative humidity is over 100 per cent. Suppose now that a small droplet of *pure* water was introduced in supersaturated air with such high humidity that the drop begins to grow. The curvature of the droplet then decreases, and as the growth progresses the effect of curvature tends to vanish, more or less as shown by curve *B* in Fig. 46. When the droplet has grown so that its radius is 2 to 3 microns, the curvature effect is so small that, for all practical purposes, the drop behaves as if it had a plane surface. It will thus be seen that both the solute effect and the curvature effect are important only at the very beginning;

later the process is almost the same as if the water were pure and the surface plane.

The actual growth comes out as a compromise between the solute effect and the curvature effect, as shown in Fig. 46. Suppose that a nucleus of salt is introduced into air which is not saturated. The nucleus

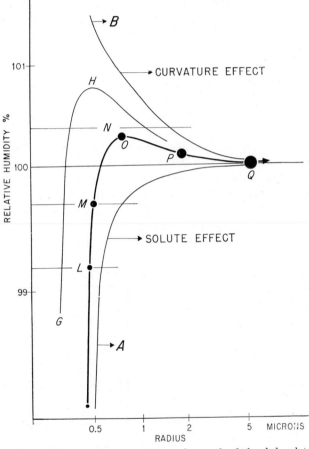

Fig. 46.   Showing the formation and growth of cloud droplets.

will then absorb water until it is in equilibrium with the surrounding air. Let this point be indicated by *L* in Fig. 46. Next let the air be cooled so that the relative humidity increases a little. The droplet will then grow further until a new equilibrium is reached, say, at *M*. We cool the air again so that the relative humidity increases to the value indicated by *N*. The droplet will then grow along the curve *LMOP* without coming into equilibrium with the surrounding air. After the hump *O* has been passed, the growth is *unstable* in the sense that it does not result in an approach to equilibrium.

Suppose next that a much smaller nucleus were used. The solute effect would then be smaller and the curvature effect larger. The result would be that the hump H would be higher, as indicated by the curve GH.

The condensation process may now be summarized as follows. When the air is cooled the relative humidity increases, but before it reaches 100 per cent (in terms of a plane surface of pure water), condensation begins on the larger and more active nuclei, and these grow to full-sized cloud droplets when the humidity is close to 100 per cent. The solute effect is opposed by the curvature effect, and for this reason the small and less active nuclei do not come into play, for the available water vapor is used up by the larger nuclei. Hence, the number of cloud droplets in a unit volume is much smaller than the number of nuclei.

Computations show that it takes an average nucleus about 1 sec to grow to 10 microns, a few minutes to grow to 100 microns, 3 hr to grow to 1,000 microns (or 1 mm), and about a day to grow to 3 mm. Since heavy rain may develop within an hour or two after the cloud has formed, it is evident that the condensation process is far too slow to account for the formation of raindrops, although it is able to produce drops of drizzle size.

The Fall Velocity of Drops. Before we discuss the rain-producing mechanisms, it is useful to know something about the rates at which

Table 4. Terminal Velocity of Raindrops and Cloud Droplets in Still Air

Diameter, microns	Rate of fall		Type of drop
	ft/min	m/sec	
5,000	1,750	8.9	Large raindrop
1,000	790	4.0	Small raindrop
500	555	2.8	Fine rain or large drizzle
200	300	1.5	Drizzle
100	59	0.3	Large cloud droplet
50	15	0.076	Ordinary cloud droplet
10	0.6	0.003	
2	0.023	0.00012	Incipient droplets and nuclei
1	0.007	0.00004	

drops of various sizes fall relative to the air. A water drop will be accelerated downward by gravity. As the velocity increases, the frictional drag against the surrounding air increases, and after a short while the two forces balance. Thereafter the drop falls with a constant speed which is called the *terminal velocity*. Some typical values for spherical drops are given in Table 4.

If the air itself had vertical motion, the drops would fall *relative* to the air with the speeds indicated. It will be seen that a large raindrop can be kept aloft if the updraft is about 9 m/sec (30 ft/sec), and that the smaller drops would be carried upward in the cloud. Updrafts with such speeds are commonly observed in thunderstorms. When drops of various sizes are present, their rates of fall will vary over wide ranges, and this provides plenty of opportunity for collisions.

Another interesting feature should be mentioned here. When a drop grows to about 7,000 microns in diameter, the fall velocity will be somewhat larger than 30 ft/sec. At such high speeds the drop flattens out and breaks up into a few smaller drops, such as small raindrops and drizzle. Thus there is an upper limit to the size of the drops that can exist in the atmosphere. If a bucket of water were emptied into the air from the top of a skyscraper, the water would come down as ordinary raindrops unless the air was so dry that the drops evaporated before they came down.

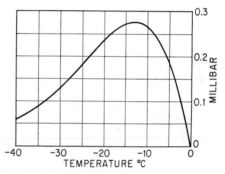

Fig. 47. The saturation vapor pressure over ice is lower than over water, and this permits condensation on ice particles before the air is saturated in respect to water.

Precipitation Processes. In the main there are two processes which will cause the clouds to release precipitation. The first of these is commonly called the *ice-crystal process*, and the latter may be called the *capture process*.

The ice-crystal process is readily explained as follows. When the air ascends it cools by expansion, and as it cools, the relative humidity increases. When the air reaches saturation, cloud droplets form. These droplets do not freeze until the temperature is far below the melting point (32°F or 0°C). Observations from aircraft show that at temperatures between 32 and 10°F the clouds normally consist of water droplets. In the range from 10 to −20°F, one usually finds a mixture of water droplets and ice crystals. At still lower temperatures ice crystals predominate, and at very low temperatures only ice crystals are present. These are the cirrus clouds which were discussed in the foregoing chapter.

The layer with a mixture of water droplets and ice crystals is of particular interest. The reason is that the saturation vapor pressure over ice is lower than over water. Although the difference is small (see Fig. 47) it is significant. In a cloud which consists of both droplets and crystals the actual vapor pressure will be a compromise between the two saturation pressures, so that the air is not quite saturated in respect to water while it is slightly supersaturated in respect to ice. This will cause the droplets to evaporate while water vapor condenses on the ice crystals. In other words, we have here a process which will cause some of the cloud elements to grow at the expense of the others. This effect is often called the *Bergeron effect*, after Bergeron, who discovered it in 1928. The essence of the Bergeron effect is shown schematically in Fig. 48.

As soon as some of the cloud elements have outgrown the others, the larger ones will fall through the cloud and further growth will result from collisions. When an ordinary raindrop falls through a cloud, the smallest cloud droplets are swept aside but the larger ones are captured on the forward side of the falling drop (Fig. 49*a*). We call this *direct capture*.

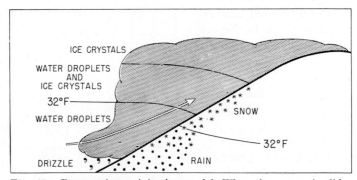

Fig. 48.   Bergeron's precipitation model. When the warm air glides up over the cold wedge, it cools adiabatically and cloud droplets form. Precipitation begins to form in the layer where ice crystals and water droplets are present. The larger elements fall through the cloud and grow further by collision with other drops and droplets.

There is, however, another capture process which is important. When a drop falls, the streamlines diverge rapidly (Fig. 49*b*) on its forward side while they converge slowly in the rear. In the wake which the drop leaves behind, the air resistance is reduced, so that other drops, of almost the same size as the leading drop, will fall fast in the wake and overtake the leading drop. This is called *wake capture*.

In high and mid-latitudes the freezing level is so low that many clouds reach up to subfreezing temperatures, and here the ice-crystal process is important for starting the release, while the capture processes come into play later. In low latitudes only few clouds reach up to subfreezing temperatures, and in such clouds precipitation is released because some cloud droplets are appreciably larger than the others. To ensure further growth, to the size of raindrops, it is important that the cloud be deep. Observations show that tropical clouds which are less than about 6,000 ft deep do not produce rain. The probability for rain to occur increases with the depth of the cloud, and clouds which are more than 12,000 ft deep are almost certain to produce rain.

In a thundercloud the updrafts are so strong that ordinary raindrops may be carried upward in the cloud. Such drops will grow by collisions while they are carried upward as well as when they later fall downward. When such drops grow to the critical size (see foregoing section), they break up into smaller drops which then are carried by the updraft. This may lead to repeated growths and splinterings, with the result that a vast

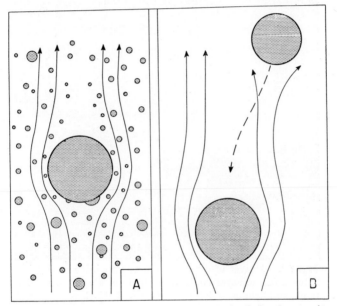

Fig. 49. A falling raindrop will capture cloud droplets on its forward side (*a*), and it will be overtaken by other raindrops coming into its wake (*b*).

number of raindrops is produced. As soon as the updraft weakens, or changes into a downdraft, a heavy downpour sets in. In the large and widespread cloud systems, the vertical velocities are very small (2 to 4 in./sec), and the drops are generally smaller and far less numerous.

Artificial Stimulation of Precipitation. A cloud that reaches up to freezing temperatures may not contain any ice crystals, and in such cases it will not be very effective as a producer of rain; everything is there except the freezing nuclei which are necessary to start the process. Therefore, if we could add ice crystals the process would start. Instead of adding ice crystals we could cool the air so that ice crystals would form in the cloud. One way of doing this is to drop dry ice in the upper portion of the cloud. The air in the wakes of the falling lumps of dry ice would be cooled;

natural ice crystals would form and spread through the cloud, thus initiating precipitation. Another way of inducing the cloud to release precipitation consists in "fooling" the water-vapor molecules into behaving as if ice crystals were present. For this purpose silver iodide has been used, since its structure is very similar to that of natural ice crystals.

Experiments have shown that when dry ice or silver iodide is sprinkled over a layer of undercooled stratus, snow begins to fall, and

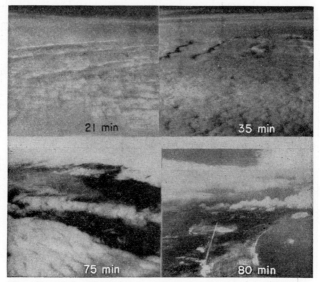

Fig. 50. A layer of dense stratus was seeded with dry ice. After a few minutes lanes began to form along the seeding track, and light snow fell out of the cloud. The lanes deepened and widened, and after 80 min a clear area of about 100 sq miles was produced. Thunder Bay, Michigan, Dec. 12, 1953. (*Courtesy Dr. Helmut K. Weikmann, Signal Corps Laboratories.*)

after a few minutes the cloud dissolves (see Fig. 50). The amount of snowfall from such clouds is, however, exceedingly small. Similar experiments with clouds of great depth have shown positive results, although it has been difficult to determine precisely how much of the precipitation was due to the artificial stimulation and how much would have occurred anyway.

In the tropics most clouds are "warm clouds" in the sense that their tops do not reach up to freezing temperatures. The precipitation (tropical showers) from such clouds is released when there are a few drops which are much larger than the others, enabling the capture processes to become effective. These large drops are thought to form on the relatively few giant salt nuclei which are often present. In the absence of such giant nuclei, it would seem possible to induce precipitation by sprinkling the cloud either by salt particles or by water drops. Such experiments seem to indicate success.

Research in the field of artificial stimulation of precipitation is still in its infancy, and it is likely that a long series of carefully designed experiments will be needed to determine the circumstances in which artificial stimulation will prove effective.

5

Heat and Temperature Changes

For convenience the discussion of heat and temperature changes will be divided into two parts. The present chapter will deal with certain laws that govern the behavior of the air, particularly in regard to temperature changes. The following chapter will give an account of how the radiation from the sun is converted into heat and shared by the earth and the atmosphere.

Various Forms of Heat. Before going into details it may be useful to recall some simple observations on heat and temperature changes.

If a kettle of cold water is placed over a fire, the temperature of the water will rise. We can ascertain this by using a thermometer or more simply by feeling the change. Such heat is called *sensible heat* because it can be felt. However, if we continue to heat the water so that the boiling point is reached the temperature rise stops, for the excess heat goes to transforming liquid water into water vapor. The heat thus used is no longer present as sensible heat; we call it *latent heat* or, more precisely, the *latent heat of vaporization.* This heat can be recovered as sensible heat when the vapor subsequently condenses. These are the processes that go on all the time in steam engines, and we encounter them in the atmosphere in connection with evaporation and condensation processes.

Another kind of latent heat may be illustrated as follows. Take a bucket of cold snow into a warm room and insert a thermometer in the snow. The temperature of the snow will then be seen to rise, but when the melting point is reached the temperature rise stops. If we stir the mixture of ice and water well we shall find that the temperature stays at 32°F (0°C) until all the snow is melted. Thereafter the temperature of the water will rise and approach the room temperature. During the melting process the heat was used to transform ice into liquid water, and we call this the *latent heat of fusion.* The heat thus expended can be recovered as sensible heat when the water subsequently is frozen. We encounter these processes in the atmosphere in connection with the formation and melting of ice crystals, snow, and hail.

Next, we pump air into a bicycle tire and notice that the valve becomes warm. Here no heat was applied, but we used mechanical work to compress the air, and this work was transferred into an equivalent amount of heat. If we open the valve, the air will expand; it will do work on the surrounding air and therefore cool. We meet these processes in the atmosphere frequently. For example, air that descends will come under higher pressure; it will be compressed and warm up. Similarly, air that ascends will come under lower pressure, expand, and cool. In an ascending current, the air may cool so much that it becomes saturated. If it ascends further it will continue to cool by expansion, but, at the same time, it will gain some heat in proportion to the amount of water vapor that condenses. This is nothing but the recovery of heat which once was used to evaporate the water. In the meantime this heat has been latent in the vapor.

Another experience with heat may be illustrated as follows. On a cold, sunny day we sit on a sun porch and notice that the temperature there is much higher than it is outside. It appears as if the sun's rays are able to heat the air inside the porch but have little effect on the outside air. We interpret this in the following manner. The radiative surface of the sun is very warm, somewhere near 6000°A (11,000°F). At such high temperatures the radiation is mainly in the short wavelengths. The atmosphere is, however, fairly transparent relative to such radiation, with the result that the sun's rays come down to the earth without much reduction in strength. Ordinary window glass is also transparent relative to such radiation, so that the radiant energy goes through the glass and becomes absorbed in the floor, walls, and furniture of the porch. Through this absorption the radiant energy becomes transformed into sensible heat. However, the porch must also radiate, and since its temperature is relatively low (say 293°A, or 68°F) the radiation is in the long waves. The glass is not transparent to such radiation; if it were, heat would be lost through closed windows,[1] and greenhouses of the kind commonly used would serve no useful purpose. In a manner of speaking, the function of the glass is to form a *radiation trap.*

In a broad sense, the atmosphere acts in the same manner as the glass in a greenhouse. It lets in much of the high-temperature radiation

[1] In this discussion we are not considering conduction of sensible heat through the glass.

from the sun, but its water vapor and carbon dioxide prevent much of the low-temperature radiation of the earth from escaping to space. The glass of the atmospheric greenhouse is not perfect, and its efficiency varies very much with the water-vapor content.

We may go a step further and say that the floor of the atmospheric greenhouse is also very variable. Much of the radiation that hits the oceans is used to evaporate water, and the remainder is distributed through a deep layer, so that the net temperature changes are very small. On the other hand, dry and sandy land will store the absorbed heat in a shallow layer, and the temperature changes become large.

Specific Heat and Heat Capacity. The amount of heat stored in a body may be expressed in various units, but most frequently used is the *calorie*. This unit is the amount of heat required to warm one gram of water one degree centigrade when the temperature of the water is fifteen degrees centigrade. The specification 15°C is necessary because the relation between the added heat and the temperature rise varies slightly with the temperature of the water.

If we apply equal amounts of heat to equal masses of different substances, we shall find that their temperature changes are not the same. For example, if we apply 1 cal to 1 g of silver the temperature rise will be 10°C, while in the case of water the temperature rise will be only 1°C. We say that different substances have different specific heats.

The term specific heat is defined in the following manner. If Δh is the number of calories which is given to 1 g of any substance, there will be a certain temperature rise which we call ΔT. The two quantities Δh and ΔT are connected by a factor C which we call the specific heat. We may then write

$$\Delta h = C \, \Delta T \qquad \text{or} \qquad \frac{\Delta h}{\Delta T} = C$$

The *specific heat* may now be defined as the ratio of the added heat to the resulting rise in temperature.

The foregoing definition refers to a unit mass. There is another measure which is called the heat capacity, and it refers to a unit volume. If V is the volume and ρ the density, the mass of the substance is $V\rho$. If a certain amount of heat (Δh) is given to this mass, we may write

$$\Delta h = V\rho C \, \Delta T \qquad \text{or} \qquad \frac{\Delta h}{V \, \Delta T} = \rho C \qquad (2)$$

For a unit volume ($V = 1$), the ratio of the heat to the temperature rise is ρC, and this is called the *heat capacity*. Thus,

$$\text{Heat capacity} = \text{density} \times \text{specific heat}$$

In the following chapter we shall see how the temperature changes are related to the heat capacity and the conductivity of the earth and the atmosphere. But before we do so we must explain certain laws which govern the behavior of the air.

The Gas Law. This law states that the relation between the pressure (p), the density (ρ), and the absolute temperature (T) of a gas is

$$p = R\rho T \tag{3}$$

Here R is a constant which characterizes the gas in question.

According to the molecular theory, a gas, or a mixture of gases, may be regarded as being made up of a large number of minute molecules which are in a state of incessant and irregular motion leading to frequent collisions between the individual molecules. The effect of the impacts of the molecules produces the pressure of the gas. This pressure depends, therefore, on the number and the mass of the molecules and the speed with which they are moving. The number and the mass of the molecules define the density of the gas. It follows, then, that the pressure must be proportional to the density ρ. The average speed with which the molecules move depends on the absolute temperature. If the temperature were 0°A, the molecules would be at rest and there would be no pressure. The higher the temperature, the more the molecules are agitated and the greater is the frequency of the collisions. Therefore the pressure must be proportional to the absolute temperature, as indicated in the foregoing equation.

The factor R, which is called the *gas constant*, characterizes the gas, or the mixture of gases, and its numerical value depends on the units used. If the atmospheric pressure is expressed in millibars, the density in grams per cubic centimeter, and the temperature in °A, the gas constant for dry air is very nearly 2,870. Since the amount of water vapor in the atmosphere is variable, the gas content varies slightly with the moisture content; but this variation is so small that it may be neglected unless great accuracy is required.

The density of any substance is defined as the mass contained in a unit volume. Instead of the density it is sometimes convenient to use the volume occupied by a unit mass. This is called the *specific volume*, and we denote it by α. Thus

$$\alpha = \frac{1}{\rho} \quad \text{or} \quad \alpha\rho = 1$$

and the gas equation may be written

$$\alpha p = RT \tag{4}$$

This shows that the product of the specific volume and the pressure is proportional to the absolute temperature.

The First Law of Thermodynamics. This law is a statement of the physical changes that take place when heat is supplied to (or withdrawn from) a gas. It is a very important law for, together with the gas law and the hydrostatic law (page 6), it accounts for many of the processes which occur in the atmosphere.

To introduce this law we may make a very simple experiment. Take an airtight vessel which contains a unit mass (say 1 g) of air. The volume of the air is then what we have called the specific volume, and since the gas is confined to a solid container, the volume will remain constant. Suppose now that we supply a small amount of heat, say Δh. The temperature of the gas will then increase by a small amount, say ΔT. As shown in the section on specific heat, we may write

$$\Delta h = C_v \, \Delta T \tag{5}$$

We have here added subscript v to emphasize that the volume is kept constant, and we call C_v the *specific heat at constant volume.*

Since the temperature has been increased while the volume was kept constant, we see from the gas equation that the pressure must have increased by a corresponding amount.

Suppose now that the walls of the container are removed. The heated air will then expand, and its pressure will adjust itself to the environment. In the expansion the volume of the gas increases by a certain amount, say $\Delta \alpha$. Through this expansion the air must push away the surrounding air and thus do work against the outer pressure. This work is equal to the outer pressure p multiplied by the amount of expansion, which is $\Delta \alpha$. The amount of work is therefore $p \, \Delta \alpha$. We see then that when heat is supplied to air (which is free to expand), part of the heat is used in the work of expansion, and the remainder is used to increase the temperature. Since no energy can be lost, we have

$$\Delta h = C_v \, \Delta T + p \, \Delta \alpha \tag{6}$$

or, in plain language,

Added heat = increase in internal energy + work due to expansion

Since the specific volume is not observed it is convenient to use Eq. (4) and replace the volume expansion by the corresponding pressure change. This can be done in the following manner. Suppose that a unit mass of air undergoes a small change so that the pressure increases from p to $p + \Delta p$. The specific volume and the temperature will then undergo small changes from α to $\alpha + \Delta \alpha$, and from T to $T + \Delta T$. At the beginning of the process the gas equation is $\alpha p = RT$, and after the changes have taken place we have

$$(\alpha + \Delta\alpha)(p + \Delta p) = R(T + \Delta T)$$

or
$$\alpha p + p\,\Delta\alpha + \alpha\,\Delta p + \Delta\alpha\,\Delta p = RT + R\,\Delta T$$

But since $\alpha p = RT$, this reduces to

$$p\,\Delta\alpha + \alpha\,\Delta p + \Delta\alpha\,\Delta p = R\,\Delta T \tag{7}$$

The product of the two small quantities $\Delta\alpha$ and Δp is very much smaller than the other terms and may be neglected, so that

$$p\,\Delta\alpha = R\,\Delta T - \alpha\,\Delta p \tag{8}$$

If this is substituted in Eq. (6), we obtain

$$\Delta h = (R + C_v)\Delta T - \alpha\,\Delta p \tag{9}$$

At the beginning of this section we considered what happened when heat was supplied at constant volume. We shall now see what happens when heat is supplied while keeping the pressure constant. In this case, $\Delta p = 0$, and Eq. (9) reduces to

$$\Delta h = (R + C_v)\Delta T \qquad \text{or} \qquad \frac{\Delta h}{\Delta T} = R + C_v \tag{10}$$

Now, the ratio $\Delta h/\Delta T$ defines a specific heat, and since the pressure was kept constant we write

$$C_p = R + C_v$$

and call it the *specific heat at constant pressure*. With this notation, Eq. (9) is written

$$\Delta h = C_p\,\Delta T - \alpha\,\Delta p \tag{11}$$

Equations (6) and (11) are but different forms of the first law of thermodynamics, but Eq. (11) is most convenient since the temperature and pressure changes are readily observed.

Adiabatic Processes. At the beginning of this chapter we referred to the pumping of a bicycle tire as an example of temperature changes without supply of heat. Any process in which no heat is supplied to, or withdrawn from, the air is said to be *adiabatic*, and if heat is involved the process is said to be *nonadiabatic*.

Near the earth's surface nonadiabatic processes are common, since the air readily exchanges heat with the underlying surface. At higher levels, the air is so far removed from heat and cold sources that we can disregard the heat and consider the processes to be very nearly adiabatic.

However, we must distinguish between two cases. If the air is non-saturated and no heat is supplied, we say that the process is *dryadiabatic*, and the temperature changes are entirely due to expansion or contraction. It is this process that we experience when pumping a bicycle tire. On the other hand, if the air is saturated and no heat is supplied from outside sources, latent heat will be liberated if water vapor condenses. In this case we speak of a saturated, or *wetadiabatic*, process. The temperature changes of the air are then partly due to expansion (or contraction) and partly due to liberation of latent heat.

The Dryadiabatic Rate of Cooling. We consider a parcel of dry air which moves along the vertical without heat being supplied to, or withdrawn, from it. In this case, $\Delta h = 0$, and Eq. (11) reduces to

$$C_p \, \Delta T = \alpha \, \Delta p \tag{12}$$

We see then that the air cools when it comes under lower pressure and warms when it comes under higher pressure. The pressure change Δp is related to the height change Δz through the hydrostatic equation (page 6), so that $-\Delta p = \rho g \Delta z$. We substitute this in Eq. (12) and note that $\alpha \rho = 1$ (see page 73). This gives

$$-\frac{\Delta T}{\Delta z} = \frac{g}{C_p}$$

We see that the air cools when it ascends and warms when it descends. The quantity $-\Delta T/\Delta z$ is the rate at which the air cools, and since the process is dryadiabatic, we call it the *dryadiabatic rate of cooling*. It is customary to denote this rate by γ_d, so that

$$-\frac{\Delta T}{\Delta z} = \frac{g}{C_p} = \gamma_d \tag{13}$$

It is of interest to note that the rate of cooling is constant. Using the numerical values for the acceleration of gravity g and the specific heat at constant pressure C_p, we find $\gamma_d = 0.0098°\text{C/m}$, that is, very nearly $1°\text{C}/100$ m, or $5.4°\text{F}/1,000$ ft.

The Wetadiabatic Rate of Cooling. If a saturated parcel of air ascends adiabatically, the air will cool by expansion, but this cooling will be counteracted, or retarded, by the liberated latent heat. As a result we find that the wetadiabatic rate of cooling is slower than the dryadiabatic one.

We can account for the difference in the following manner. We consider a parcel of air which is made up of 1 g of dry air and r g of water vapor. Here, r is the mixing ratio as defined on page 26. Through condensation a small amount of gaseous water is changed from vapor to liquid, so that the mixing ratio decreases by the small amount Δr. If L is the latent heat of vaporization, the liberated heat is $-L\,\Delta r$, for Δr is negative. Now, if no heat is supplied from other sources, the first law of thermodynamics, as expressed by Eq. (11), may be written

$$-L\,\Delta r = C_p\,\Delta T - \alpha\,\Delta p$$

or
$$\Delta T = \frac{\alpha\,\Delta p - L\,\Delta r}{C_p} \tag{14}$$

Again, we may use the hydrostatic equation and replace Δp by Δz. This gives for the rate of cooling in a wetadiabatic process

$$-\frac{\Delta T}{\Delta z} = \frac{g}{C_p} + \frac{L}{C_p}\frac{\Delta r}{\Delta z} = \gamma_d + \frac{L}{C_p}\frac{\Delta r}{\Delta z} = \gamma_s \tag{15}$$

Here, subscript s has been used to distinguish the saturated rate of cooling from the dry one.

Since Δr is negative, we see that the effect of condensation is to cause the rising air to cool more slowly than in a dryadiabatic process. Unlike the dryadiabatic rate, the wetadiabatic one is not a constant. It will be seen from Fig. 4 that the amount of water vapor that saturated air can hold increases rapidly with the temperature. The term containing Δr will therefore be large at high temperatures and small at low temperatures. For example, in warm tropical air the wetadiabatic rate is about 35 per cent of the dryadiabatic one, while at such low temperatures as prevail in the polar regions in winter and in the upper troposphere in all seasons, the two rates are barely distinguishable.

The Temperature-Height Diagram. The adiabatic laws expressed by Eqs. (13) and (15) are illustrated in Fig. 51. The straight diagonals (— — — —) represent the dryadiabatic rate of cooling, and the slightly curved diagonals (— · — · —) show the wetadiabatic rate. These lines are called *dry* and *wet adiabats*, respectively.

The use of the diagram may be indicated by the following example. If the observed temperature is plotted against height, we obtain a curve such as AB. The rate at which the observed temperature decreases along the vertical is called the *lapse rate*. This lapse is customarily indicated by γ. We have then the following temperature characteristics to consider:

$$\gamma = \text{the actual lapse rate}$$
$$\gamma_d = \text{the dryadiabatic rate of cooling}$$
$$\gamma_s = \text{the wetadiabatic rate of cooling}$$

Suppose now that the parcel of air at A is lifted; it will then follow the dry adiabat until it has cooled so much that it has become saturated at, say, C. This level is called the *lifting condensation level* (LCL). If the parcel is lifted farther it will cool along the wet adiabat CDE. Below the level *D* the parcel would be colder, and above *D* it would be warmer than the surrounding air.

Temperature-height diagrams are rarely used in meteorology, for it is far more convenient to use pressure rather than height to indicate distance along the vertical.

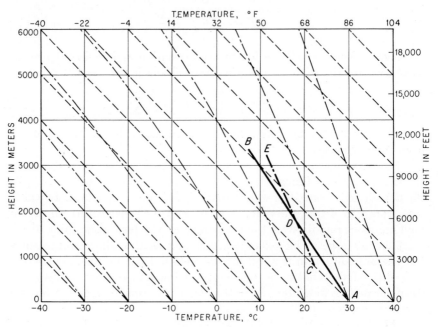

Fig. 51. A temperature-height diagram. The straight diagonals (— — —) are the dry adiabats, and the slightly curved diagonals (— · — · —) are the wet adiabats.

Adiabatic Charts. The relationships discussed in the foregoing sections are conveniently represented in a diagram of the type shown in Fig. 52. Such diagrams may be constructed in various ways but they all have the same basic properties. In the diagram shown the ordinate is divided into equal parts of the logarithm of pressure, and the horizontal lines (the isobars) are labeled in millibars. The temperature is represented on a linear scale along the abscissa. For practical convenience the temperature lines (or the isotherms) are skewed so that they form an angle of 45° with the abscissa. This skewing is introduced in order to distinguish more clearly between dry and saturated adiabatic processes.

In addition to the isobars and the isotherms the chart contains three families of curves. The first of these (— — —) represents the dry adiabats; the second (— · — · —) represents the saturated adiabats; and the third (· · · ·) represents the mixing ratio and the dewpoint temperature.

To illustrate the use of the diagram more clearly we consider Fig. 52, where the background is a skeleton specimen of the adiabatic chart. Suppose that we have a sounding of pressure p, temperature T, and dew-point temperature T_d, as shown in Table 5. We first plot T against p and obtain the curve on the right. Next we plot T_d against p and obtain the

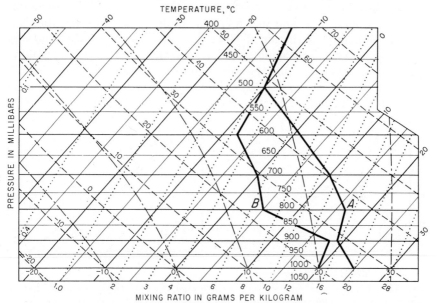

TEMPERATURE, °C

PRESSURE IN MILLIBARS

MIXING RATIO IN GRAMS PER KILOGRAM

Fig. 52. An adiabatic chart. The horizontal lines are isobars, and the lines slanting upward to the right are isotherms (°C). Other lines are dry adiabats (— — —), wet adiabats (— · — · —), and mixing-ratio lines (· · · · ·). The heavy curves are plots of temperature and dewpoint temperature (see Table 5).

curve on the left. We see immediately that the temperature decreases rapidly up to 900 mb, and at this level the dewpoint temperature is almost the same as the temperature, showing that the air is nearly saturated. Above 900 mb the dewpoint depression becomes large, indicating that the relative humidity is low. As we ascend to lower pressure the dewpoint depression decreases, and above 500 mb the air is saturated.

Table 5. Example of Sounding

p, mb	T, °C	T_d, °C	U, %
1,000	25	20	78
900	19	18	98
800	17	5	45
700	10	0	49
600	1	−8	46
500	−10	−10	100
400	−13	−13	100

The relative humidity is readily obtained in the following manner. If the air, say, at 800 mb were saturated, the dewpoint temperature would be equal to the temperature. If we used a detailed diagram and read the mixing ratio at A on the scale on the upper right, we would find 19.4. This is the saturation value. Next we read the mixing ratio corresponding to the dewpoint at B and find 8.7. This is the actual mixing ratio. The relative humidity of the air at 800 mb is then $100 \times 8.7/19.4$, or very nearly 45 per cent. In a similar manner we compute the relative humidity for the other levels and find the values given in the last column of Table 5.

Returning again to Fig. 52, the following may be noted. In the layer from 1,000 to 900 mb the actual lapse rate of temperature is smaller than

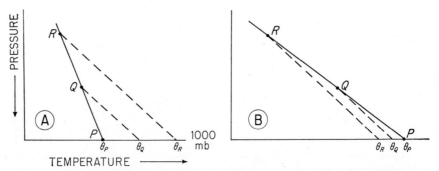

Fig. 53. The potential temperature is the temperature which the air would have if it were brought dryadiabatically to the level where the pressure is 1,000 mb.

the dryadiabatic rate and larger than the saturated rate of cooling. In the layer from 900 to 800 mb, the actual lapse rate is smaller than both of the adiabatic rates. Furthermore, between 800 and 500 mb the actual lapse rate is between the adiabatic ones. It will be shown later that the differences $(\gamma_d - \gamma)$ and $(\gamma_s - \gamma)$ are of great importance as far as weather processes are concerned.

Potential Temperature. We have seen in the foregoing sections that the temperature of a parcel of air changes considerably when the parcel moves toward higher or lower pressure. It is sometimes of interest to compare two parcels and see what temperature they would have if they were brought adiabatically to the same pressure. It is customary to choose 1,000 mb as a standard pressure for such comparisons, and we say that the potential temperature is the temperature that a parcel of air would have if it were brought dryadiabatically to the level where the pressure is 1,000 mb. It is customary to denote the potential temperature by θ.

To illustrate we consider Fig. 53. Let the curve PQR (Fig. 53a) represent the observed temperature as a function of pressure. In this case the temperature decreases upward at a rate which is less than the dryadiabatic rate, so that γ_d is larger than γ. In the first place we note that the parcel P is at 1,000 mb, so that its actual temperature is the same as its potential temperature. Next, if we moved the parcel at Q downward it would follow the dry adiabat through Q and arrive at 1,000 mb with the temperature indicated by θ_Q, which would be higher than the potential temperature of the parcel at P. Finally, if we bring the parcel at R dryadiabatically down to 1,000 mb its potential temperature would be θ_R. We see then that the potential temperature in an air column increases upward when the actual lapse rate is smaller than the dryadiabatic rate.

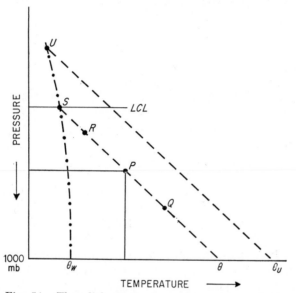

Fig. 54. The adiabatic chart may be used to evaluate the physical changes that a parcel of air undergoes when it moves along the vertical. For explanation, see text.

In Fig. 53*b* the full line shows the temperature distribution along the vertical in a case where the actual lapse rate is steeper than the dryadiabatic rate. By moving parcels of air along the dry adiabat it is readily seen that the potential temperature decreases upward through the column. In the limiting case, when $\gamma = \gamma_d$, the potential temperature is the same for all parcels in the column, and the potential temperature is constant along the vertical.

Another interesting property of the potential temperature may be illustrated as follows. Let P in Fig. 54 represent a parcel of air. If it were brought down to 1,000 mb the potential temperature would be θ, and the value of θ would be determined by the intersection of the dry adiabat through P with the 1,000-mb line. Now if the parcel were brought downward from P to Q, or upward from P to R, this intersection would stay the same. We see then that the potential temperature of a parcel of air remains constant as long as the process is dryadiabatic. We say that the *potential temperature of a parcel is conserved in dryadiabatic motion.*

Next we let the parcel P rise until it becomes saturated at S in Fig. 54. Below this level it follows the dry adiabat and its potential temperature remains constant. If the parcel moved further toward lower pressure, water vapor would condense, and the parcel would follow the saturated adiabat above S and arrive at, say, U. During the saturated ascent the potential temperature would not remain constant. Let us assume that the condensed water fell out. If the parcel now at U descended to 1,000 mb its potential temperature would then be θ_u. The difference $\theta_u - \theta$ reflects the effect of the latent heat that was liberated while the parcel ascended from S to U.

A further point may be noted. While the parcel moves from S to U (Fig. 54) its temperature is equal to the wet-bulb temperature (see page 25), and it moves along the saturated adiabat through S. If this saturated adiabat is prolonged downward to 1,000 mb, we obtain the *potential wet-bulb temperature* θ_W.

Now, the parcel of air at P is characterized by its pressure, temperature, and moisture content. These three variables determine the lifting condensation level, or the point S where the parcel becomes saturated in adiabatic motion. Whether the parcel ascends or descends, and whether or not saturation occurs, this point remains fixed, and so does the intersection between the saturated adiabat through S and the 1,000-mb line. We see then that the wet-bulb potential temperature θ_W is conserved in dryadiabatic as well as wetadiabatic motion. The wet-bulb potential temperature is often used as a label for identifying traveling air masses in cases where heat and cold sources are unimportant.

The Lifting Condensation Level. We shall now examine the changes of the dewpoint temperature when the air moves adiabatically. Consider Fig. 55, in which P represents a plot of the temperature and pressure of a parcel of air. If the parcel is not saturated, the dewpoint is lower than the temperature, and Q represents the dewpoint. Now, if the parcel moves dryadiabatically with constant water-vapor content, the mixing ratio will remain constant. The dewpoint will then move along the mixing-ratio line ($\cdots\cdots\cdots$) through Q, while the temperature moves along the dry adiabat (———) through P. So, if the parcel is lifted upward, the temperature approaches the dewpoint, and the parcel becomes saturated at S. This level is called the lifting condensation level.

It will be seen from Fig. 55 that the temperature of the moving parcel changes far more rapidly than does the dewpoint temperature. In fact, the actual temperature decreases at the dryadiabatic rate of 1°C/100 m, while the dewpoint decreases at a rate of about 0.17°C/100 m. Thus, when a parcel of air ascends, the temperature will approach the dewpoint at a rate of 0.83°C/100 m ascent. Suppose now that we have observed a certain air temperature T and dewpoint T_d. We may then ask: At what level H would this air become saturated if it were lifted adiabatically with

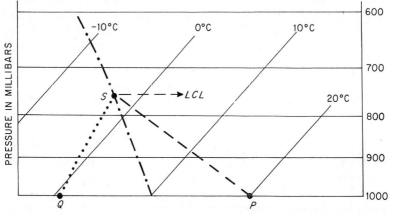

Fig. 55. Here P represents the temperature and Q the dewpoint of a parcel of air. If the parcel is lifted, the temperature changes along the dry adiabat (— — — —), and the dewpoint changes along the dewpoint line (· · · · ·). The parcel becomes saturated at S, which is called the lifting condensation level (LCL). If the parcel is lifted farther, it will follow the wet adiabat through S (— · — · — · —).

constant moisture content? We then find

$$\frac{0.83}{100 \text{ m}} °\text{C} = \frac{T - T_d}{H} \tag{16}$$

or very nearly

$$\begin{aligned} H &= 120(T - T_d) \quad (°\text{C and m}) \\ H &= 220(T - T_d) \quad (°\text{F and ft}) \end{aligned} \tag{17}$$

This formula will normally give only a rough estimate of the condensation level, for vertical mixing will occur while the air moves along.

Mixing. The motion of the air is always turbulent in the sense that the speed and direction of the wind exhibit irregular variations. These are due to a succession of eddies which move about in an irregular manner, mix with the surrounding air, and die out while new eddies form all the time. The movement of the eddies and their mixing with the environment are important, for through these processes heat, moisture, and similar properties become redistributed through deep layers.

To illustrate the effect of mixing we shall consider a very simple experiment. A vessel is partly filled with cold salt water, on top of which is an equal mass of warm fresh water. If we now stir the two masses we shall find that the end result of the mixing is characterized by a uniform temperature and a uniform salinity throughout. Since the water is incompressible, there are no adiabatic temperature changes. When air moves along the vertical the temperature will change adiabatically. However, the potential temperature of the moving parcels will not be affected, so that the potential temperature of the air mixes in the same way as the temperature of the water. The end result of mixing of air is, therefore, a uniform potential temperature. It was shown in a foregoing section that

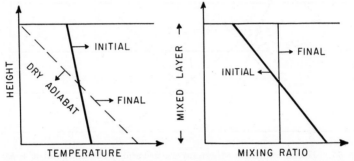

Fig. 56. If a layer of dry air is stirred thoroughly, the temperature will change so that the lapse rate becomes equal to the dryadiabatic rate. At the same time the mixing ratio will become uniform along the vertical.

when the potential temperature is uniform, the actual temperature decreases upward at the adiabatic rate. The end result of such mixing will be characterized by a lapse rate of temperature which is equal to the dryadiabatic rate of cooling. Now, if the lapse rate initially were smaller than the dryadiabatic rate (which is normally the case), the result of mixing would be a temperature decrease at the top and a temperature increase at the base of the layer, as shown in Fig. 56.

Next, we consider the effect of mixing on the moisture distribution. It is useful first to recall that the humidity mixing ratio was defined (page 26) as the number of grams of water vapor mixed with one gram of dry air. Obviously the weight of a mass does not change with expansion and contraction; the mixing ratio is conserved, and the end result of mixing will be a uniform distribution of the mixing ratio along the vertical.

Normally the mixing ratio will increase from the ground upward. Mixing by turbulent eddies will then increase the moisture content in the top of the layer and dry out the lower part of the layer. At the same time the temperature will decrease in the upper part and increase in the lower part of the layer. Thus it is readily seen that saturation may occur in the upper part of the layer, for this part will gain moisture while its temperature decreases. An example is shown in Fig. 57. For simplicity we have taken a layer of saturated air and uniform temperature between 1,000 and 900 mb. If this layer were thoroughly stirred the relative humidity at the base would decrease from 100 to about 80 per cent while at the top it would increase from 100 to 138 per cent. If there were no condensation nuclei in the air, large amounts of supersaturation would occur. However, with condensation nuclei, a layer of stratus would form in the upper part of the mixed layer. Most of the stratus clouds observed in the lowest part of the atmosphere are produced by such mixing.

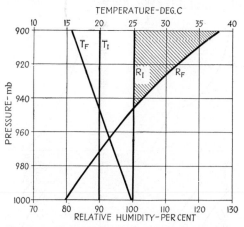

Fig. 57. T_I and R_I represent an initial distribution of temperature and relative humidity. After complete mixing the distributions will be shown by the curves T_F and R_F.

Subsidence and Inversions. The term *subsidence* is commonly used to denote large-scale downward motion in the atmosphere. Although these motions are small (500 to 1,000 ft/hr) they are very important. For example, the adiabatic heating associated with a descent of 1,000 to 2,000 ft will suffice to evaporate the water droplets of an average cloud. Moreover, when subsidence occurs it usually affects a major part of the air column below the tropopause, with the result that the clouds often dissolve at all levels. The clearing that ends a prolonged period of rain is usually due to widespread subsidence.

Mixing along the vertical is most pronounced near the earth's surface, where turbulence, due to surface heating and the roughness of the ground, is active. Normally, the subsided layer will be warm and dry, while the mixed layer below will remain cool and moist. Such structures occur frequently along subtropical west coasts. For example, if we drive from Los Angeles to Mount Wilson we first pass through a layer of relatively cool and moist air, to emerge into warm and dry air above the lowlands.

The typical structure of subsided air over a mixed layer is shown in

Fig. 58. It will be seen that above the mixed layer the temperature first increases with elevation and then resumes a normal lapse. The high temperature and the low dewpoint are due to the adiabatic heating of the subsided air.

A layer within which the temperature increases with elevation is called an *inversion*, and the case shown in Fig. 58a illustrates an inversion produced by subsidence aloft and mixing in the ground layer. Only rarely do the subsidence inversions reach down to the ground, except on the slopes of hills and mountains (Fig. 58b).

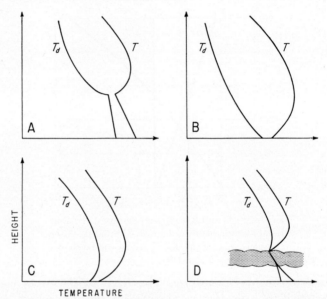

Fig. 58. Types of temperature inversions: (a) subsidence above a mixed surface layer; (b) subsidence reaching the ground; (c) ground inversion caused by cooling of stagnant air; (d) inversion caused by cooling and mixing of the surface layer.

Inversion layers, without subsidence, form frequently when the air is cooled from below. Typical examples are shown in the lower part of Fig. 58. If the wind is light, so that there is not much turbulent mixing, the surface layer will cool faster than the air above. As this air cools the temperature approaches the dewpoint, and a fog may form. Inversions of the type shown in Fig. 58c are frequent occurrences on calm and clear nights. They are also frequent over the polar ice fields in all seasons and over cold continents in winter. If the wind is sufficiently strong, the surface layer will be mixed, and the structure will be as shown in Fig. 58d. Quite frequently a layer of stratus may be present at and below the base of the inversion. The subsidence inversions can always be distinguished from the other types by the dryness of the air above their bases.

6

Radiation and Exchange of Heat

While the sun is the source of all the energy that drives the atmospheric machinery, it is well to bear in mind that the earth's surface plays an important part in converting the solar radiation into sensible heat and in determining how this heat is to be divided between the earth and the atmosphere.

The Heat Budget. What we call weather and climate is mainly determined by the temperature and moisture regimes. In order to understand how these regimes are distributed over the face of the earth it is necessary to examine the heat and moisture budget under which the system earth-atmosphere has to operate. In doing so we cannot regard the earth and the atmosphere as separate entities, for heat and moisture are continuously exchanged between them. Nor can we establish a heat budget without considering the moisture. Most of the water in the atmosphere is present in the form of vapor which, at some earlier time, was evaporated from the earth's surface. In the evaporation, vast amounts of heat were used; this heat is latent in the vapor and becomes liberated as sensible heat when the vapor subsequently condenses. It is evident, therefore, that any transfer of moisture from one place to another is equivalent to a transfer of heat.

Climate and weather are customarily defined and measured in terms of atmospheric conditions, but these conditions depend intimately upon the composition of the earth's surface (land, ice, sea, etc.) and the exchange of heat and moisture between the surface substances and the atmosphere. Thus, in order to establish a heat budget for the atmosphere we must consider the items in two stages. First, we must account for what

87

is available to the single system of earth *plus* atmosphere and, second, what concerns the atmosphere alone. The second problem includes all the processes that enter into the first and, in addition, the processes associated with the exchanges between the earth and the atmosphere. In a manner of speaking, we may say that the processes associated with climate and weather reach down to some distance below the surface of the earth.

Over a long span of time the system earth-atmosphere must return to space as much energy as it receives from the sun. However, at any particular time and place the gain is rarely equal to the loss, and this accounts for much of the variability of the weather sequences.

Radiation Processes. The origin of the energy that maintains all atmospheric processes lies in the radiation from the sun. This energy comes to the earth in the form of short-wave radiation (see page 71) which goes through the atmosphere without much absorption. If clouds intercept a beam of such radiation, they reflect most of it back to space. A further part of the incoming radiation is reflected from the earth's surface and from the dust in the air.

The fraction of the total incoming radiation which is reflected back to space is called the *albedo*. Under average conditions the albedo of the earth as a whole is about 40 per cent. Of the remaining 60 per cent a small part is absorbed in the atmosphere, but the bulk is absorbed in the earth's surface. However, if we consider the system earth-atmosphere, the 60 per cent represents the amount with which we have to deal.

The *average* value of this energy amounts to a supply of about 0.30 cal/cm²/min of the earth's surface. However, its distribution over the face of the earth varies greatly with latitude and season, and it also varies with the atmospheric conditions. If all this heat were used to warm up the atmosphere, it would cause the temperature to rise about 1.5°C (3°F) a day.

As mentioned on page 71, energy may be converted into various forms, but the total must be conserved. Furthermore, since the climate of the earth does not change perceptibly, it is evident that, on the average, there must be a loss almost exactly equal to the afore-mentioned 0.30 cal/cm²/min. This loss must be sought in the long-wave radiation that goes from the system earth-atmosphere back to space. We have then to consider how this loss is brought about.

There is a fundamental law of radiation, called *Stefan's law*, which states that a black body will emit radiation from its surface in proportion to the fourth power of its absolute temperature. The qualification *black* has little to do with the actual color, and the term "black body" may be thought of as indicating a good radiator. In fact, the earth's surface and the clouds radiate very nearly as a black body, so that a stream of long-wave radiation passes outward at a rate which is determined by the temperature of the earth's surface and the temperature of the upper surface of the clouds. Some of this radiation passes directly out to space, but some of it is absorbed by the water vapor and the carbon dioxide of the air, for these gases are not transparent to long-wave radiation.

There is another fundamental law of radiation, known as *Kirchhoff's law*, which states that a body which is a good absorber is also a good emitter in the same wavelengths. Thus, the outgoing long-wave radiation from the earth and the clouds is absorbed by the water vapor and carbon dioxide at higher levels and reemitted at correspondingly lower temperatures.

For the system earth-atmosphere as a whole, the average outgoing radiation must be equal to the incoming, which is about 0.30 cal/cm^2/min, and this would be the radiation of a black body having a temperature of about 240°A (-33°C, or -27°F) radiating into vacuum. This, then, must be the temperature of the atmosphere at some distance above the earth's surface and yet well below the height where the atmosphere becomes tenuous. This principle of radiation balance explains why the temperatures are what they are and not, say, 100° lower or higher. The general level of atmospheric temperatures being determined in this way, the variation with height, above and below this level, is governed by the principle of the lapse rate. If the air were perfectly stirred, the lapse rate would be equal to the adiabatic rate of cooling. As a compromise between the effects of stirring and transfer of heat, the average lapse rate of the troposphere comes out to about 6.5°C/km. In the uppermost layers of the atmosphere the temperature distribution along the vertical is greatly influenced by the chemical processes discussed on page 4.

Variation with Latitude. The amount of incoming radiation varies strongly with latitude and depends essentially upon the altitude of the sun. The variation with latitude undergoes seasonal changes, but for the purpose of this discussion it suffices to consider the yearly average.

It is convenient to divide the hemisphere into zonal bands, as shown in the first column of Table 6. These bands will not be of equal size (see second column), and to obtain a balanced budget it is necessary to account for the areas involved. The third column gives the mean incoming short-wave radiation per unit area and time in each of the zonal bands, and the fourth column shows the corresponding values of the outgoing long-wave radiation. It will be seen that the amount of absorbed radiation decreases rapidly with increasing latitude while the amount emitted remains almost constant. Although the amounts of incoming and outgoing radiation must balance for the system as a whole, this need not be the case for each of the zones, for heat will be carried from one zone to another without escaping from the system. The carrying agents are the moving parts of the system or the winds of the atmosphere and the currents of the oceans.

Because of the greater mobility of the air, the winds play a major role in bringing about the exchange of heat between low and high latitudes. A north wind (in the Northern Hemisphere) will normally carry cold air equatorward, while a south wind will carry warm air poleward. The net effect of all the wind systems is to export heat from the zones where the sun provides it generously to the regions less endowed. The amounts of heat thus transported across the latitude circles 20, 40, and 60° are shown in the last column of Table 6. The amounts are enormous and show a maximum in the mid-latitudes. This, as will be shown in Chap.

Table 6. The Annual Heat Balance, by Latitude Zones

Zones of latitude, deg	Fraction of total area	Short-wave radiation absorbed, cal/cm²/min	Long-wave radiation emitted, cal/cm²/min	Poleward transport of heat across latitude parallels,* cal/min
0–20	0.34	0.39	0.3	
				57 × 10¹⁵ (20°)
20–40	0.30	0.34	0.3	
				77 × 10¹⁵ (40°)
40–60	0.22	0.23	0.3	
				50 × 10¹⁵ (60°)
60–90	0.14	0.13	0.3	
Weighted mean.......... 0.30		0.30		

* If a kilocalorie is used to denote 1000 calories, 10¹⁵ signifies a million million kilocalories.

14, is the zone where the traveling cyclones and anticyclones are most frequent and most strongly developed. The north and south winds associated with these systems are very effective as carriers of heat.

Because the low-latitude belts export some of the heat received from the sun, they need radiate less than would otherwise be the case. For the high-latitude belts the reverse is true. Thus, if there were no moving parts in the system, the temperature would decrease in the polar regions and increase near the equator. As a result of the exchange across latitude circles the outgoing long-wave radiation varies with latitude much more slowly than does the incoming short-wave radiation.

It is difficult to estimate accurately the meridional variation in the outgoing radiation, and for this reason the values in Table 6 have been rounded off generously. It is probable that the outgoing radiation has a slight increase from pole to equator, but the precise value is not important since it has been clearly established that there is a large excess of incoming radiation in low latitudes and a large deficit in high latitudes and that the balance is brought about mainly by motions in the atmosphere and the oceans.

Some insight into the causes underlying the annual variation of temperature can be gained from the figures reproduced in Table 7. For the time being we disregard the heat transfer due to motion in the ocean and the atmosphere. As a crude approximation we may say that in midsummer and in midwinter there is a near balance between the absorbed incoming radiation and the outgoing radiation. Now, according to Stefan's law the outgoing radiation is proportional to the fourth power of the absolute temperature, which is the same as saying that the temperature is proportional to the fourth root of the radiation. It will be seen from the last column of Table 7 that the difference between the fourth roots in summer

Table 7. *Incoming Radiation in Latitude Zones*

Zone	Short-wave radiation absorbed, cal/cm²/min*		
	Summer	Winter	Difference
0–20°	0.42 (0.805)	0.36 (0.775)	0.06 (0.030)
20–40°	0.42 (0.805)	0.26 (0.714)	0.16 (0.091)
40–60°	0.35 (0.769)	0.12 (0.589)	0.23 (0.180)
60–90°	0.24 (0.700)	0.02 (0.376)	0.22 (0.324)

* Figures in parentheses are the fourth roots of the radiation.

and winter increases rapidly with increasing latitude, showing that there will be a tendency for the annual range of temperature to be large in the polar regions and to decrease toward the equator. This is true for the earth and atmosphere considered jointly. However, in any given place the annual variation of the air temperature will depend upon how the heat is apportioned between the uppermost layer of the earth's surface and the air. It will be shown later that the annual variation of air temperature at any latitude is much larger over land than over the oceans.

In regard to the diurnal variation of temperature, it is of interest to note that the amplitude is small in high latitudes and increases equatorward. This is due to the circumstance that the variation in the elevation of the sun is small in high latitudes and large in low latitudes. In addition to the meridional variation in radiation one has to consider the properties of the underlying surfaces. Again, we shall find that the variation is much larger over land than over oceans and water bodies.

The Equation of Balance. Though some of the processes that enter into the full balance have yet to be discussed, it is useful at this stage to form a picture of all the factors involved in the heat budget. Figure 59 shows schematically the heat budget of a column which begins at some distance down in the ocean or the ground and contains all the air above.

The total incoming radiation I may be divided into two parts, I_a and I_r. Of these, I_a is the part that is absorbed, and I_r is that reflected, either from the earth or from the clouds. R_1 represents the long-wave radiation from the ground which passes straight into space, and R_2 is the long-wave radiation which is absorbed either by the clouds or by the water vapor and other absorbing gases. Furthermore, r_u and r_d are the radiation emitted upward or downward by the atmosphere; G is the sensible heat that flows into the ground, and H is the sensible heat that flows into the

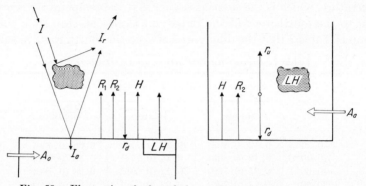

Fig. 59.   Illustrating the heat balance. For explanation, see text.

air; LH is the latent heat of water evaporated from the ground and later yielded up in condensation. Finally, A_a and A_o are the amounts of heat carried horizontally into the column by the winds of the atmosphere and the currents of the oceans.

It should be noted that G, H, LH, A_a, and A_o may be positive or negative. If our column extends so far into the earth that it takes in the layer affected by the heat exchanged and also extends to the top of the atmosphere, we may write the following equations:

$$\text{Warming the ground} = G = I_a - R_1 - R_2 + r_d - H - LH + A_o$$
$$\text{Warming the air} = R_2 - r_d - r_u + H + LH + A_a$$
$$\text{Warming the ground and air} = I_a - R_1 - r_u + A_o + A_a$$

The third equation represents the balance which was discussed in the foregoing sections. It results from adding the first two equations, and is rather simpler than the others because certain terms which represent the exchanges between the two parts cancel in the grand total. We must, however, consider these exchanges if we are to acquire an understanding of the heat balance of the atmosphere and the climates which result from it.

If we take totals over the whole globe, the terms A_o and A_a will disappear, for these represent horizontal exchanges between different parts of the system. Finally, if in any of the equations the total over a year or several years is taken, we shall find that the terms on the right add up to zero, or very nearly so, for the net warming over a long span of time must be negligibly small.

The Conduction Process. If the earth's surface were smooth and of uniform composition, the mean temperature over a long span of time would be uniform along each latitude circle and there would be no variation with longitude. Observations show, however, that there are very large temperature variations within any latitude zone, and these varia-

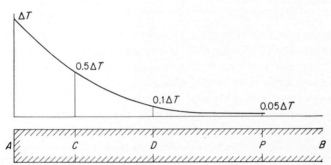

Fig. 60.   If a rod (*AB*) is heated at *A* so that the temperature there rises by the amount Δ*T*, the rise will be progressively smaller at *C* and *D*. The distance of penetration is taken to be the point *P* where the temperature rise is only 5 per cent of that at *A*.

tions reflect the influences of the varying configuration and composition of the earth's surface, in particular the influences due to the distribution of land and sea.

It has been customary to attribute such temperature variations to the difference in heat capacity between land and water. Such an explanation is, however, inadequate, and to obtain a better understanding of how such temperature differences become established, we must examine the process of heat conduction. To illustrate, let us consider a long rod *AB*, as shown in Fig. 60. Suppose that the rod initially has a uniform temperature and that heat is steadily applied at the end *A*. Heat will then be conducted along the rod toward *B*. After a certain time we shall find that the temperature at *A* has increased by a certain amount, say Δ*T*, and that the temperature rises are progressively smaller, say ½Δ*T* and $\frac{1}{10}$Δ*T*, at the points *C* and *D*.

For practical purposes we may define the *distance of penetration* at a given time *t* by the point *P* at which the temperature rise is a small fraction, say $\frac{1}{20}$, of the rise at *A*. Similarly, we say that the rate of penetration is the speed with which the point *P* moves away from *A*. At first, when t is small, the rate of penetration is rapid and then slows down as the temperature contrast along the rod decreases. From the theory of conduction it can be shown that the distance of penetration at any time t is proportional to the square root of t. However, at all times the rate of penetration is determined by a *single property* of the material, which is known as the *temperature conductivity*, or the *thermal diffusivity*, of the substance. This property, which is denoted by K, is commonly expressed in square centimeters per second. From the theory of conductivity it can be shown that the distance of penetration at the end of a time interval t is proportional to the square root of K. Thus, at any given time

Distance of penetration is proportional to $\sqrt{K}$

Suppose now that A is subject not to a steady rate of heating but to a periodic variation of heating and cooling, such as will occur at the earth's surface every day and every year. Temperature waves will then spread along the rod, with their amplitudes diminishing progressively as we go farther away from A. Eventually, we reach a point where the temperature change is so small that we can say that the wave does not effectively penetrate. If the oscillations at A are rapid (as in the daily cycle), the heating phase will be short, with shallow penetration before the cooling phase sets in; with slower oscillations, the penetration will be deeper.

To find the actual rise in temperature of the medium we recall (see page 72) that the heat required to raise the temperature of a unit volume by an amount ΔT is proportional to ΔT and to the heat capacity of the substance, that is, $\rho C \, \Delta T$. Since the distance of penetration is proportional to $\sqrt{K}$, the volume must also be proportional to $\sqrt{K}$. We then find that $\rho C \sqrt{K} \, \Delta T$ must be proportional to the rate of heating; in other words, ΔT is inversely proportional to $\rho C \sqrt{K}$.

The combination of the physical properties of any medium represented by $\rho C \sqrt{K}$ occupies a central place in all problems concerning conduction of heat, in the earth as well as in the atmosphere, and it is convenient to call it the *conductive capacity*. The larger the conductive capacity, the greater is the ability of the substance to conduct heat away, and the smaller will be the temperature rise at the place where the heat is applied.

From this discussion it follows that the heat capacity in itself has but little bearing on the problem of temperature changes. The important properties are (1) the conductive capacity, which determines the temperature change, and (2) the temperature conductivity, which determines the depth of penetration of the warming.

We may now go a step further and apply heat at the interface between two media of different physical properties. The heat will then be shared in proportion to their conductive capacities and will penetrate each in proportion to their respective values of $\sqrt{K}$. The range of temperature at the interface must be the same for both media, and it will be determined approximately by the sum of the two conductive capacities.

The Influence of Land and Sea. We are now in position to discuss more fully the interactions between the atmosphere and the earth. Incoming solar radiation is absorbed at the interface between the atmosphere and the earth, which also emits long-wave radiation. The composition of the earth's surface is very variable, and may consist of water, ice, snow, or a variety of soils in different conditions. The physical properties of some of these substances have been summarized in Table 8. The depth of penetration is given as the depth at which the temperature change falls below one-twentieth of that at the surface.

Table 8. Conduction Properties of Air and Various Surface Substances*

Substance	Heat capacity, ρC, cal/cm³/°C	Temperature conductivity, K, cm²/sec	Conductivity capacity, $\rho C, \sqrt{K}$	Penetration	
				Diurnal, ft	Annual, ft
Ice.............	0.45	0.012	0.05	1.8	34
Dry sand......	0.3	0.0013	0.011	0.6	11
Wet soil.......	0.4	0.01	0.04	1.6	30
Still water.....	1.0	0.0015	0.0015	0.6	12
Stirred water...	1.0	50*	7*	100*	
Still air........	0.0003	0.2	0.00013		
Stirred air.....	0.0003	100,000*	0.1*	5,000*	Tropopause*

* Values marked by asterisk are not determined, as are the others, by molecular properties and so cannot be measured precisely as in laboratory experiments. The stirring of water decreases with the depth, and the annual penetration will not exceed a few hundred feet. The values for stirred air vary within wide limits (see text).

In still water the heat conduction would take place by molecular processes, and the conductive capacity, penetration, etc., would not differ much from those of ordinary land substances. Thus, if the oceans were still, there would be little difference between the heat exchanges over oceans and over continents. However, the oceans are stirred by the action of the winds, and heat is transferred along the vertical by motion and mixing of water in bulk, rather than by the much slower molecular processes; as a result, the conductivity and the conductive capacity of stirred water are very much larger than in still water. The difference is entirely due to the mobility of water.

The air is even more mobile than water, and here we meet with vast differences. Even in apparently calm air there is a small amount of turbulence. In such air the conductivity may be very low. The value given in Table 8 refers to the average conditions at some considerable distance above the ground. Near the earth's surface, the mobility (along the vertical) of the air is considerably reduced, and values of the conductivity in the range from 500 to 5,000 are typical. The mobility of air depends very greatly upon the lapse rate, with the result that it increases as the lapse rate steepens. Thus, when and where the lapse rate is steep, a deep layer of air will take part in the exchange, and the temperature change will be small. On the other hand, when the lapse rate is small, the mobility is much reduced, and only a shallow layer will be affected.

The temperature conductivities of the various land substances are rather uniform; there is very little difference between ice and wet soil, while dry sand stands out as a somewhat poorer conductor. As compared with stirred water, all land substances are poor conductors, and water is, in turn, inferior to air. As a result of these differences, the periodic heatings and coolings (diurnal and annual) will penetrate only to a very short distance into the land, to a moderate depth in the oceans, and to a considerable height in the atmosphere.

The actual range of temperature will be greatest at the surfaces, and there it will be inversely proportional to the sum of the conductive capacities of the air and the substance in contact with it. This sum is about 7 for air and ocean, and about 0.14 for air and land, so that the temperature range would be about 50 times larger over continents than over oceans. Furthermore, the heat is shared between the two media in proportion to their conductive capacities. Thus, air in contact with land gains more than one-half of the available heat, while air over oceans gains only a negligible amount.

If we look closely at the figures in Table 8 and note the way the conductive capacity $\rho C \sqrt{K}$ is compounded, it is clear that the enormous difference between the land and ocean effects is not much influenced by the difference in heat capacity but is primarily due to the difference in the temperature conductivity K, which, in turn, depends upon the mobility of the water. If these differences are translated into sea-surface temperatures, we find a diurnal range of about 0.2 to 0.5°C. For land areas we find values about 50 times larger, that is, from 10 to 25°C. These values are somewhat larger than those observed. The difference is partly due to the horizontal heat exchange, which tends to circulate air near the earth's surface from cold to warm regions, and partly due to loss of heat due to evaporation from the ground, particularly during the sunny hours.

If radiation and conduction were the only processes at work, the annual range of temperature would be much larger than what is actually observed. The moderating influence is primarily due to the horizontal transfer and mixing of air. During the warm season, vast masses of air from the oceans invade the continents, while in winter a reverse circulation is active. These horizontal exchanges between the oceans and continents exert a strong moderating influence on the annual range of temperature.

In every respect, the mobility proves to be an important factor in governing the heat balance.

Evaporation and Condensation. If we consider radiation alone, we shall find that, over a long span of time, there is balance between the gain and the loss as far as the system earth-atmosphere is concerned. If we consider the atmosphere alone and compare radiation and conduction, we shall find that the budget is not balanced, and we conclude that there must be some additional process at work. Before we identify this process it might be of interest to examine the function it has to perform.

From its long-wave and short-wave radiation exchange, the earth's surface emerges as the gainer. This gain is finally balanced by an equal radiation loss which takes place entirely from the atmosphere. We have therefore to consider how the gain at the surface is compensated for by loss from the upper layers of the atmosphere. The gain over land goes as sensible heat partly into the air and partly into the ground, while over the oceans (which occupy about 70 per cent of the whole) the gain goes almost exclusively into the water. The process that we are looking for must therefore be one in which the share gained by the land and the oceans is passed into the atmosphere to offset its loss through radiation. This process must be of greater intensity over oceans than over land, and from Table 6 it will be seen that it must, in general, be more intense in lower than in higher latitudes.

The process that fulfills these conditions is the evaporation-condensation cycle. The evaporation of water from the earth requires the consumption of heat from the immediate surroundings, and this will reduce the heat content at the surface and also reduce the conduction of heat away from it. When the water vapor resulting from this evaporation subsequently condenses into clouds in the atmosphere, the latent heat of vaporization is yielded up, with the atmosphere as the sole beneficiary. The water cycle thus achieves a net transfer of heat from the earth to the atmosphere (see Fig. 61) and permits the establishment of a balanced budget for each of the two parts of the system. While the evaporated water is returned to the earth as rain, the heat is not returned.

The water cycle accounts also for the greater humidity over oceanic regions and the low-latitude belts. However, the precipitation will normally not fall out where the evaporation takes place. The water vapor and the latent heat may be carried vast distances from the place of origin. In fact, much of the water vapor which originates in low latitudes is carried northward by the air currents and yielded up in mid- and high latitudes. This is equivalent to an export of heat from low to high latitudes; it has been included in the heat transport calculated in the last column of Table 8 and is part of the great equalizing influence which the wind systems exert on the temperature distribution over the globe.

Horizontal Exchanges. As mentioned on page 92, the horizontal exchanges do not contribute to the total budget for the system earth-atmosphere. Nevertheless, they are important regionally, and also for invigorating the exchange between the earth and the atmosphere. For example, when winter air streams from Canada southward over the Gulf Stream, a temperature difference is set up such that heat flows from the

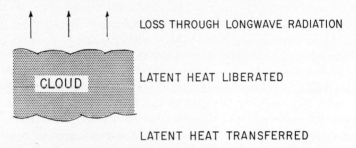

LOSS THROUGH LONGWAVE RADIATION

LATENT HEAT LIBERATED

LATENT HEAT TRANSFERRED

HEAT USED IN EVAPORATION

Fig. 61. A sketch showing the role of evaporation and condensation in the heat budget.

ocean into the air. This steepens the lapse rate of temperature and increases the mobility (along the vertical) and the temperature conductivity of the air, with the result that the absorbed heat penetrates to great heights. On the other hand, on account of the large conductive capacity of the ocean, the sea-surface temperature undergoes little change. On the whole, when air streams over sea, the air temperature will tend to adapt itself to the sea-surface temperature, and the latter will change but little. On the other hand, under similar conditions over land it is more nearly true to say that it is the land surface that adjusts itself to the air temperature. Thus, alternation between northerly and southerly winds will bring about much stronger temperature changes over land than over oceans.

Further Remarks on the Heat Balance. We may now summarize the main points concerning the heat balance. The system earth-atmosphere gains heat (mostly at the earth's surfaces) by absorbing short-wave radiation from the sun, and it loses heat by means of long-wave radiation. When these are added algebraically, a net heat source is found in low latitudes and a net sink in high latitudes. The equator-to-pole variation of the mean temperature results primarily from radiation. The same is true of the general increase from equator to pole of the annual variation of temperature and the increase from pole to equator of the diurnal variation of temperature. The horizontal exchanges tend, however, to moderate the contrasts that radiation alone would provide.

The sharing of the heat between the earth and the atmosphere affects a very shallow layer of the land areas, a moderately deep layer of the oceans, and a very deep layer of the atmosphere. In consequence, one finds large yearly and daily ranges of temperature over the continents, particularly over dry and sandy soils, and much smaller ranges over the oceans. The variations in temperature due to the swinging of the wind from northerly to southerly directions are also much larger over land than at sea.

While part of the net radiation gain at the surface goes directly into the atmosphere as sensible heat, a large part of it, particularly over the oceans, has to reach the atmosphere through evaporation and horizontal exchanges. The importance of the evaporation-condensation-precipitation cycle can hardly be stressed too much, for without it the atmosphere would be forced into a very different temperature regime. But above all, we must emphasize the importance of mobility. It is through the mobility of the water that the difference between oceans and continents arises. And it is the mobility of the air that moderates the differences between pole and equator and between continents and oceans. Without this mobility, the climatic extremes would be intolerable to life as we know it.

Annual Variation of Temperature. The processes that determine these changes have been described in the foregoing sections, and we shall now outline the general aspects of their geographical distribution. We consider first Fig. 62, which may be taken to represent the conditions in a belt through Asia extending from the equator to the North Pole.

In the equatorial zone the sun is in the zenith twice a year (at the equinoxes), and there is a tendency for the temperature to be highest at the equinoxes and lowest at the solstices. A typical example is the curve for Batavia (now called Jakarta) (Fig. 62). However, the sun is high in the sky throughout the year, and the annual range of temperature is very small. Inhabitants of the equatorial belt are far more concerned with the seasonal changes of moisture and rainfall than with the range of temperature.

The tendency for a double oscillation of temperature is usually disturbed where there are marked seasonal variations in rainfall and wind. During the rainy season the cloud cover is large, and this increases the albedo (page 88), with the result that less radiation is absorbed by the earth. Furthermore, the rain, coming from colder air aloft, will cool the air, and some heat is used to evaporate falling and fallen rain. The rainy season is therefore generally cooler than the dry one.

On the Asiatic side, vast masses of air stream northward across the equator during the northern summer and invade South Asia, while a reverse current is present during the northern winter. These currents, which are known as the summer and winter monsoons, will be discussed in Chap. 11. Such annual migrations of vast masses of air bring about horizontal heat exchanges, and these affect the annual range of temperature.

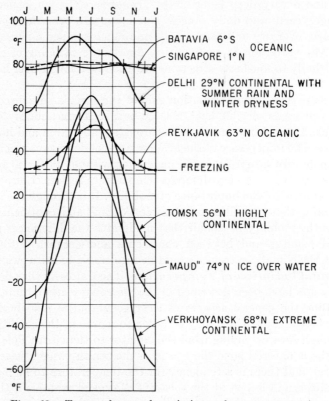

Fig. 62. Types of annual variations of temperature. At Batavia (now called Jakarta) and Singapore the annual range is very small. At Delhi the range is moderate, and the monsoon rain tends to depress the temperature in July and August. Tomsk and Verkhoyansk, which are typical of the interior of large continents, have much larger annual ranges than Reykjavík, which is under oceanic influences. Over the polar ice (Maud) the summer maximum is determined by the melting point of ice, and the winter minimum is moderate because heat is conducted through the ice from the warmer water underneath.

A typical example is the curve for Singapore (Fig. 62). Being situated at 1° N, Singapore would be expected to have a double oscillation of temperature, with maxima near the equinoxes. While rainfall is plentiful in all months, the driest period is midsummer, and the wettest, midwinter. Furthermore, during the winter months the air that arrives at Singapore has come from the continent of Asia. Thus, both the variation in rainfall and in the general wind direction tend to depress the temperature during the northern winter. However, before the continental air arrives at Singapore, it has adapted itself so well to the sea surface that the annual range of temperature is very small.

Considering next the curve for Delhi we see a marked annual change, indicating a continental regime. The curve is typical of large land areas in the subtropics with distinct winter dryness and summer rain. The rainy season sets in in May with the arrival of the southwest monsoon (see Chap. 11). The combined effect of increased albedo and cooling by rain suffices to arrest the temperature rise before the sun reaches its maximum altitude. The rain abates in late August and September, and the temperature curve tends to recover. However, heat is used to evaporate water, and as the season advances, the southwest monsoon dies out; the northeast monsoon develops, and the temperature curve reverts to a normal trend.

It is of considerable interest to note that the mean January temperature in Delhi is as high as 58°F. This is about 10° higher than the January temperature in Alabama. The relatively high winter temperatures in northern India are to a large extent due to the protection afforded by the Himalayas and their extensions toward the west and northeast. These lofty mountains form a barrier against invasions of cold air from the polar continents farther to the north, and hinder horizontal exchanges with the cold source.

The importance of the mountain range in hindering horizontal exchanges can best be seen by comparing the temperature curves for Delhi and Tomsk (Fig. 62). The latter station is situated far from any maritime influence, and the region as a whole is barred from exchanging air with the subtropical belt. These conditions are even more pronounced at Verkhoyansk, which is situated in a valley to the east of the Lena River. Apart from the remoteness from oceanic influences, the local mountains and hills hinder exchange and favor drainage of cold air down to the floor of the valley. Verkhoyansk has often been called the cold pole of the world. The lowest temperature ever recorded there was close to −95°F. For comparison we have inserted the temperature curve for Reykjavík, Iceland, which is in about the same latitude; we see clearly the vast modifying influence that the oceans exert.

Even the coldest regions of Siberia receive some air, in occasional bursts, from the Atlantic, and they export cold air to the Pacific Ocean. Without these horizontal exchanges, the mean winter temperature in the Baikal region would be lower than that observed. In still air the winter temperature in the zone of midwinter darkness would be determined by a balance between the outgoing radiation and the conduction of heat from the interior of the earth. This theoretical minimum would be somewhere in the vicinity of $-100°F$.

If we go from the continent of Asia to the polar fields of snow and ice, we shall meet with a different temperature regime. The annual variation of temperature, as determined by Sverdrup on the Maud Expedition, is shown in Fig. 62. Although midnight sun and midwinter darkness prevail, the annual range is moderate. In summer, heat is used to melt ice, and the mean temperature does not exceed the melting point. During the long winter the snow loses heat at a rapid rate by radiation. However, ocean currents from lower latitudes (notably from the Atlantic) dive under the ice sheet and bring in vast amounts of heat. The average polar ice is about 6 to 10 ft thick, and since its conductive capacity is moderately high (see page 95), a balance between loss through radiation and gain through conduction from the water below is reached. As far as winter temperature is concerned, the arctic is not nearly as forbidding as are some polar continental areas. The difference comes entirely from the mobility of the ocean waters.

Over the water close to the ice edge the average winter temperature of the air does not deviate much from the freezing point of sea water, which is about $29°F$. On the other hand, the average summer temperature does not deviate much from the melting point of fresh ice, or $32°F$. A seal living along the ice edge would probably conclude that the sun, while controlling the light, has little influence on the temperature.

The influence of oceans and continents is shown also in Fig. 63. Here is plotted the annual range of temperature from the west coast of North America eastward to the east coast of Asia, broadly along the 50th parallel.

Seattle, about 80 miles from the main coast, has a moderate maritime trend. Spokane, which to some extent is sheltered by the Cascade Range, is distinctly continental; the annual range is large, and there is frost in winter. The main barrier against horizontal heat exchanges from the Pacific is the Rocky Mountains. To the east of the Rockies we find temperature curves of the type represented by Minneapolis and Quebec. Even St. John's, on the east coast of Newfoundland, has a continental trend, the reason being that the prevailing winds are from the continent.

On the North Atlantic, the annual range of the air temperature is the same as that of the sea surface, and generally of the order of $10°F$. On the European side Dublin shows a typical maritime trend, more so than Seattle. The maritime influence in Europe extends a considerable distance inland. Here there are no extensive mountain barriers, and the horizontal exchanges are lively. As a result, Berlin (Fig. 63) has a cooler summer and a milder winter than Spokane, and Kiev has a milder winter than Minneapolis and Quebec. Only when we go deep into the Eurasian continent do we find an annual range which is larger than that along the Canadian border to the east of the Rocky Mountains.

The data in Fig. 63 show the very great difference between the temperature regimes along west coasts and east coasts in mid-latitudes. We shall return to the discussion of these differences in a later chapter.

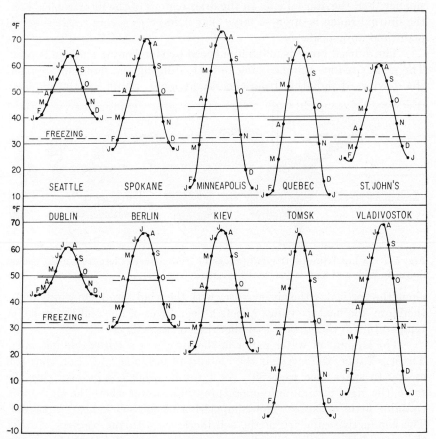

Fig. 63. Types of annual variations of temperature, showing the influence of oceans and continents.

Diurnal Variations. The processes are the same as those in the annual cycle, but there are differences in degree. First, since the daily cycle is short the penetration is shallow, and the diurnal range of temperature is relatively large. Second, on account of the shortness of the cycle, the horizontal exchanges of heat are relatively unimportant, except along coasts where an alternating system of land and sea breeze (see Chap. 10) develops. On a small scale, drainage of cold air down to low ground may depress the night temperature. Third, since the daily variation in the elevation of the sun is large in low latitudes and small in high latitudes, the diurnal range will, on the whole, decrease from the equator toward the poles. Over the oceans the diurnal range rarely exceeds 1°F and is everywhere smaller than the annual range. Over land we find a broad belt around the equator (Fig. 64) within which the annual range is smaller than the diurnal one. In the drier regions of the intertropical belt, the diurnal range is often so large that it imposes severe restrictions on plant and animal life.

The diurnal range is much influenced by cloud cover and wind speed. The clouds reduce the incoming radiation during the day and augment the downward radiation from the sky at night. Similarly, the mobility

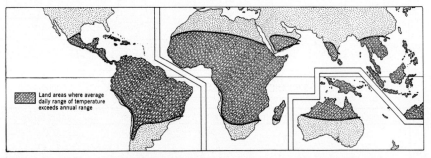

Land areas where average daily range of temperature exceeds annual range

Fig. 64.   In low latitudes the daily range of temperature is larger than the annual range. In mid- and high latitudes the reverse is true.

along the vertical of the air increases with the wind speed. On windy days, therefore, the heat exchange affects a deep layer of air, and the range of temperature at the surface is smaller than on calm days.

The amount of water vapor in the air exerts a noticeable influence. The less vapor, the larger is the amount of outgoing radiation that can escape to space (see page 89). As a result, other conditions being the same, the night minimum temperature will be lower where the air column contains little moisture. The composition of the soil is also important. The conductive capacity of the soil increases with the wetness, so that the diurnal range will be smaller over wet than over dry land. Also, since heat is used to evaporate water and yielded up in the formation of dew, the wetness of the ground has a moderating influence on the range. The two effects combined tend to produce very large diurnal changes over deserts (where both the air and the ground are dry) and smaller changes in more humid regions.

Over snow cover the maximum temperature will be limited by the melting point, but, since snow is a good radiator, the minimum temperature may be low.

With the diurnal cycle of temperature goes a corresponding change in lapse rate near the ground. The daily range of temperature is largest at the ground and decreases rapidly with height. As a result, the lapse rate is, on the average, small in the early morning and steep in the early afternoon. The mobility of the air (along the vertical) increases with the lapse rate and so undergoes a diurnal cycle in tune with the temperature.

The mobility does not only affect the exchange of heat but also the exchange of moisture. After sunrise, water begins to evaporate from the ground. The lapse rate is, however, small, so that the vapor accumulates

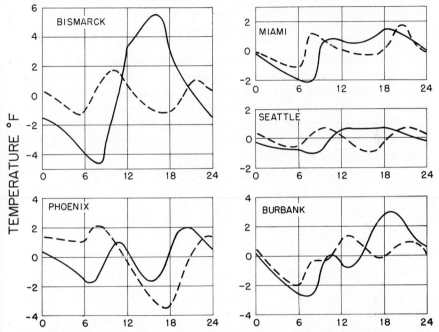

Fig. 65. Examples of daily variation of dewpoint temperature. Dashed lines refer to summer, and solid lines refer to winter conditions.

in the lowest layer. About 3 to 4 hr after sunrise the lapse rate has become so steep and the exchange so lively that there is balance between the removal and supply of vapor. At this time we normally find the first diurnal maximum in water vapor and dewpoint temperature at the ground. After this time the ground is so dry that the evaporation fails to keep up with the heating; the removal dominates, and the amount of water vapor and the dewpoint temperature decrease toward a minimum in the afternoon. Thereafter, the exchange weakens, and the dewpoint rises again until the air has cooled so much that dew begins to form. The second maximum in the dewpoint temperature usually occurs about 3 to 4 hr after sunset. During the night the air loses water vapor to the ground, and the dewpoint decreases until the sun again rises.

Some typical examples of diurnal variations in dewpoint are shown in Fig. 65. The lowest daily minimum is found over relatively dry land (Phoenix), but even moist places (Miami and Seattle) show a double oscillation. At Burbank (Southern California) the normal trend is distorted somewhat by local breezes. The curves for Bismarck, North Dakota, are of special interest. In summer, the land is relatively dry and the midday minimum is well developed. In winter, when snow is present on the ground, while the lapse rate of temperature is generally small, the removal of moisture during the sunny hours is insufficient to produce an afternoon minimum. The winter curve for Bismarck is typical of the snow covered regions, while a double oscillation is typical of bare land.

The variations described in this section refer to the conditions at the level of the instrument shelter (see page 27). It should be emphasized, however, that the diurnal variations will be very much larger at the level where the plants grow. The agriculturist will be interested not only in the broad aspects of weather and climate, as revealed by the customary observations, but also in the very local weather and climate that affects the roots and leaves of the plants.

7

Showers, Thunderstorms, Hail, and Tornadoes

There is a large group of weather phenomena which develop when the lapse rate of temperature becomes too steep. These are the manifestations of instability in vertical columns of air, and it is typical of all such developments that their horizontal dimensions are small while their vertical extents are large.

Stability and Instability. It is necessary first to state precisely what we mean by the terms stability and instability, and to do so we consider Fig. 66. Let the parcel of air at P_0 be displaced a small distance Δz upward (positive) or downward (negative) so that it arrives at P_1 or P_2, where it is brought to rest. Since the air is compressible, the parcel will expand (in upward motion) and contract (in downward motion), and we may inquire whether the parcel will be lighter or heavier than the surrounding air when it arrives at P_1 or P_2. If it is lighter at P_1 or heavier at P_2, it will be accelerated farther away from its original level. The state is then said to be *unstable*, since a small disturbance will cause the parcel to move farther and farther away from its original level. What characterizes instability is that the vertical acceleration A has the same sign as the displacement Δz, so that the product $A \Delta z$ is positive.

On the other hand, if the conditions are such that the parcel R_0, when displaced, becomes heavier than the environment at R_1 or lighter than the environment at R_2, the acceleration will be opposite to the displacement, and we say that the stratification is *stable*.

In the limiting case, the density of the displaced parcel Q will be the same as that of the environment. There is then no buoyancy, and the stratification is said to be in neutral equilibrium. We may symbolize these

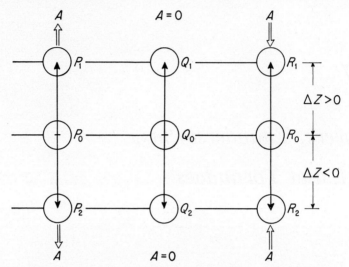

Fig. 66. Showing the definition of instability and stability.

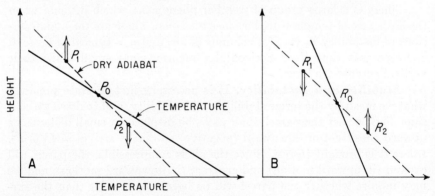

Fig. 67. Showing how stability and instability depend upon the lapse rate of temperature.

definitions by writing

$$A \, \Delta z > 0 \qquad \text{instability}$$
$$A \, \Delta z = 0 \qquad \text{neutrality}$$
$$A \, \Delta z < 0 \qquad \text{stability}$$

To determine what kind of equilibrium exists in a given case we consider Fig. 67. For the time being, we assume that the air is not saturated. Now, if the parcel at P_0 is moved upward or downward, it will follow the dry adiabat through P_0 and arrive at P_1 or P_2. At P_1 it would be warmer, and at P_2 colder, than the environment. The accelerations would be away from the original level, and the case would be unstable. What characterizes this case is that the *actual lapse rate* γ is larger than the *dryadiabatic rate* γ_d.

We consider next Fig. 67*b*. Here γ is smaller than γ_d. It will be seen that if the parcel were moved up or down, buoyancy would be present, and the parcel would become accelerated back toward its level of origin. The case is one of stability.

In the limiting case, when $\gamma = \gamma_d$, the density of the parcel would be the same as that of the environment, and the equilibrium would be neutral. We see then that the criteria for instability, neutrality, and stability may be written

$$\gamma > \gamma_d \quad \text{instability}$$
$$\gamma = \gamma_d \quad \text{neutrality}$$
$$\gamma < \gamma_d \quad \text{stability}$$

If the air were saturated, the same reasoning would hold, except that the saturated adiabat would replace the dry adiabat. Thus, for saturated air

$$\gamma > \gamma_s \quad \text{instability}$$
$$\gamma = \gamma_s \quad \text{neutrality}$$
$$\gamma < \gamma_s \quad \text{stability}$$

Types of Soundings. Although the above definitions are straightforward, certain complications arise when a parcel of air undergoes such large vertical displacements that it becomes saturated with moisture. The "path" of the parcel, as depicted on an adiabatic chart, will then be partly along a dry adiabat and partly along a saturated adiabat. Three typical cases are shown in Fig. 68.

We consider first the sounding on the left. If the parcel at P is moved upward, it will follow the dry adiabat through P and become saturated at its lifting condensation level (LCL) (see page 82). Above this level it will follow the saturated adiabat. The parcel temperature will be that indicated by curve T'. This temperature will everywhere be lower than the environment temperature, as indicated by curve T. What is typical of this case is that the actual lapse rate is smaller than the saturated adiabatic rate, so that $\gamma < \gamma_s$. Throughout, the lifted parcel (whether saturated or not) is colder than the environment. This case is called *absolute stability*.

We consider next the case shown in the middle part of Fig. 68. If the parcel at Q is lifted it will follow the dry adiabat through Q, and be warmer than the environment. As soon as it reaches its lifting condensation level (LCL) it will move along the saturated adiabat, and throughout it will be warmer than the environment. This case is called *absolute instability*.

Finally we consider the case shown on the right of Fig. 68. Here the actual lapse rate is smaller than the dryadiabatic rate and larger than the saturated adiabatic rate. If the parcel at R is lifted, it will at first be colder than the environment. However, as soon as it reaches its lifting condensation level (LCL), it begins to move along the saturated adiabat, and when it comes to the level indicated by LFC it has the same temperature as the environment. If the parcel now is displaced farther, it will be

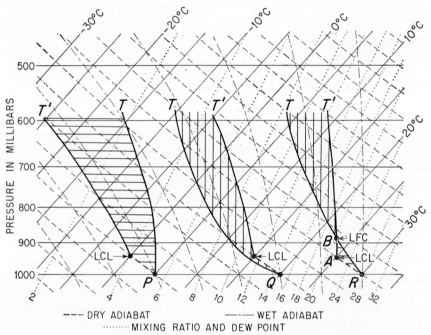

Fig. 68. Three soundings indicating absolute stability (left), absolute instability (middle), and conditional instability (right).

warmer than the environment, and there will be an upward acceleration. Below the level LFC, energy must be supplied to the parcel to move it against the buoyancy forces. The amount of energy needed is represented by the area $RABR$, which is called the *negative area*. The level LFC is called the *level of free convection*, for above this level the parcel will move freely, and convective overturnings will result. The area between the curves T and T' above the level LFC is called the *positive area*, for here potential energy is available for the creation of convective currents. The case shown on the right of Fig. 68 is called *conditional instability*. The word *conditional* means that if the parcel could be moved upward to LFC, instability would result.

Comparing the three cases shown in Fig. 68, we see that the case on the left is characterized by a negative area; the case in the middle is characterized by a positive area; and the case on the right is characterized by a lower negative area and an upper positive area. The three cases illustrate what we have called absolute stability, absolute instability, and conditional instability.

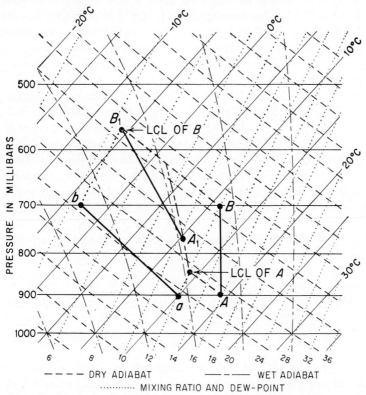

Fig. 69. If a mass of air is lifted bodily so much that it becomes saturated, its internal structure may change from a stable to an unstable stratification. For explanation, see text.

Bodily Lifting of Air. In the foregoing section we considered the stability of an individual parcel of air moving through an undisturbed environment. In certain circumstances, a large mass of air may be moved upward or downward. This happens normally when air streams over a mountain range, or when warm air glides up or down a wedge of cold air. To explain the stability changes associated with such vertical motions, we consider Fig. 69. Here the line *AB* represents the temperature distribution through a layer which, for convenience, is chosen 200 mb deep. We imagine that this layer is lifted, and we assume that there is no outflow of mass through the vertical walls. The layer must then remain 200 mb deep.

Now, if the line *ab* represents the dewpoint temperature, the air at the base of the column (that is, *A*) will become saturated at its lifting condensation level (see page 82), and if it is lifted further it will follow the saturated adiabat to A_1. Next, the air at the top of the column (that is, *B*) will become saturated at B_1. Since the layer is 200 mb deep, the base will be at A_1 when the top becomes saturated. It will be seen that the column was initially dry and stable. However, after being lifted so much that the column becomes saturated, the stratification is unstable, for $\gamma > \gamma_s$. In the case shown, the instability develops because the humidity decreases rapidly with elevation.

Suppose that the humidity at the top of the column were higher; the lifting condensation level of the top of the column would then be somewhere on the line BB_1. As long as the lifting condensation level of *B* falls to the *left* of the saturated adiabat through the lifting condensation level of *A*, the column will be unstable when lifted to saturation. On the other hand, if the moisture distribution is such that the lifting condensation level of *B* falls to the *right* of the saturated adiabat through the lifting condensation level of *A*, the stratification will be stable after saturation is reached.

The type of instability here described is called *convective instability*. Initially, the stratification is stable, but if the column is lifted so much that it becomes saturated throughout, instability, neutrality, or stability will develop according to the following rules:

1. Instability if LCL of *B* is to the left of saturated adiabat through LCL of *A*.

2. Neutrality if LCL of *B* is on the saturated adiabat through LCL of *A*.

3. Stability if LCL of *B* is to the right of saturated adiabat through LCL of *A*.

These rules may be applied to any layer of air to determine whether or not instability will develop as a result of bodily lifting. We shall see later that this type of instability is a prominent feature in connection with thunderstorms, squalls, and tornadoes.

Types of Cumulus Clouds. Few clouds are so variable in appearance and so interesting to watch as are the cumulus clouds. The three principal types are illustrated schematically in Fig. 70. Here the upper row shows an outline of the cloud structure, and the lower row shows the typical temperature distribution along the vertical.

Cumulus humilis, or fair-weather cumulus (Fig. 70*a*), are shallow clouds; they have no towers and protuberances and they show little sign of growth and internal motion. They develop when the layer below the condensation level is unstable while the air above is stable. On occasions, the clouds may cover a major part of the sky, and they are then hard to distinguish from stratocumulus.

Cumulus congestus, or towering cumulus (Fig. 70b), are easily recognized by the presence of towers and protuberances. By careful watching one gains the impression that large bubbles of air rise through the cloud and form a cauliflower pattern on its upper surface. Although each

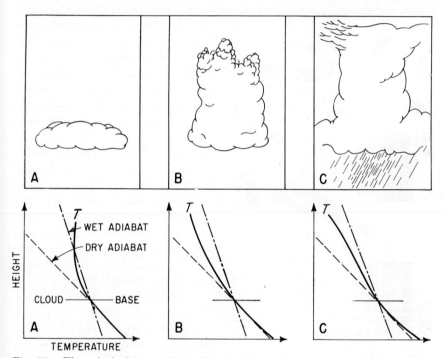

Fig. 70. The principal types of cumulus clouds and the corresponding temperature distributions.

bubble is short-lived, new ones form and the cloud continues to grow. The towering cumulus form when there is a relatively deep layer of conditionally unstable air above the condensation level. If this layer is sufficiently deep, the cloud may grow into a cumulonimbus.

Cumulonimbus clouds form when there is a very deep layer of conditional instability above the condensation level. In mid- and high latitudes these clouds reach up to such heights that the temperature is well below freezing. The upper portion will then consist of ice crystals or a mixture of ice crystals and water droplets. Most frequently these clouds release precipitation in the form of showers or snow flurries; in pronounced cases they may produce hail and thunderstorms.

Patterns of Thunderstorms. Thunderstorms develop from cumulonimbus clouds or aggregations of such clouds, and they differ from the shower clouds in that they produce thunder and lightning. Observations show that thunder and lightning occur only when large masses of liquid and frozen water have been carried up to such heights that the temperature is well below $-20°C$ ($-4°F$). Since large masses of such water can accumulate at these high levels only when the air originally was warm and humid, thunderstorms are rarely observed without warm and humid air being present in the lower layers. Furthermore, since large masses of condensed water can be carried to great heights only if the updrafts are strong, thunderstorms develop only when the lapse rate of temperature is steep through deep layers of air. As a general rule, therefore, thunderstorms occur in connection with warm, humid, and unstable air.

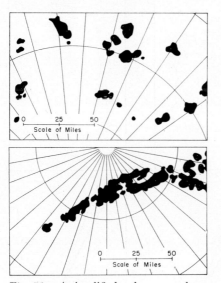

Fig. 71. A simplified radar scope showing scattered thunderstorms (upper) and line thunderstorms (lower).

Observations show that the thunderstorms often occur in more or less distinct patterns, and it is customary to speak of air-mass thunderstorms, line thunderstorms, and frontal thunderstorms.

1. *Air-mass Thunderstorms.* Within a more or less uniform mass of air one finds that the storms are scattered; they develop locally where the lapse rate becomes steep as a result of diurnal heating, and they have a maximum frequency in the afternoon hours.

2. *Line Thunderstorms.* These storms are organized into narrow belts or bands in the direction of the winds at low levels. Typical examples of air-mass and line storms are shown in Fig. 71. In North America the line pattern is more frequent than the scattered type, and the line storms are usually more intense. Thunderstorms of the line type may develop at any time, but there is a distinct tendency for maximum occurrence in the afternoon hours.

3. *Frontal Thunderstorms.* As explained in connection with Fig. 45, a front is a sloping layer which separates cold and warm air. When the warm air glides up over the cold wedge, thunderstorms may develop if the warm air is convectively unstable. Although the frontal thunderstorms may be scattered, they move along with the fronts and can be recognized

as belonging to the general frontal cloud region. These storms may occur
at any time of the day, and there is hardly any preference for the afternoon hours.

  Stages in Thunderstorm Development. The life of an individual
thundercloud is quite short, and its whole life cycle is often a matter of
1 or 2 hr. In the developing stage (Fig. 72) the cloud is warmer than the

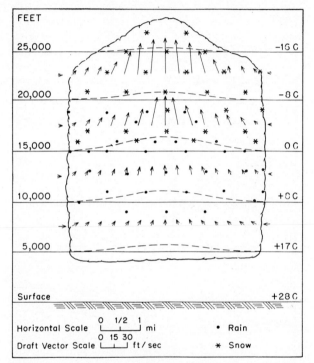

Fig. 72. A thundercloud in the developing stage. The cloud
air is warmer than the outside air, and there is updraft
throughout the cloud. (*After Byers and Braham.*)

outside air so that the cloud air is accelerated upward (see page 109).
The updraft increases with elevation, and the cloud builds rapidly to
heights where the temperature is well below freezing. In the meantime
large amounts of cloud droplets, raindrops, and snowflakes accumulate in
the cloud. Eventually, the amount of accumulated water becomes so large
that the heavier elements cannot be supported by the updrafts; water
then begins to fall through the cloud. The frictional drag exerted by the
falling water turns the updraft into a downdraft, and a heavy downpour
sets in, marking the beginning of the mature stage shown in Fig. 73.

  In the mature stage updrafts and downdrafts exist side by side. The
falling snow and rain (coming from the colder air aloft) cools the down-

draft, which spreads out horizontally over the ground as a wet and cool pool of air, more or less as shown in Fig. 74.

The onset of the downdraft at the ground is usually sharp and marked by strong gusts. An outstanding example is shown in Fig. 75. After a more or less normal rise in temperature from morning to early afternoon, a sudden drop set in at about 3 P.M. At the same time a heavy

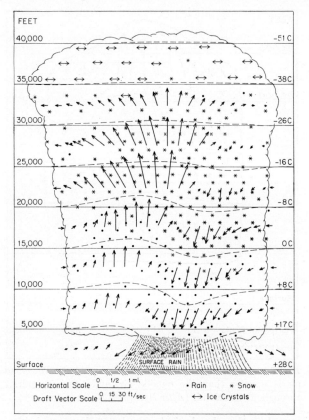

Fig. 73. A thunderstorm in the mature stage. Part of the cloud is occupied by a downdraft which is colder than the neighboring air. (*After Byers and Braham.*)

downpour began, lasted a little more than 1 hr, and resulted in about 2 in. of rainfall. The arrival of the downdraft is clearly indicated by the sharp gust which set in about 3 P.M. with a peak velocity of about 70 mph. At the same time a sharp and irregular rise in pressure occurred.

During the mature stage the downdrafts gain over the updrafts, and after some time the stage shown in Fig. 76 is reached. This is called the dissipating stage. The cloud then exhausts its water supply; the rain intensity decreases, and, eventually, the cloud dissolves or disintegrates into

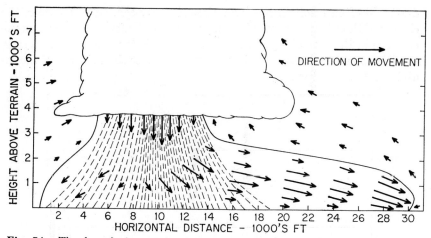

Fig. 74. The downdraft spreads out and advances like a cold wedge. (*After Byers and Braham.*)

irregular lumps of scud at low levels and dense patches and streaks of cirrus at high levels.

Thunderstorm Cells and Clusters. The above description applies to an individual thundercloud. Most frequently, a thunderstorm consists of a cluster of thunderclouds. A typical example is shown in Fig. 77, where five cells are present. Cell I is an old thundercloud in which only downdraft is present. Cell V is relatively young since only updrafts are observed, while the other cells correspond to the mature stage in which updrafts and downdrafts are present side by side.

Observations show that there is a distinct tendency for new cells to form on the forward side of the downdraft of an older cell. Referring back to Fig. 74, it will be seen that the forward spreading of the cold downdraft will give an upward impulse to the warm air. When the downdraft has spread sufficiently far from the mother cloud, the upward motion ahead of the down-

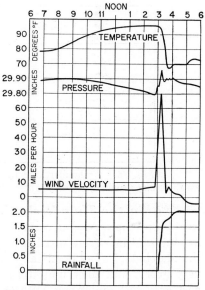

Fig. 75. Showing the temperature drop, the pressure peak, the gust, and the rain associated with a line thunderstorm. Washington, D.C., July 30, 1913. (*After Humphreys.*)

draft will often result in the formation of a new cell. In this manner the cluster of thunderstorms will be replenished on the forward side while the old cells in the rear dissipate. As a result of this tendency for clustering, the life span of a cluster will be very much longer than the life of the individual thunderstorms.

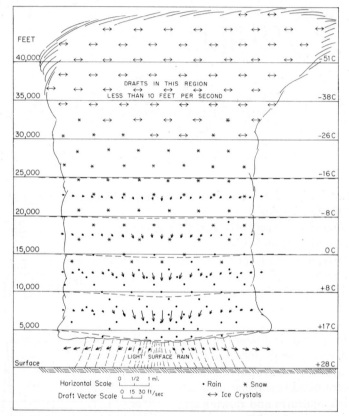

Fig. 76. A thundercloud in the dissipating stage. (*After Byers and Braham.*)

Within the Thundercloud. While everyone is familiar with the weather on the ground associated with the passage of thunderstorms, it is less known that severe weather may be encountered at all levels within a thundercloud. For all practical purposes, the visibility is zero. The wind is very gusty, and since updrafts and downdrafts exist side by side, the gust gradients are strong, with the result that aircraft flying through a thundercloud will experience strong jerks. Above the freezing level aircraft icing may be intense, but the total amount of accumulated ice is usually small, since the length of the path through the cloud is relatively short.

In addition to the vast number of cloud droplets, a thundercloud will contain a large variety of hydrometeors, such as rain, snow, hail, etc., and these may be present simultaneously through deep layers. Some typical distributions in summer thunderstorms in Ohio are shown in Table 9. It will be seen that raindrops may be encountered at all levels

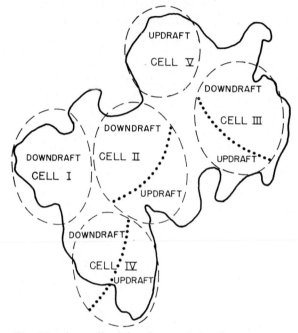

Fig. 77.   An outline of a cluster of thunderstorms consisting of five cells. Wilmington, Ohio, Aug. 14, 1947. (*After Byers and Braham.*)

up to about 25,000 ft (8 km), or to about 10,000 ft above the freezing level. The occurrence of raindrops at these heights is due to strong updrafts, which may carry even large drops upward in the cloud. Mixture of snow and rain is most frequent near the freezing level, which, during the

Table 9. *Percentage Frequency of Hydrometers in Thunder-clouds*[*]

Type	Height, ft				
	5,000	10,000	15,000	20,000	25,000
Rain............	87	95	78	18	5
Snow............	2	15	79	88	91
Hail............	2	12	5	6	3

[*] After Byers and Braham.

summer season in Ohio, is near the 15,000-ft level. Hailstones are more frequent within the cloud than at the ground since many of them melt on their way down.

Observations show that lightning discharges do not occur until the cloud has built up to such heights that the temperature at its top is about $-28°C$ ($-18°F$). A center of positive charge is then found near the $-20°C$ isotherm ($-4°F$), with a lower negative center between about 0

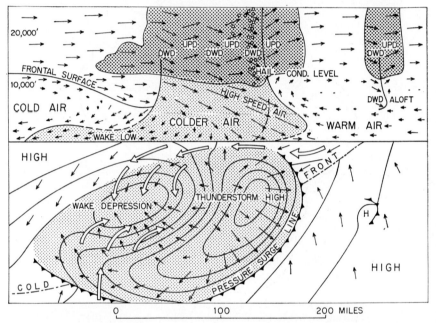

Fig. 78. Typical structure of a line thunderstorm. (*After Fujita.*)

and $-10°C$ (32 and 14°F). These are the main charge centers, and the first discharge takes place between them. On occasions, a positive center may be present at lower levels.

The greatest lightning activity is in the region of the downdraft and heavy rain. On the whole, thunder and lightning are most likely to occur in warm and humid air in which the lapse rate is so steep that strong vertical currents can develop.

Squall Lines. Some examples of weather charts were shown at the end of Chap. 3. In those examples we were concerned with such large-scale features as extensive fronts, large cyclones, and anticyclones. If the pressure distribution in the vicinity of a thunderstorm, or a cluster of such storms, is analyzed in great detail, one often finds that a dwarf anti-cyclone (or high) is present under the storm. This dwarf anticyclone, which occupies much of the area covered by the downdraft, is called the *thunderstorm high.* Often a small low is found upwind from the high, and this is called the *wake depression.*

The typical structure of a line thunderstorm is illustrated in Fig. 78, where the upper portion shows a vertical cross section through the storm, and the lower section shows the horizontal pressure distribution under the

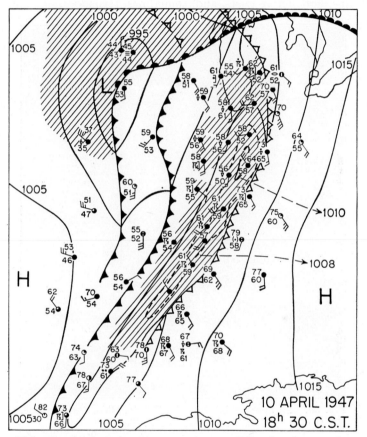

Fig. 79.   An example of an extensive squall line in advance of a cold front. (*After Bergeron.*)

storm. The line along which the downdraft meets with the warm air is called the *squall line* or the *pressure surge line.* Here the wind direction shifts suddenly; there is a strong sharp-edged gust, with a sudden drop in temperature and brisk rise in pressure (see also Fig. 75).

The squall lines are often so short that they are difficult to identify on weather charts of the type shown on page 59. On occasion, and particularly when the thunderstorms are associated with cold fronts, the storms may be organized in long narrow bands. The thundery area is then usually preceded by an irregular squall line which may be several hundred miles long. A somewhat extreme case is shown in Fig. 79. Here a squall line in advance of the thundery area can be traced all the way from northeastern Texas to northern Michigan. In the United States squall lines are most frequent in spring and summer. They are often accompanied by hailstorms, destructive gusts, and, sometimes, tornadoes.

Fig. 80. An approaching tornado. Toledo, Ohio, June 8, 1953. (*Photograph by J. Burde. Courtesy of U.S. Weather Bureau.*)

Tornadoes. A tornado is a vortex of small horizontal extent and great intensity which extends downward from a thundercloud. It is usually visible as a funnel-shaped cloud with a broad base in the cumulonimbus and a narrow tubular extension down to the ground. An example of a relatively wide tornado is shown in Fig. 80.

The lower part of the tornado cloud is often surrounded by an ugly column of dust and debris, which are sucked up from the ground and thrown outward by the centrifugal force in the whirl. At the time of inception the funnel is more or less vertical, but as the mother cloud moves on, the upper portion of the whirl becomes slanted and sometimes detached. On occasions several funnels may build down from the mother cloud, and some of these may not reach the ground.

The diameter of a tornado may vary from a few yards to a few hundred yards, with an average of about 250 yd. The winds are strong also outside the funnel cloud, and the width of the path, as determined by the destructive effects on the ground, may exceed ½ mile. The passage of a tornado is accompanied by a sudden pressure drop of the order of 25 mb, though on occasions much larger pressure changes have been observed. The decrease in pressure from the rim to the center of the tornado represents a tremendous force, which few buildings can withstand. As a tornado goes over a building the outside pressure drops so suddenly that the pressure within cannot follow suit; much of the damage caused by tornadoes is due to the pressure differential through the walls and roof.

The circulation of the wind around a tornado is almost always in a counterclockwise (cyclonic) direction. The wind speed near the core varies within wide limits. Since no anemometer has survived the passage of a severe tornado, no reliable measurements of the wind speed have been made. Estimates, however, indicate that the wind speed is of the order of 100 m/sec, or over 200 mph, and may be twice as large in extreme cases. From the formula given on page 32 it follows that, in extreme cases, the wind pressure may be as large as 700 lb/ft². Only few structures can withstand such wind pressures.

The life of a tornado varies within wide limits. On the average, the length of the path, as determined from the destructive effects on the ground, is about 3 to 6 miles. On occasion paths as long as 200 miles have been observed.

The majority of the tornadoes in the United States occur in connection with squall lines or severe cold fronts. These tornadoes often occur in families and move in the direction of the wind in the warm air; they usually have long paths. Tornadoes are observed also in connection with scattered thunderstorms of great intensity. Such tornadoes are usually short-lived and have irregular paths. Although tornadoes may occur anywhere, except in the polar regions and over cold northern continents in winter, they are most frequent to the east of the Rocky Mountains, to the east of the Andes, and in eastern India. This suggests that the influences of mountains on the air currents and the distributions of temperature and moisture along the vertical are important, but little is known about the mechanisms that produce tornadoes. In the United States about 95 per cent of all tornadoes move from a direction between south and northwest, with a strong preference (61 per cent) for a southwesterly direction.

Most of the tornadoes in the United States occur in connection with squall lines and cold fronts when there is a layer of warm and moist air near the ground overlain by a layer of dry air. The typical structure of the air masses preceding tornado development is shown in Fig. 81. The lapse rate of temperature is steep in both air masses, and the air above the inversion (above about 820 mb) is strongly convectively unstable. When this air becomes lifted along a squall line or a cold front, excessive instability will result.

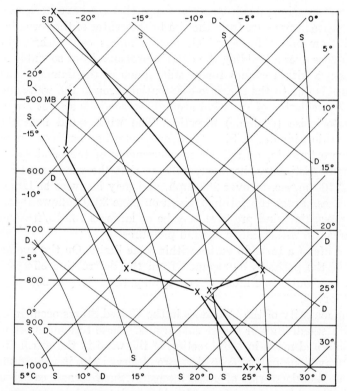

Fig. 81. A sounding through a dry inversion preceding tornado development. (*After Faubush and Miller.*)

Severe-local-weather Warnings. In the United States such warnings are issued when the thunderstorms are expected to result in destructive gusts, hail, free-air turbulence, or tornadoes. The practice is to identify the areas which are likely to experience the most severe conditions, it being understood that adjacent areas will be affected by storms of lesser intensity. The warnings are usually issued 6 to 12 hr in advance of events and are valid for a period of about 6 hr.

While the thunderstorms and the related weather may be widespread, the areas that qualify for severe-weather warnings and alerts are usually quite small, generally about 30,000 sq miles. Since the distance between observing stations ordinarily varies from 50 to 150 miles, the occurrence of the individual storms cannot be pinpointed. It is possible, however, to forecast the likelihood of severe local weather within the area as a whole.

The forecasting procedure may be described briefly as follows. In the first place, the temperature and humidity soundings are analyzed, the regions of pronounced conditional and convective instability are identified, and the movements of such regions are charted. The lifting condensation level, the level of free convection, and the magnitudes of the positive and negative areas are evaluated and used as indexes of the intensity of the convective currents. Second, the effects of diurnal heating or cooling are evaluated to determine the changes in the stability parameters. Third, the movement of cold fronts and squall lines are charted to determine when and where the unstable regions will be subjected to lifting. Fourth, the influx of moist and warm air at low levels and the advance of cold and dry air aloft are considered. Fifth, the details of the air currents at various levels are analyzed in great detail. In general, it is found that the most severe weather occurs where a strong and narrow current from a westerly direction aloft begins to overrun a strong and narrow current from a southerly direction at low levels. These currents are often referred to as the high-level and low-level jet, respectively.

Although the severe-local-weather service is of a relatively recent date, it has already proved to be of very great value in minimizing losses of life and property.

Thunderstorms in the United States. Although thunderstorms may occur throughout the year, there is a strong preference for the summer season. The number of days with one or more storms is shown in Fig. 82. In many places the number of thunderstorms occurring during the three summer months accounts for more than 50 per cent of the annual total.

Winter storms are rare everywhere except in Louisiana and the neighboring Gulf states. In spring the frequency increases, and the maximum is found between northeastern Texas and southern Illinois, with moderate frequency of storms elsewhere between the Continental Divide and the Atlantic Coast. In summer (see Fig. 82) a strong maximum is present over Florida, and a well-developed secondary maximum is found in northern New Mexico and Colorado. In late August the thundery activity decreases sharply everywhere.

Loss of life and property due to lightning is considerable, particularly in Texas, Oklahoma, Illinois, New York, Tennessee, Kentucky, and West Virginia. Far greater losses are incurred by the occasional hailstorms and tornadoes which accompany the severe thunderstorms.

Hailstorms in the United States. According to the records of the U.S. Weather Bureau, the average annual property damage due to hailstorms in the United States during the 10-year period 1944–1953 amounted to 53 million dollars. This is about 15 per cent more than the average damage due to tornadoes during the same period. While the tornadoes mostly destroy buildings and structures, most of the hail

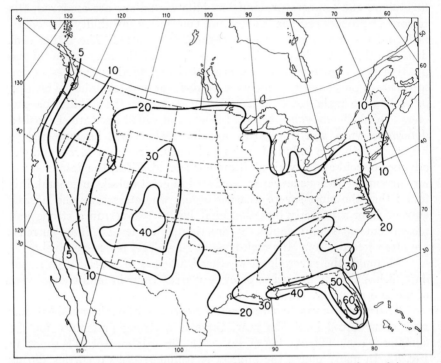

Fig. 82.   Number of days with one or more thunderstorms in June, July, and August.

damage (about 80 per cent) is due to destruction of crops. With considerable justification hailstorms have been referred to as the "white plague." In the most disastrous year on record (1951), Kansas alone suffered a loss of 15 million dollars.

While hailstorms occur in all the 48 states, some states are worse off than others. As far as damage is concerned, Kansas leads the nation, and is followed by several other states in the general area between the Continental Divide and the Mississippi River. The damage is, however, no strict measure of the severity of the storms, for it depends much on the type of crop and the time of occurrence as related to the life cycle of the crop. It so happens that the frequency and severity of hailstorms rises sharply from April to June, with the result that much damage is done during the growing season. Damage to wheat and corn exceeds that to any other crop, particularly since they cover very large areas. Damage to tobacco and fruit is also severe, particularly since these are sensitive also to relatively small hailstones.

The annual variation of hailstorms for the United States as a whole is shown in Fig. 83. It will be seen that the storms are relatively rare from late August to early April. In most states with numerous storms the season is from May to July, except in Montana, where the frequency rises sharply in early June, reaches a maximum in early August, and ends

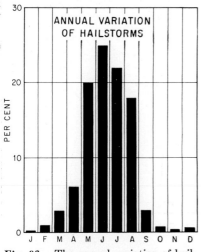

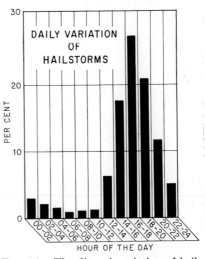

Fig. 83. The annual variation of hailstorms in the United States. On the whole, storms are rare from late August to early April.

Fig. 84. The diurnal variation of hailstorms in the United States. About 85 per cent occur between noon and 9 P.M.

rather abruptly toward the end of that month. On the whole, the hail season begins and ends later in the Northern than in the Southern states. For the United States as a whole, about 77 per cent of the hailstorms occur in May, June, and July, 18 per cent in August, and 5 per cent during the other months.

The diurnal variation of hail is shown in Fig. 84. It will be seen that there is a sharp rise after noon local time, with a maximum between 4 and 6 P.M. About 85 per cent of all storms occur between noon and 9 P.M.

The average annual loss due to hailstorms is shown in Fig. 85. Noteworthy are the large losses in the states commonly called the "breadbasket" of the nation. Much of this area also suffers severe damage by tornadoes.

Tornadoes in the United States. The geographical distribution and the seasonal variation of tornadoes are shown in Fig. 86. Broadly speaking, the United States may be divided into seven main regions.

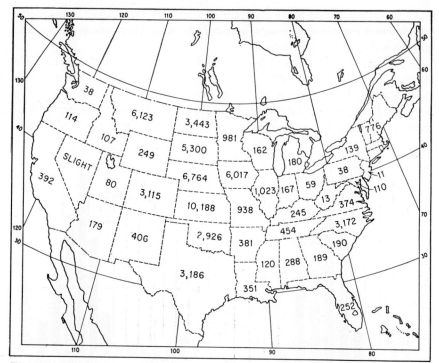

Fig. 85. The average annual loss due to hailstorms expressed in thousands of dollars.

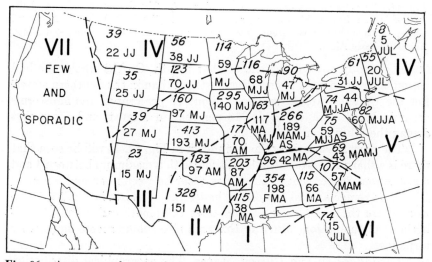

Fig. 86. Average number of tornadoes by states. The upper figure shows the average annual number. The lower figure shows the average number during the months indicated. The Roman numerals indicate broad tornado regions.

Early in the year (February to April) a tornado maximum is found in Mississippi and Alabama. As the seasons advance, the maximum moves north-northwestward through the regions I to IV, with a maximum frequency in Kansas in May and June. In region V the annual maximum is

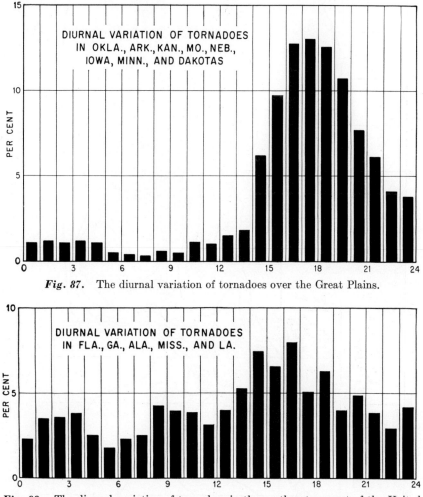

Fig. 87. The diurnal variation of tornadoes over the Great Plains.

Fig. 88. The diurnal variation of tornadoes in the southeastern part of the United States.

indistinct, although there is a preference for the warmer part of the year. In region VI there is a slight preference for July, but otherwise the occurrence of tornadoes is almost evenly distributed throughout the year. To the west of the Continental Divide (region VII) tornadoes are very rare.

In most regions the occurrence of tornadoes shows a strong prefer-

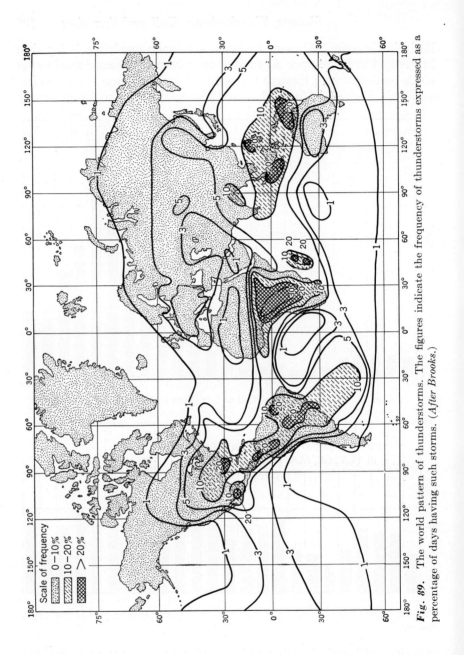

Fig. 89. The world pattern of thunderstorms. The figures indicate the frequency of thunderstorms expressed as a percentage of days having such storms. (*After Brooks.*)

Scale of frequency
0—10%
10—20%
> 20%

ence for the afternoon hours. The diurnal variation of the frequency of tornadoes is shown in Fig. 87 for the belt extending from Oklahoma and Arkansas northward to the Canadian border. It will be seen that there is a sharp rise in the frequency at about 2 P.M., with a distinct maximum between about 4 and 7 P.M. On the other hand, as will be seen from Fig. 88, the diurnal variation in the southern states (Florida, Georgia, Alabama, Mississippi, and Louisiana) is very small, although there is a slight preference for the afternoon hours.

An impression of the damage wrought by tornadoes can be obtained from the figures reproduced in Table 10.

Table 10. Tornado Summary for the United States, 1915 to 1950

Item	Total	Annual average
Number of tornadoes............	5,204	145
Number of tornado days.........	2,306	64
Number of deaths..............	7,961	221
Property damage...............	$476,000,000	$13,200,000

World Patterns. While little is known about the normal distribution of the frequencies of tornadoes and hailstorms over the face of the earth, a considerable amount of information on thunderstorms is available. It will be seen from Fig. 89 that, on the whole, thunderstorms are very rare on the poleward side of the 60th parallels. In these high latitudes, the air is rarely so warm and moist that thundery developments are possible. The highest frequency of thunderstorms is found near the equator, and central Africa stands out as the thunderstorm center of the world. Other regions of high frequency are South America to the east of the Andes, Central America, the southern part of North America to the east of the Rocky Mountains, Madagascar, and the entire region between South Asia and the north coast of Australia.

The difference between land and sea is striking. Within the equatorial belt, the number of thunderstorm days is about three times larger over land than over oceans. The reason is that instability develops more readily over land during hours of sunshine. Although the diurnal variation of temperature is large over the deserts, the air there is too dry for thundery developments to occur.

Noteworthy is the low frequency of thunderstorms along the subtropical west coasts (California, Chile, Morocco, and South Africa). Here the prevailing winds blow toward the equator, and cold water wells up along the coasts, so that the air is cooled far below the average for the latitude. As a result, the air masses as a whole are stable; fogs, rather than thunderstorms, are typical of these coastal regions.

8

Haze, Mist, Smog, and Fog

To obtain uniformity in the reporting system, a fog is defined as a cloud that envelops the observer (on the ground) and reduces the horizontal visibility to ⅝ mile (1 km). If in similar circumstances the visibility exceeds ⅝ mile, the cloud is called a mist. While these definitions are convenient, there is, of course, no physical difference between a stratus cloud and a fog, and a mist is nothing but a very thin fog. It should be noted that the word mist is popularly used in North America to indicate a fine drizzling rain.

The Complexities of Smog. If a fog or mist were made up of droplets of pure water, the relative humidity would be very close to 100 per cent. Particularly in industrial areas (such as London, Pittsburgh, Los Angeles, etc.) the air contains a very large number of soot and dust particles, and many of these have such a high affinity to water vapor that the droplets form well before the air is saturated in the customary sense, that is, in respect to pure water. Such dirty fogs are usually called "smog." In many respects the dust and smoke particles may be as important as the water component. For example, the very dense London smog of December, 1952, which was about 500 ft deep, had the composition shown in Table 11.

Table 11. Composition of a Typical Smog

Weight of	Tons per Cubic Mile
Dry air	2,000,000
Liquid water	18,000
Water vapor	68,000
Smoke	40
Sulfur dioxide	40

From these figures we see that the weight of the smoke and sulfur dioxide amounted to only 0.4 per cent of the weight of liquid water; nevertheless, the smog was very dirty and unpleasant. At the end of the foggy period, the amount of carbon dioxide was 0.4 per cent, or about 10 times the usual value (see page 3). The average concentration of carbon monoxide was about 0.014 per cent, which is a very high value. The death rate rose early in the foggy period, before much carbon monoxide could have accumulated, and medical opinion attributed the high mortality mainly to the presence of sulfuric acid in the smog.

Haze, Mist, and Fog. Polluted air, such as dirty city air, is often seen to become increasingly misty when the air is cooled so that the relative humidity rises above about 70 per cent. When the relative humidity is lower, the dust particles are dry, and we speak of a dry haze. Distant mountains seen through such a haze look as if they were covered by a uniform bluish veil which subdues the colors and details and makes the contours stand out as a silhouette against the sky. When the relative humidity increases above about 70 per cent, condensation begins on the largest and most active nuclei. If the air is cooled, so that the relative humidity

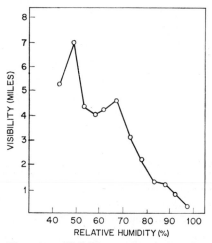

Fig. 90. Visibility and relative humidity at Los Angeles Airport. Note the steady decrease in visibility before the onset of fog (visibility less than $\frac{5}{8}$ mile). (*After Neiburger and Wurtele.*)

increases, the haze thickens and changes gradually into a grayish mist. When the air is cooled further, so that the relative humidity increases to over 90 per cent, the mist thickens into a fog. The visibility is then $\frac{5}{8}$ mile or less. A typical example of the decrease in visibility preceding the formation of fog in polluted air is shown in Fig. 90. It will be seen that the visibility decreases almost uniformly as the relative humidity increases above about 70 per cent, and, also, that the fog forms without the relative humidity reaching 100 per cent. When fogs form in highly polluted air there is a gradual transition from dry haze to mist and fog.

On the high seas and in the polar regions, where the air is relatively pure, the decrease in visibility before the onset of the fog is very small. Since dirty city air contains a large number of active nuclei, the number of fog droplets will be large and the average drop size relatively small. In a typical sea fog the number of nuclei is relatively small, and the droplets will be larger and less numerous than in the city fog. For this reason the visibility in a dirty city fog will be lower than in a sea fog, even when both have the same amount of liquid water.

The amount of liquid water in fogs varies within wide limits. In a dense sea fog, with visibility less than 100 ft, there may be as much as 3 g/m³ of air. On the other hand, in a light city fog, with visibility about 3,000 ft, the water content may be less than 0.02 g/m³.

Fog-producing Processes. Most fogs are produced by cooling of the air in contact with the earth's surface. On occasions, fogs may form when water is evaporated into the air. We may therefore speak of fogs caused by cooling and fogs caused by evaporation. Each of these may be divided into subclasses according to the circumstances that surround the cooling and the evaporation processes.

1. *Cooling Fogs.* To explain the formation of such fogs we return to Eq. (11) (page 75). The temperature change suffered by a unit mass of air may be written

$$\Delta T = \frac{\Delta h}{C_p} + \frac{\Delta p}{C_p \rho}$$

Here, Δh is the amount of heat given to, or withdrawn from, the air; Δp is the pressure change, C_p the specific heat at constant pressure, and ρ is the density of the air.

According to the hydrostatic law (page 6) $\Delta p = -\rho g \, \Delta z$, so that

$$\Delta T = \frac{\Delta h}{C_p} - \frac{g}{C_p} \Delta z$$

We divide this by the time interval, Δt, over which the temperature change takes place. The quantity $\Delta z/\Delta t$ is then simply the vertical velocity of the air, and we denote it by w. Furthermore, as was shown on page 76, $g/C_p = \gamma_d$, or the adiabatic rate of cooling. The foregoing equation may then be written

$$\frac{\Delta T}{\Delta t} = \frac{1}{C_p} \frac{\Delta h}{\Delta t} - \gamma_d w \tag{18}$$

This equation states that the temperature of the air may decrease either because heat is removed from it or because the air expands adiabatically as a result of upward motion ($w > 0$).

At sea level, or other level ground, the air is constrained to move horizontally, so that $w = 0$. In such cases, a fog can form only if heat is removed from the air.

This removal of heat may be brought about in different ways. In the first place, during calm and clear nights the ground loses much heat because of outgoing radiation, and the air in contact with the ground will cool. If, in such cases, the air is sufficiently humid, the cooling will bring the air to the saturation point, and a fog will form. This is called *radiation fog*. Second, if the air streams toward a colder region, it will surrender heat to the underlying surface, and a fog may develop. This is called *advection fog*.

Over the oceans the diurnal change in temperature is very small (about 1°F), and radiation fogs do not develop. Most sea fogs are advection fogs. Such fogs are particularly frequent where the air streams from a warm ocean current to a cold one. Over land, both advection and radiation fogs occur, and most land fogs are brought about by advection of warm and moist air followed by nocturnal cooling.

When the air streams upward over a mountain, the second term on the right of Eq. (18) will be important, and a fog may form as a result of adiabatic cooling. Such fogs are called *upslope fogs*, or *mountain fogs*.

2. *Evaporation Fogs.* To explain these fogs we shall consider the following combination. A body of water has a temperature T_W, and to this temperature corresponds a saturation vapor pressure E_W. The air over the water has a temperature T, and to this temperature corresponds a saturation vapor pressure E. If the air is not saturated, the actual vapor pressure of the air (call it e) will be less than E. Now, if the temperature of the water initially is higher than that of the air, E_W will be larger than E, which, in turn, is larger than e. Thus, initially,

$$E_W > E > e$$

The evaporation of water into the air is proportional to the difference

$$E_W - e$$

and the evaporation will continue until this difference vanishes, so that the end of the process is characterized by

$$e = E_W > E$$

Since the actual vapor pressure now would be greater than the saturation value, the air would be supersaturated. However, since condensation nuclei are present in abundant amounts, the superfluous water vapor will condense. It is readily seen, then, that a fog may form if warm water is evaporated into colder air. Such fogs may form in two ways.

In the first place, when cold air streams over much warmer water, a fog may form. This happens only when the temperature contrasts are rather extreme. Fogs of this type are frequently observed along the edge of the arctic fields of snow and ice when the bitterly cold arctic air streams over open water. For this reason, such fogs are commonly called *arctic sea smoke*.

Second, when rain from warm air aloft falls through a cold and

shallow layer near the earth's surface, the evaporation of the warm rain-
drops into the colder air will produce a fog. Such fogs are called *rain fogs*.
In most cases, the rain falls from the warm air above a frontal surface
(Fig. 91), and for this reason these fogs are often called *frontal fogs*.

Most fogs are either of the radiation or the advection type, and in
the following we shall be concerned only with such fogs.

Radiation Fog. Such fogs develop as a result of nocturnal cooling
of relatively windless air over land, particularly when the air has been
previously moistened by rain or by evaporation. The essential features of

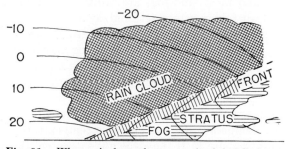

Fig. 91. When rain from the warm air aloft falls into a
layer of cold air, evaporation from the warm raindrops
may produce a fog.

radiation fogs may be described in connection with the example shown in
Fig. 92.

When the outgoing radiation exceeds the incoming radiation, the
temperature of the topsoil begins to fall, and so does the temperature of
the air in contact with it. If the wind is sufficiently light, the downward
eddy flux of heat from the air above will not suffice to maintain a normal
lapse rate, and a shallow temperature inversion forms at the ground. As
the cooling progresses, the temperature falls steadily and the inversion
sharpens. At the same time the moisture content of the air decreases because dew is deposited on the ground. However, the relative humidity
increases because the temperature decrease outweighs the loss of water
vapor. At a certain relative humidity, which depends upon the composition and the number of the condensation nuclei, a mist forms at the
ground and gradually deepens and thickens into a fog. In the case shown
in Fig. 92, the fog commenced when the relative humidity was 92 per cent,
and although the fog became quite dense during the night, the relative
humidity did not exceed 96 per cent. In air with less impurities, the relative humidity would be close to 100 per cent and the fog would be wet and
clammy.

During the formation of a radiation fog a temperature inversion becomes established at the ground, so that the temperature increases up-

ward (see Fig. 92a). The density of the water vapor is lowest at the ground because dew is deposited on the ground (see Fig. 92c). The relative humidity is, however, highest at the ground (see Fig. 92b).

As the cooling progresses the temperature inversion deepens, and so does the water-vapor inversion. Within the fog, radiation is absorbed and

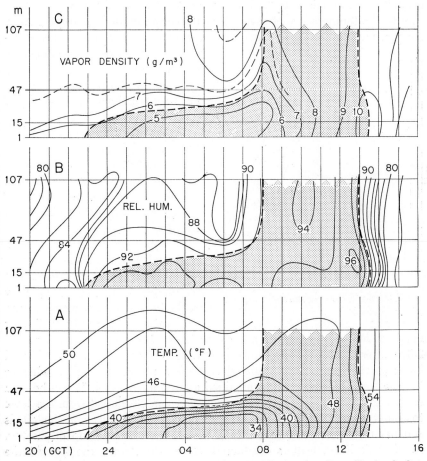

Fig. 92. Showing the development of a typical radiation fog. Rye, England, Oct. 30–31, 1945.

reemitted both upward and downward. However, the maximum rate of cooling is found at the top of the foggy layer rather than at the ground, with the result that the temperature inversion gradually rises as the fog thickens. During the later part of the night, the temperature is almost uniform within the fog while the temperature increases rapidly through its upper surface. After sunrise the incoming radiation warms the air, and the fog gradually dissipates. Normally, the fog dissipates within 3 hr after sunrise. However, in the case shown here the fog was deep and dense, and it did not dissipate until after midday.

Advection Fog. These fogs develop when the air streams from a warmer to a cooler region. The air then loses heat to the underlying surface. Such fogs are particularly frequent at sea. Since the conductive capacity of water is very high (see page 95), the air adjusts its temperature to the temperature of the water surface, which undergoes very little change. Over land, the air and the soil divide the heat more evenly between them, and advection fogs are less frequent.

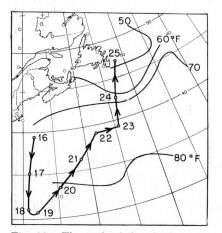

Fig. 93. The path of the air that produced the advection fog shown in Fig. 94. (*After Taylor.*)

The favored regions for advection fogs are those where cold and warm ocean currents are adjacent to one another. The general region of the Grand Bank, where the Gulf Stream borders the icy waters of the Labrador Current, is an example. The typical features of such fog development are shown in Figs. 93 and 94.

On July 18 and 19 (Fig. 93) a warm and stagnant mass of air was present over the Gulf Stream. The air temperature was 81°F, very nearly the same as the sea-surface temperature. After July 19 the air mass moved northward and arrived to the east of Newfoundland on the 25th, where the sounding shown in Fig. 94 was made. On the northward journey the air temperature decreased from 81 to 53°F, whereas the sea-surface temperature remained almost unchanged. It will be seen from Fig. 94 that a temperature inversion has developed from sea level to about 600 m (2,000 ft). The relative humidity (the curve on the left) is 100 per cent up to 210 m (700 ft), and this marks the top of the fog. Above this level, heat is conducted downward toward the fog. At the same time the base of the fog loses heat to the sea, for the air temperature is about 1.8°C (3°F) higher than the sea-surface temperature (see arrow).

From the middle curve of Fig. 94 we see that the moisture content decreases downward below about 600 m. This downward decrease is due to loss of water vapor during the cooling of the air. Part of this loss is due to condensation directly on the colder sea surface, but the bulk is due to condensation in the air. An average fog droplet has a fall velocity of about 5 ft/min (see page 64), so that the average life of a droplet in the air would be about 1 to 2 hr (since the fog was about 700 ft deep). Without cooling, the fog would clear itself in about this time. To maintain the fog it is necessary that the air be cooled at an appreciable rate, so that new droplets form all the time.

This precarious balance between loss of droplets to the ground and formation of new drops through cooling is typical of all fogs. The sea fogs consist of relatively large droplets, and these have relatively large velocities of fall. The dirty city fogs are made up mostly of very small droplets, and such fogs may linger long after the cooling has ended. If we compare Figs. 92 and 94 we see that the relative humidity in Fig. 92

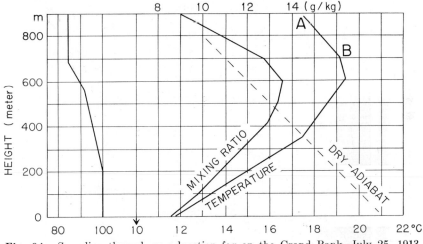

Fig. 94. Sounding through an advection fog on the Grand Bank, July 25, 1913. (*After Taylor.*)

never exceeded 96 per cent, whereas in Fig. 94 it was 100 per cent. The difference is due to the circumstance that the fog shown in Fig. 92 was a land fog which formed in polluted air, while that shown in Fig. 94 was a sea fog which formed in relatively clean air.

Some Modifying Influences. As mentioned earlier, most land fogs are mixed, in the sense that the effects of advection, radiation, upslope motion, and rain often combine. In Fig. 95 is shown schematically the regions in the United States where advection and night radiation often combine to produce fog. When moisture-laden air, either from the Great Lakes or from the ocean, is cooled over land, fogs develop readily. The favored belt is broader in winter than in summer because the land is colder and the nights longer.

Certain fogs are very sensitive to the speed of the wind. In particular, this is true of the radiation fogs. In moderate or strong winds mixing is active and there will be a tendency for stratus rather than fog to develop. The reasons were explained on page 83. Advection fogs are, however, less sensitive, for the cooling is often so rapid that it outweighs the effect of mixing. As a general rule, radiation fogs occur only with very light winds, while advection fogs may exist with a moderate or fresh breeze.

Over snow-covered ground one often sees that the fogs prefer a belt along the freezing isotherm. The reason may be explained as follows. When the snow is melting, the air temperature above the snow is above freezing, and the temperature of the air that is in contact with the snow is

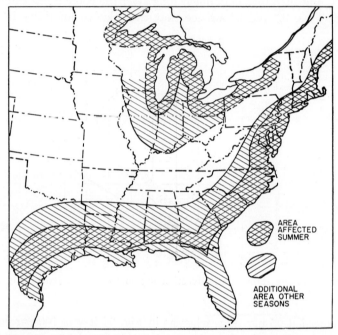

AREA
AFFECTED
SUMMER

ADDITIONAL
AREA OTHER
SEASONS

Fig. 95. Schematic chart showing regions where fogs often occur as a result of advection followed by radiative cooling during the night. (*After George.*)

0°C. There is then a temperature inversion at the ground, and the transfer of heat will be directed downward toward the snowy surface. The heat thus carried downward is consumed in the melting of the snow, without benefit to the surface.

Under normal conditions, the moisture content of the air increases with elevation when there is a temperature inversion above the snow. The transfer of moisture will then be directed downward, and the water vapor will condense on the snow. Thus, when snow is melting, heat and moisture are carried toward the snowy surface, and the process tends to cause the air to become drier. It follows, then, that fogs do not readily form over melting snow when the air temperature is *much* over freezing.

On the other hand, when the temperature of the snow is much below freezing it becomes difficult for fogs to develop. The reason is that the saturation vapor pressure over cold snow is lower than over water (see page 65). As a result, condensation will begin on the snow before the air becomes saturated. As will be seen from Fig. 47, this effect (the Bergeron effect) is largest in the interval from 10 to 15°C, and few fogs survive cooling through this interval. The effect of snow cover is clearly shown in Fig. 96. In October, when there is no snow on the ground, the highest probability of fog is found at the lowest temperatures observed (0 to −5°C). In January, February, and March, when snow is present, the

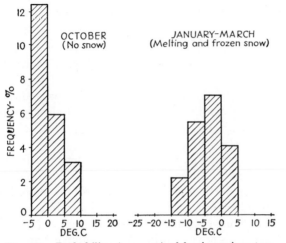

Fig. 96. Probability (per cent) of fog in various temperature intervals. When snow is present on the ground the highest probability is found near freezing.

highest probability is found in the vicinity of the freezing point, and fogs are absent when the temperature is above 5°C (41°F) and below −15°C (5°F). In colder regions, where the air temperature sinks below −35°C (−31°F), the fogs usually consist of ice crystals. Such fogs are in equilibrium with the snow cover, and they may be very persistent.

Regions with Frequent Fogs. Since the sea fogs are mostly of the advection type, the ocean areas noted for high frequency coincide with the cold ocean currents.[1] The Grand Bank is noted for hazards to shipping due to fog and icebergs. Here the Labrador Current brings southward vast masses of icy water and runs adjacent to the warm Gulf Stream. In winter, fogs develop with winds from a southerly direction (from warm to cold), while in summer, fogs develop also when warm air from Canada moves over the cold water. Though the frequency is high throughout the year, it is highest in summer. The Grand Bank regime extends south-

[1] Charts showing these currents are reproduced in Chap. 16.

westward along the coast of Massachusetts and, with diminishing frequency, to the coast of the Carolinas (see Fig. 97). It extends also northeastward along the Greenland Current and continues over the northern part of the Norwegian Sea to the Barents Sea. Here fogs are particularly frequent in summer, when the air from the much warmer continent streams northward. In winter, fogs are frequent along the edge of the arctic ice, and in summer it is frequent all over the arctic.

A fog regime similar to the one described above is present over the Oyashio, or Okhotsk Current, and other cold waters along the coast of Asia.

Winter fogs are fairly frequent along the coast from Texas to Florida. During winter and early spring the Mississippi and its tributaries furnish much cold water, which depresses the sea-surface temperature along the coast. As a result, fogs form with southerly flow of air from the Gulf of Mexico. The Great Lakes have a high frequency of fog, but the season here is late spring and early summer, when the water is much colder than the surrounding land. Similar spring regimes exist elsewhere where warm land surrounds water cooled by melted snow. The Baltic and North Seas are examples.

It will be seen from Fig. 97 that the frequency of fog is high along the Appalachian ranges. These are mixed fogs, which occur in warm and moist air streaming northeastward from the Gulf. While these fogs are primarily due to advection, upslope motion and rain contribute much to the concentration along the range.

The vast expanses of the Middle West and West are notably free of fogs, but the frequency is high along the Pacific Coast and in the neighboring valleys. Summer fogs are frequent along the coast of California. Here the prevailing winds in summer are from a northerly direction. These winds set up a southward ocean current (see Chap. 16), and cold water wells up along the coast. The air passing over the cold coastal waters adapts itself to the sea-surface temperature, with the result that the temperature is low and the relative humidity high. Fogs are very frequent off the coast, and during the night, when the land cools off, they penetrate inland. Above the cool moist layer is a subsidence inversion of the type shown in Fig. 58a. The California fog is therefore overlain by warm and dry air.

Winter fogs are frequent in the valley all along the Pacific Coast. These form when moist maritime air becomes trapped in the valleys and cooled by outgoing radiation. These are typical examples of fogs produced by advection followed by radiation.

The California type of regime is typical of all west coasts in the subtropics; along them the prevailing winds are equatorward, with upwelling of cool water. Noted regions are the west coast of South America from

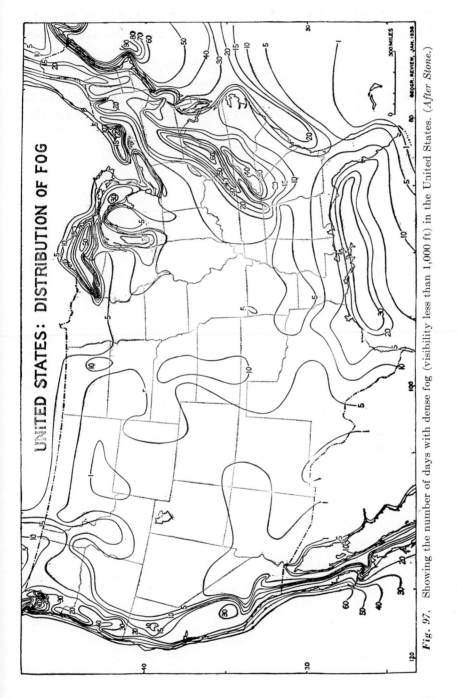

UNITED STATES: DISTRIBUTION OF FOG

GEOGR. REVIEW, JAN. 1936.

300 MILES

Fig. 97. Showing the number of days with dense fog (visibility less than 1,000 ft) in the United States. (*After Stone.*)

143

4 to 31 °S (August to September), the west coast of North Africa from Casablanca to Senegal (summer), the west coast of South Africa from 8 to 32 °S (June to August).

In the Southern Hemisphere fog is frequent along the antarctic ice. Mild versions of fogs of the Grand Bank type are found along the east coast of South America to the south of Rio de la Plata (July to September), and along the east coast of Africa to the south of Cape Guardafui (June to September).

9

The Laws of Motion

It is probably not going too far to say that fluid motion is one of the most complex and fascinating branches of the physical sciences. Since the theories cannot be dealt with without elaborate mathematical derivations, we must here be satisfied to discuss only some very simple aspects of the motions of the atmosphere.

Some Typical Features. The reader is invited to examine Fig. 98 and try to relate the observed winds to the distribution of pressure. When this has been done some general rules will emerge.

In the first place, we note that the wind blows mainly along the isobars, with low pressure to the left and high pressure to the right of the wind. If a similar chart were prepared for any region in the Southern Hemisphere, we should find the reverse rule; namely, that the wind blows mainly along the isobars with low pressure to the right of the wind. Since the rotation of the earth's surface in the Southern Hemisphere is opposite to that in the Northern Hemisphere, we suspect that the different behavior of the winds is due to the rotation of the earth.

Second, we find that the wind is not altogether along the isobars but tends to stream toward the side where the pressure is low. However, if we prepared charts for any level above 2,000 or 3,000 ft, we should find no systematic drift toward lower pressure. We are thus led to believe that the drift toward lower pressure is caused by friction along the earth's surface, and that its effect is not noticeable above about 2,000 to 3,000 ft above the ground. This would be true in both hemispheres.

Third, we find that the wind is strong where the isobars are crowded, and weak where they are wide apart. If we ignore the drift toward lower pressure, we gain the impression that the wind blows in isobaric channels in such a manner that the speed stands in inverse proportion to the width of the channel. This would be true in both hemispheres.

Fourth, if we extended our chart from pole to pole, we should find that the relation between isobar spacing and wind speed is rather firm in high and mid-latitudes but weakens as we approach the equator. Between

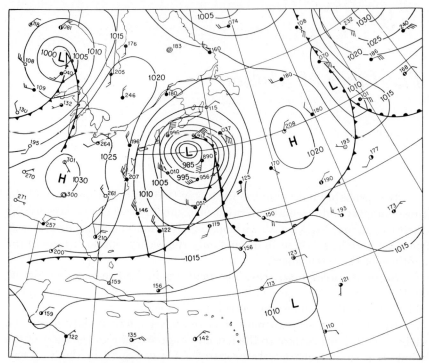

Fig. 98. Simplified sea-level chart Nov. 20, 1955, 1200 GCT. The symbols are explained at the end of Chap. 3.

about 10° N and 10° S, we should have considerable difficulty in relating the winds to the pressure distribution.

Fifth, if we were in a position to follow the motion of an individual parcel of air and measure the rate at which its speed changes (that is, its acceleration), we should find that the accelerations are very small. In fact, if we consider the large-scale currents and ignore the fluctuations due to short-period gusts and lulls, we should find accelerations which are about 0.0002 m/sec² (0.0006 ft/sec²). In the large wind systems the air is a slow starter, but when it has worked up speed it will carry on for a long time.

Sixth, if we could measure the vertical component of the motion, we should find that it is large in thunderstorms, tornadoes, etc., and also in the very small eddies which we call turbulence. However, if we consider the large-scale currents of the atmosphere we shall find that the motion is overwhelmingly horizontal.

The knowledge summarized here has accumulated gradually, most of it since the middle of the last century, when weather charts first came into use. The relation between the wind and the isobars is often called the *baric wind law*, or Buys-Ballot's law, after Buys-Ballot (1817–1890), who did much to clarify the relation between wind and pressure.

In the following discussion we shall be concerned only with the large-scale currents, and the six features mentioned above are those which we wish to explore in further detail.

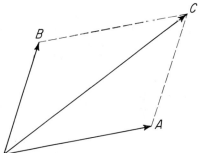

Forces and Motion. In any discussion of the relation between motion and forces the starting point is Newton's second law. This law states that the *rate of change of momentum is equal to the sum of the forces*. The forces may be represented by arrows and their sum obtained as shown in Fig. 99.

Fig. 99. If the arrows A and B represent two forces, their sum is represented by C.

Now, if v is the volume and ρ the density of a parcel of air, the mass is ρv. If V is the velocity, the momentum is $\rho v V$. The boldface V indicates that the velocity is characterized by a direction as well as a magnitude. Now, since mass can be neither created nor destroyed, the mass ρv is constant, and the rate of change of momentum is equal to the mass multiplied by the rate of change of velocity. The rate of change of velocity is what we call *acceleration* (A), so that the rate of change of momentum is equal to $\rho v A$.

It is convenient to consider a parcel of air which occupies a unit volume (say, 1 cm³). If all forces are referred to a unit volume, we may write

$$\text{Density} \times \text{acceleration} = \text{sum of the forces}$$

As it stands, this equation will account for what is called *absolute motion*. However, when we discuss the wind we must bear in mind that we are dealing with *relative motion*. The anemometer (say, in Chicago) does not measure the absolute velocity of the air but the velocity relative to the earth's surface, which itself is moving. For example, a west wind is air that moves eastward with a speed greater than that of the earth, and an east wind is air that moves eastward slower than the earth under it. By the same token, a calm is air that moves with the speed of the earth.

When considering the motion of the air relative to the rotating earth we have to consider not only the *real forces* due to pressure, gravity, and friction but also the *apparent force* due to the rotation of the earth.

For the time being we shall ignore the effect of friction. The real forces that act upon the air are then the pressure force **P** and the gravity force **G**. Now if *A* is the acceleration relative to the earth's surface, we

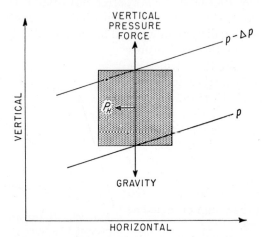

Fig. 100. The decrease in pressure from the base to the top of the cube is equivalent to a pressure force pointing upward. This force is compensated for by the gravity. The decrease in pressure from the right to the left is equivalent to a horizontal pressure force P_H.

may write

$$\rho A = P + G + D \tag{19}$$

Here **D** symbolizes some apparent force which is due to the rotation of the earth. The nature of this force will be discussed presently.

Pressure and Gravity. To clarify the meaning of the pressure force we consider a cube of air with unit volume (say, 1 cm³), as shown in Fig. 100. In the first place, the pressure decreases along the vertical so that the pressure on the base of the cube is larger than on the top. This is equivalent to a force directed upward, from high to low pressure. This force is, however, almost exactly equal to the force of gravity acting on the air within the cube. The reason for this was explained on page 6, where we derived the hydrostatic law. We see, then, that the vertical component of the pressure force is compensated for by the gravity force, and their combined effect need not be considered. There remains, however, the horizontal pressure force, and if this force is denoted by P_H,

Eq. (19) reduces to

$$\rho A = P_H + D \tag{19a}$$

To explain the meaning of the horizontal pressure force we consider Fig. 101. Here the hatched area represents a horizontal rod of air with unit cross section and length ΔH. At the left end of the rod the pressure is

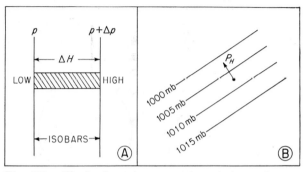

Fig. 101. The horizontal pressure force is inversely proportionate to the isobar spacing.

p and at the right end it is $p + \Delta p$. The pressure difference Δp represents a force acting along the rod, in the direction from high to low pressure. The force per unit volume is then Δp divided by ΔH. If P_H is the magnitude of this force, we may write

$$P_H = \frac{\Delta p}{\Delta H} \tag{20}$$

If isobars are drawn for standard intervals of pressure (say, 5 mb), the horizontal pressure force is inversely proportional to the isobar spacing; its direction is perpendicular to the isobars, from *high* to *low* pressure.

The Earth's Rotation. To clarify the meaning of the force due to the earth's rotation we consider the conditions at the North Pole (Fig. 102). A man stands at the pole N and aims his rifle at a target which is fixed to the earth. At the time when the rifle is fired, the target occupies the position B, and right behind it is an

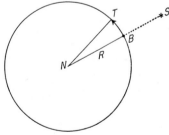

Fig. 102. Showing the relation between absolute and relative motion.

object S (say, a star) which does not take part in the earth's rotation. The bullet will travel along the straight line NBS while the earth rotates under it. By the time the bullet has traveled the distance NB, the target (which moves with the earth) will occupy the position T. Now, if the path of the bullet is viewed in relation to the moving target, we see that, initially, it moves straight toward the target but, as time passes, it deviates more and more to the right. The reader may say that this is contrary to experience, for a hunter at the North Pole is able to shoot a polar bear at some short distance away from the pole. The explanation is that the distance traveled by the bullet is very short. Moreover, rifles are constructed so as to reduce the deflection to a minimum.

The deviation to the right of the straight line NT can be accounted for by introducing a force D, which always acts at right angles and to the right of the path of the bullet. This force comes into the picture because

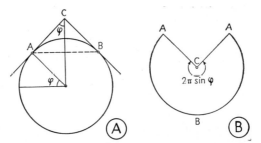

Fig. 103.   (*a*) Meridional section through the earth, with a cone tangent to latitude φ. (*b*) The cone unfolded, representing the horizon plane in latitude φ.

the motion is considered relative to the rotating earth, and we call it the *deviating force due to the earth's rotation.*

Now, the earth rotates an angle 2π in 24 (sidereal) hr, and this is the angular velocity Ω of the horizon plane at the pole. Its numerical value is very nearly 0.000073 radian/sec. If t is the time it took for the bullet to travel from N to B, the angle BNT is Ωt. Next, if R is the distance from N to B, and V is the speed of the bullet, $R = Vt$, and the length of the arc BT is $R\Omega t = V\Omega t^2$. This deviation can be accounted for by an acceleration a acting at right angles to the right of the path, for the distance corresponding to this acceleration is $\frac{1}{2}at^2$. We thus find

$$\frac{1}{2}at^2 = V\Omega t^2 \qquad \text{or} \qquad a = V2\Omega$$

This applies to the conditions at the North Pole. To find the general expression for this acceleration in any latitude (say φ), we consider Fig. 103, which represents a cross section through the earth along a meridian. We place a cone tangent to the earth along the latitude circle φ. This cone unfolded is shown on the right; it represents the horizon plane in the latitude φ. Now, while the earth rotates an angle 2π in 24 hr, a point A on the horizon plane in latitude φ will rotate the angle ACA (through B), which is equal to $2\pi \sin \varphi$. We see, then, that while the angular velocity of the horizon plane at the pole is Ω, the corresponding velocity in latitude φ is $\Omega \sin \varphi$. From the foregoing formula it follows that the deviating acceleration a in an arbitrary latitude φ is expressed by

$$a = V2\Omega \sin \varphi$$

The experiment shown in Fig. 102 was carried out in the Northern Hemisphere, and it was shown that the acceleration was at right angles *to the right* of the velocity. If the experiment were carried out in the Southern Hemisphere, the horizon plane would rotate in the opposite direction. Hence, the deviation would be at right angles *to the left* of the velocity.

Next, a force can always be written as the mass that it acts upon multiplied by the acceleration that it produces. Since we are here considering the force per unit volume, the mass is equal to the density. Hence, the magnitude of the deviating force D is

$$D = \rho V2\Omega \sin \varphi \qquad (21)$$

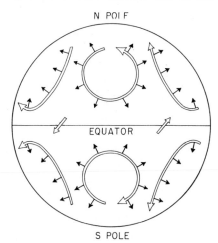

The direction of this force is to the right of the wind in the Northern Hemisphere, and to the left in the Southern Hemisphere (see Fig. 104).

Fig. 104. The double arrows represent the wind direction, and the single arrows show the direction of the deviating force. In the Northern Hemisphere, the deviating force is at right angles to the right, and in the Southern Hemisphere it is at right angles to the left, of the wind. There is no deviating force at the equator.

What has been said here about a bullet applies to any body that moves relative to the earth; it applies also to a parcel of air. To demonstrate how the earth's rotation affects the wind, we consider Fig. 105. Suppose that a parcel of air is kept at rest relative to the earth. If the parcel were released, the pressure force would accelerate it across the isobars, from high to low pressure. As soon as the parcel acquires a velocity, the deviating force would tend to drive it to the right (in the Northern Hemisphere), and as time passes, the motion of the parcel would tend to be along the isobars. The deviating force would be at right angles to the right, and the pressure force would be very nearly at right angles to the left of the velocity; the two forces would tend to balance, and the acceleration would be very small.

The experiment discussed in connection with Fig. 105 is rather artificial, for in the large-scale motion systems the pressure force and the velocity develop more or less simultaneously, with the result that large accelerations never occur. This, then, accounts for the first, third, and fifth characteristics of the winds mentioned at the beginning of this chapter.

The deviating force due to the earth's rotation is often called the *Coriolis force*, after Coriolis (1792–1843), who first derived the expression. Similarly, the quantity $2\Omega \sin \varphi$ is commonly called the *Coriolis parameter*. These names will be used from now on.

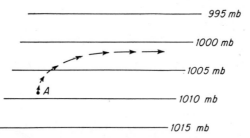

Fig. 105. If a parcel of air at A starts from rest, it will first be accelerated across the isobar and then be deflected by the Coriolis force so that it tends to move along the isobars. The diagram applies to the Northern Hemisphere.

The Geostrophic Wind. This is a very useful approximation to the actual wind. In fact, it is through this approximation that we can convert the direction and the width of the isobaric channels into wind direction and speed. Like all other approximations, it is not always equally good.

We obtain this approximation by introducing the following simplifications: (1) the current is assumed to be straight (or nearly so) so that the centripetal (or turning) acceleration can be ignored; (2) it is assumed that the wind speed changes so slowly that the acceleration along the path may be omitted; (3) the motion is assumed to be free of friction.

These three assumptions imply that the horizontal pressure force is balanced by the Coriolis force. A complete balance is rarely present in the atmosphere, but the point to bear in mind is that it is nearly realized in the large-scale currents above the layer directly influenced by surface friction. The wind calculated from this balance is what we call the *geostrophic wind*. To distinguish it from the actual wind we shall denote it by V_g. Referring back to Eq. (21) we see that the Coriolis force due to the geostrophic wind is $\rho V_g 2\Omega \sin \varphi$. Equating this to the pressure force

[Eq. (20)], we obtain

$$\rho V_g 2\Omega \sin \varphi = \frac{\Delta p}{\Delta H} \qquad (22)$$

$$V_g = \frac{1}{\rho 2\Omega \sin \varphi} \frac{\Delta p}{\Delta H} \qquad (23)$$

The horizontal variation of the air density is normally very small, and it is sufficiently accurate to replace the density by a standard value. Now, if isobars are drawn for standard intervals (say, 5 mb) the pressure difference Δp is also constant. We see then that the speed of the geostrophic wind is inversely proportional to the width ΔH of the isobaric channel (see Fig. 106). This, then, corroborates one of the observations made at the beginning of this chapter.

The relation between wind speed and isobar spacing varies with the latitude. Since $\sin 90° = 1$ and $\sin 30° = 0.5$, we see that for the same isobar spacing the wind would be twice as strong in latitude 30° as it would be at the pole. As we approach the equator $\sin \varphi$ decreases to zero, and the approximation represented by Eq. (23) becomes invalid. Near the equator the horizontal pressure force is usually very small, and the effects of friction and acceleration cannot be ignored.

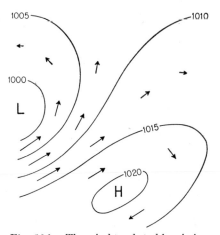

Fig. 106. The wind tends to blow in isobaric channels so that the speed is inversely proportional to the width of the channel. The diagram applies to the Northern Hemisphere.

If ρ is replaced by a standard value, Eq. (23) may be used to compute an overlay which gives the wind that corresponds to the isobar spacing in any latitude. In such computation, care must be exercised in using consistent units for wind speed, pressure, density, and distance. The scale of the chart and its variation with latitude must also be taken into account.

The Gradient Wind. This is another approximation to the actual wind; it is similar to the geostrophic wind except that the effect of the centrifugal force has been included. When the path of a moving parcel of air is strongly curved, the turning acceleration (across the path) may be appreciable, while the acceleration along the path is normally small. The gradient wind may then be defined as the wind that corresponds to balance between the pressure force, on the one hand, and the Coriolis force and the centrifugal force on the other.

To distinguish the gradient wind from the actual wind we shall use the symbol V_G. The centrifugal force corresponding to this wind is $\rho V_G{}^2/r$, where r is the radius of curvature of the path of the moving parcel of air. The Coriolis force is $\rho V_G 2\Omega \sin \varphi$, and, according to Eq. (22), the pressure force is equal to $\rho V_g 2\Omega \sin \varphi$. Now, since both the centrifugal force and the Coriolis force are at right angles to the wind, the pressure

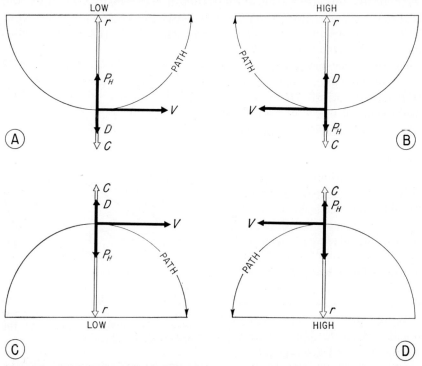

Fig. 107.   Showing the balance of the forces in curved motion. V is the wind, P_H the horizontal pressure force, C the centrifugal force, and D the deviating (or Coriolis) force. (*a*) and (*b*) apply in the Northern Hemisphere, and (*c*) and (*d*) apply in the Southern Hemisphere.

force must also be at right angles to the wind, if the forces are to balance. The balance between these forces is shown in Fig. 107. If the radius of curvature is counted positive in cyclonic motion and negative in anticyclonic motion the balance may be written

$$\frac{V_G{}^2}{r} + V_G 2\Omega \sin \varphi = V_g 2\Omega \sin \varphi \qquad (24)$$

It is convenient to write this as follows:

$$V_G = V_g - \frac{V_G{}^2}{r2\Omega \sin \varphi} \qquad (25)$$

We see then that the gradient wind is smaller than the geostrophic wind in cyclonic motion, and larger than the geostrophic wind in anticyclonic motion. Furthermore, the gradient wind approaches the geostrophic wind as the radius of curvature increases.

The meaning of Eq. (25) can be seen from Fig. 107. The Coriolis force D is proportional to the gradient wind. In cyclonic motion (Fig. 107a) this force is balanced by the difference between the pressure force P_H and the centrifugal force C, so that less wind is required to establish balance. In anticyclonic motion (Fig. 107b) the centrifugal force adds to the pressure force, so that a stronger wind is required.

The last term on the right of Eq. (25) is important only when the wind is strong and the radius of curvature small. This is the case in strong tropical storms (hurricanes) and in tornadoes. In such systems the geostrophic wind is very much larger than the actual wind, while the gradient wind is closer to the truth. On the other hand, in the large-scale systems in mid- and high latitudes, the curvature term is usually so small that it can be ignored.

Since Eq. (24) is quadratic, a solution for the gradient wind is readily obtained. The neatest expression is found by solving for $1/V_G$ and inverting. This gives

$$V_G = \frac{V_g}{\frac{1}{2} + \sqrt{\frac{1}{4} + V_g/r2\Omega \sin \varphi}} \tag{26}$$

We have here chosen plus in front of the radical since V_G must approach V_g when the radius of curvature increases.

In practice, the geostrophic wind is readily obtained from the isobar spacing, as indicated above. It is, however, far more difficult to determine the radius of curvature of the path of a moving parcel of air, and this reduces the practical value of Eq. (26).

The Influence of Friction. To illustrate the influence due to the frictional drag along the earth's surface we consider Fig. 108. We observe a certain wind velocity, which is represented by the arrow V. To this velocity corresponds a force D, which is the Coriolis force. This force is at right angles to the right (in the Northern Hemisphere) of the wind. The frictional drag at the earth's surface is represented by a force F, which is opposed to the wind. We compound the forces D and F into a resultant force R. Since the acceleration in the large-scale systems is very small, the horizontal pressure force P_H must balance, very nearly, the resultant force R. We see then that the angle between the wind and the pressure force is less than 90°. In other words, one of the effects of friction is to cause the air to move with a component across the isobars, from high to low pressure.

Another effect of friction is to reduce the speed of the wind as compared with the geostrophic wind. We see from Fig. 108 that part of the pressure force is balanced by the frictional force, while the remainder is balanced by the Coriolis force. Since the Coriolis force is proportional to the wind speed, it is evident that, for any given pressure force, the wind will be less with friction than without.

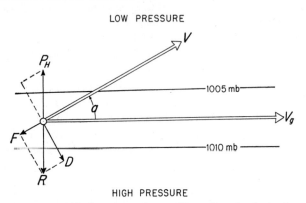

Fig. 108. Friction along the earth's surface tends to deflect the wind so that there is a drift across the isobars from high to low pressure.

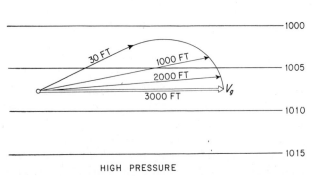

Fig. 109. The effect of friction decreases with elevation, and at 2,000 to 3,000 ft above the ground the wind blows very nearly along the isobars.

The effect of friction varies with the roughness of the ground. Over fairly smooth grassland the actual wind at the level of a well-exposed anemometer blows about 20 to 25° to the left of the isobar, and the speed is about 60 to 70 per cent of the geostrophic wind. Similar values apply also over oceans. Over very rough land the deviation may be as large as 45°, and the speed may be reduced to about 30 per cent.

As we ascend from the earth's surface the frictional influence weakens, and at 2,000 to 3,000 ft above the ground the wind blows very nearly along the isobars and the wind is very nearly equal to the geostrophic wind. The layer within which this adjustment takes place is called the *friction layer*. If the winds within this layer are plotted on a radial diagram we find a variation with height as shown in Fig. 109. To begin with, the wind varies rapidly with height, but the variation decreases upward, and the actual wind approaches the geostrophic wind very gradually.

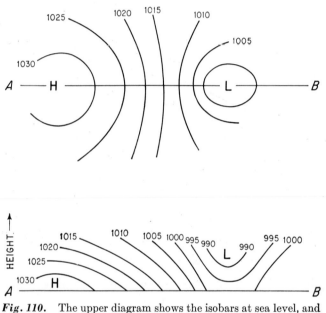

Fig. 110.   The upper diagram shows the isobars at sea level, and the lower diagram shows a vertical cross section through the isobaric surfaces.

A theory for the variation due to friction was first developed by Ekman (1874–1954), who found that it could be represented by an equiangular spiral. This is commonly called the *Ekman spiral*. Above the top of the friction layer the wind variation depends essentially upon the distribution of temperature. This will be discussed in a later section.

Isobars and Contours. If we draw isobars on a chart, such as Fig. 44, we will normally find areas of high pressure and areas of low pressure. A vertical cross section through such areas will then show domes of high pressure and hollows of low pressure, more or less as shown in Fig. 110. We direct our attention to the spacing of the isobars and note that the slope of the isobaric surface varies in proportion to the isobaric spacing. This suggests that there is a close relation between the horizontal pressure force and the slope of the isobaric surfaces.

The precise relationship can be obtained as follows. In Fig. 111 is shown a vertical cross section through two neighboring isobaric surfaces. The pressure difference from A to B is Δp. To indicate that this is along the horizontal we write Δp_H. Next, if we go vertically from B to C we experience a pressure difference of exactly the same amount but with opposite sign. We call this difference Δp_z. The two differences are related

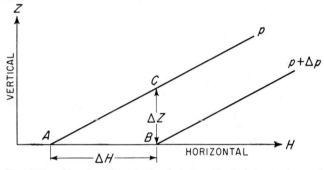

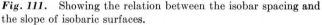

Fig. 111. Showing the relation between the isobar spacing and the slope of isobaric surfaces.

such that

$$\Delta p_H = -\Delta p_z$$

From the hydrostatic equation (page 6) we have $-\Delta p_z = \rho g \, \Delta Z$, so that

$$\Delta p_H = \rho g \, \Delta Z$$

The magnitude of the horizontal pressure force (see page 149) is $\Delta p/\Delta H$, so that

$$\frac{\Delta p}{\Delta H} = \rho g \, \frac{\Delta Z}{\Delta H} \tag{27}$$

Here subscript H has been dropped since it is now clear that Δp is taken in the horizontal.

The quantity $\Delta Z/\Delta H$ is the slope of the isobaric surface. We see then that the magnitude of the horizontal pressure force is equal to ρg times the slope. The direction of this force is, of course, from high to low pressure.

The height above sea level of an isobaric surface can be represented by contour lines in the same manner as the height of the terrain is represented on a topographic map. Thus, the pressure distribution can be represented by the contours of an isobaric surface as well as by the isobars in a level surface. This is the method now commonly used in upper-air analyses.

The advantage of using contours rather than isobars can be seen in the following manner. If Eq. (27) is substituted into the geostrophic-wind equation (23), the geostrophic wind is expressed by

$$V_g = \frac{g}{2\,\Omega\,\sin\,\varphi}\,\frac{\Delta Z}{\Delta H} \tag{28}$$

Since the density of the air varies rapidly with height, Eq. (23) is cumbersome when we have to compare the conditions at various levels. On the other hand Eq. (28) gives a relation between the wind and the contour spacing which is the same for all levels.

It is evident that the slope of an isobaric surface must be exceedingly small. Equation (28) may be written

$$\frac{\Delta Z}{\Delta H} = \frac{2\,\Omega\,\sin\,\varphi}{g}\,V_g \tag{29}$$

In mid-latitudes $2\,\Omega\,\sin\,\varphi$ is very nearly 0. 0001 per sec, and since the acceleration of gravity is about 10 m/sec², we see that the slope is related to the wind by a factor of 0.00001. If the geostrophic wind were 10 m/sec (22 mph) the slope would be about 1 in 10,000. Although the slope is exceedingly small it is important, for without it there would be no wind.

Thickness and the Thermal Wind. The wind direction and speed vary considerably as we ascend to the upper atmosphere. Often the wind regime in the middle and upper troposphere bears no resemblance to the wind regime near the earth's surface. Nevertheless, the upper and lower regimes are related, and the connecting link is the mean temperature of the air column between the levels. More specifically the connection is expressed by the hydrostatic equation (see page 6).

Let us consider an upper isobaric surface p_U whose height above sea level is Z_U, and a lower pressure surface p_L with height Z_L. Along these surfaces p_L and p_U are constant. If T_m is the mean temperature, it can be shown from the hydrostatic equation that

$$Z_U - Z_L = K T_m \tag{30}$$

Here K is a constant once the isobaric surfaces have been chosen.

The difference $Z_U - Z_L$ is called the *thickness* of the layer. Suppose now that we draw the contours of the lower pressure surface Z_L (as shown in Fig. 112) and superimpose the contours of the upper surface Z_U. The thickness of the layer is then obtained by subtracting the former from the latter. This is most conveniently done by drawing the difference diagonals (the broken lines). These lines are called the *thickness lines*.

Now, the geostrophic wind at the lower level is inversely proportional to the width of the lower contour channels, and the wind at the upper level is similarly related to the width of the upper channels. These winds are indicated by the arrows V_L and V_U in Fig. 112. The wind variation through the layer is indicated by the arrow V_T. This wind is along the thickness lines, and its speed is inversely proportional to the width of the thickness channels. Since the thickness is but another expression for the mean temperature of the air column, the wind indicated by the arrow V_T is called the *thermal wind*. It stands in the same relation to the thickness lines as the geostrophic wind to the contour lines.

If the thickness $Z_U - Z_L$ is denoted by Z_T, the speed of the thermal wind is expressed by

$$V_T = \frac{g}{2\Omega \sin \varphi} \frac{\Delta Z_T}{\Delta H} \tag{31}$$

where ΔH is the width of the thickness channel.

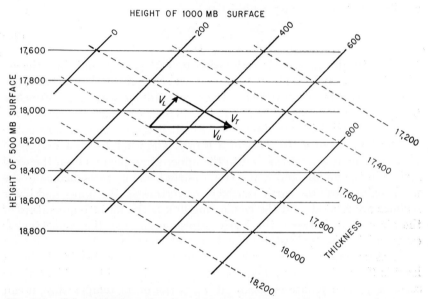

Fig. 112. Schematic chart showing the contours of the 1,000- and the 500-mb surfaces, and the thickness of the layer. The winds (V_L and V_U) are inversely proportionate to the width of the contour channels, and the thermal wind (V_T) is inversely proportional to the width of the thickness channel.

The diagram shown in Fig. 112 refers to the Northern Hemisphere. Here the thermal wind blows along the thickness lines with *cold* air on its *left* side. In the Southern Hemisphere, the thermal wind blows along the thickness lines with *cold* air on its *right* side.

From the preceding discussion we see that the change in the configuration of a pressure system and in the wind from low to high levels is determined by the horizontal variation of the mean temperature of the air. This, then, is the link which connects the upper and lower systems.

Vertical Structures. The general principles outlined above may now be used to discuss the vertical build-up of such pressure systems as cyclones (lows) and anticyclones (highs).

We see from Eq. (30) that if the mean temperature were uniform, the thickness of the layer would be uniform also, and the configuration of the pressure system aloft would be the same as that of the lower system (Fig. 113*a*). In this case the wind would not vary through a vertical column of air. We consider next Fig. 113*b*. Here the air on the right is

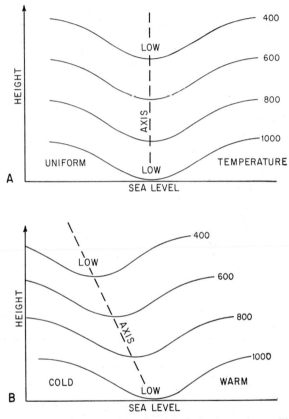

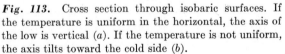

Fig. 113. Cross section through isobaric surfaces. If the temperature is uniform in the horizontal, the axis of the low is vertical (*a*). If the temperature is not uniform, the axis tilts toward the cold side (*b*).

warmer than that on the left. The axis of the low will then tilt toward the cold side, and the wind will vary with elevation.

The general aspects of the relationship between the mean temperature and the slope of isobaric surfaces may be applied to high- and low-pressure systems as shown in Fig. 114. It is readily seen that the following rules apply:

1. A sea-level low with a cold core will intensify with increasing elevation (deep low).

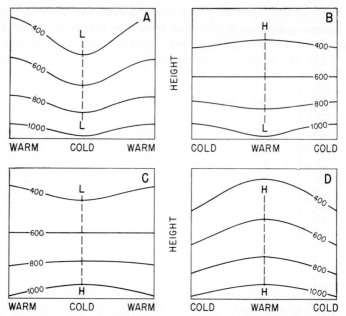

Fig. 114. Cross sections showing the vertical structures of symmetrical lows and high: (*a*) a low which intensifies with elevation; (*b*) a low which weakens and changes into a high; (*c*) a high which weakens and changes into a low; (*d*) a high which intensifies with elevation.

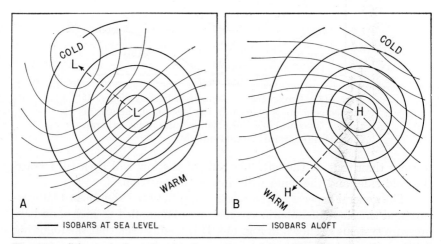

Fig. 115. Schematic chart showing the contours of the 1,000-mb surface (heavy lines) and the contours of an isobaric surface aloft (say, 500 mb). The axis of the low tilts toward the cold side, and the axis of the high tilts toward the warm side.

2. A sea-level low with a warm core will weaken with elevation and may change into a high-level high (high over low).

3. A sea-level high with a cold core will weaken with elevation and may change into a high-level low (low over high).

4. A sea-level high with a warm core will intensify with increasing elevation (deep high).

Normally the temperature distribution around sea-level highs and lows is not symmetrical. In the first place, the temperature is higher on the equatorial than on the poleward side. Secondly, the temperature varies in the east-west direction. For example, the air to the west of a sea-level low (coming from high latitudes) will normally be colder than the air to the east. The opposite is true of high-pressure areas. These conditions are shown in Fig. 115. The foregoing rules, which apply to symmetrical systems, may then be supplemented by two additional rules:

5. The axis of an asymmetrical sea-level low slants upward toward the region where the air column is coldest (slanting low).

6. The axis of an asymmetrical sea-level high slants upward toward the region where the air column is warmest (slanting high).

These general rules will be used in Chap. 11, where we shall discuss the major wind systems of the world.

Lest the reader think that the balance of forces, explained in the foregoing sections, is adequate for describing all types of motions, it should be pointed out that, in many cases, large imbalances may be present. In particular, this is true of the small-scale systems to be described in the following chapter. In these systems, the difference between the horizontal pressure force and the Coriolis force may be appreciable, and the accelerational term in Eq. (19a) will be important.

10

Local Wind Systems

While any wind is characterized by its direction and speed, certain winds, and particularly the bothersome ones, are often referred to by names. The bora of the Adriatic and the mistral of the Rhone Valley are examples of local winds which are unpleasant because of their strength and chill. The foehn in Switzerland is an example of a wind which is unpleasant because of heat and excessive dryness. The number of local winds known by such names is legion, but few of them are of any particular meteorological interest except in local descriptions of weather and climate. There are, however, some local wind systems of general interest. Some of these develop as a result of unequal heating of land and sea, others are caused by the heating and cooling of mountain slopes, and a third group is related to the deformation of air currents crossing mountain ranges.

Land and Sea Breeze. On warm days it is often observed that the wind blows across the coast line, from sea to land, during the day and reverses its direction at night. This is a very shallow wind system. The shallowness can sometimes be seen during coastal forest fires. While the fire spreads with the low-level wind, smoke and burning debris are seen to drift in the opposite direction with the countercurrent a few hundred feet above the ground.

The general features of the sea and land breeze are shown in Fig. 116. In the morning there is little difference in temperature between land and sea, and in the absence of any general wind, the isobaric surfaces would be horizontal (Fig. 116a). Now, as the sun rises higher in the sky and warms the land much faster than the sea surface, the thickness of the isobaric layer increases (see page 159) over land, and the upper pressure surface develops a downward slope from land to sea. This sets up a horizontal pressure force which accelerates the air from land to sea. This transfer of air tends to increase the sea-level pressure off the coast and to lower it over land. The result is a pressure force at sea level which tends to accelerate the air from sea to land. The early sea breeze blows mainly across the isobars, which are more or less parallel to the coast. However, as time passes and the wind increases, the deviating force due to the earth's rotation makes its influence felt, and the winds tend to swing toward the isobars and become parallel to the coast line. In the Northern Hemisphere the mature sea breeze blows with the land on its

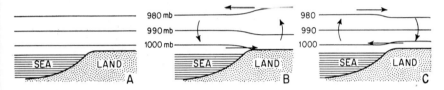

Fig. 116. Illustrating land and sea breeze.

forward left side, and in the Southern Hemisphere the land is on the forward right side.

In the evening, when the land cools and the temperature contrasts disappear, the sea breeze dies out. During the night, when the land is colder than the sea, a gentle flow from land to sea develops. This is called the land breeze.

Only rarely does one observe a pure case of land and sea breeze, for a general wind is usually present. However, the effect of differential heating is always superimposed upon the general wind.

Mountain and Valley Winds. During the sunny hours a mountain slope (and the air in contact with it) will warm up faster than the air at some distance from the slope. This differential heating sets up a circulation which is akin to the sea breeze. The air streams toward and up the mountain slope during the day and downward during the night, more or less as shown in Fig. 117. If the terrain is such that there are converging valleys, the cooled air will converge in the valley bottoms and accelerate downward through the main valley, with the result that the night wind in such places may be stronger than the day breeze.

As in the case of the land and sea breeze, the mountain and valley winds may be overshadowed by a general wind system. On an otherwise calm day the mountain and valley winds reveal their presence by cumulus clouds forming over the mountains during the day and dissolving in the evening.

Drainage Winds. During the cold season large amounts of cold air will accumulate over plateaus and inland areas sheltered by mountains.

Some of this air will seep down the slopes, gather in the valleys and fiords, and come to the coast as a gentle or moderate breeze. However, when a traveling disturbance, such as a low-pressure system, approaches, the cold air will be accelerated out through the mountain gaps, valleys, and canyons, and arrive as a cascade of cold air with strong and gusty winds. Although the air will warm up adiabatically while it descends, the temperature difference between inland and coast is normally so large that the air arrives as a cold current. These winds are particularly strong,

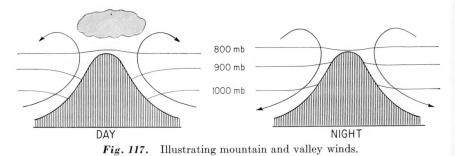

Fig. 117.   Illustrating mountain and valley winds.

and sometimes destructive, where a large reservoir of cold air has to empty itself through a narrow gap or valley, or where several converging valleys meet. A wind of this type is generally called a *katabatic* since it is caused by gravitation of cold air off high ground. Because the air is steered between the walls of a valley, the drainage winds show little relation to the isobars. Often the wind blows right across the isobars from high to low pressure.

Drainage winds occur, with variable strength, in all mountainous regions, and particularly where mountains are close to a coast. In Greenland, Spitzbergen, and in the antarctic, such winds are frequent and sometimes destructive. The "fall winds" in the valleys and fiords of Norway represent a milder variety.

Most widely known is, perhaps, the *bora*, which is a cold wind that blows from a north-northeasterly direction over the northern shores of the Adriatic. Winds in excess of 80 mph, with gusts up to 135 mph, have been recorded. A similar wind is the *mistral*, which blows southward from the Rhone Valley over the southern coast of France. In North America the best known drainage wind is the *Santa Ana*. This is a fierce wind, down the Santa Ana Canyon of Southern California, which spreads over the lowlands toward the coast. It is often laden with fine sand, which penetrates even small openings and makes life miserable indoors as well as in the open. On occasions it has played havoc with anchored ships.

Foehn and Chinook. These winds are strong, dry, and warm winds which develop occasionally along the lee slope of mountain ranges. They are most frequent and strongest along the northern slopes of the Alps, but less intense winds may occur in the lee of any mountain. In the German-speaking countries such winds are called *foehns*, and this name is generally used elsewhere. Similar winds occur occasionally to the east of the Rocky Mountains, notably in Wyoming and Montana. In North America these winds are usually called *chinooks*.

A strong foehn is distinctly unpleasant. The combination of heat and excessive dryness, together with strong and gusty winds, causes physiological as well as psychological reactions; irritableness, headaches, etc.,

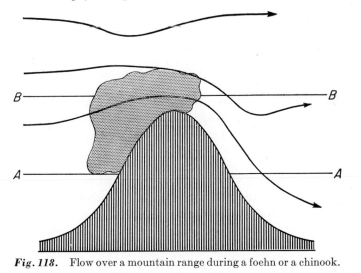

Fig. 118. Flow over a mountain range during a foehn or a chinook.

are quite common. The foehn also dries out the land, trees, and twigs, and creates favorable conditions for forest fires.

A strong foehn (or chinook) is usually preceded by an advancing low-pressure system with strong winds in the middle and upper troposphere. As the upper system approaches the mountain range, the pressure at low levels in the lee begins to fall, and a trough of low pressure forms over the lowlands. At the time when the upper system crosses the range, strong downslope winds set in between the divide and the low-level pressure trough. The high temperature and the low relative humidity that accompany these winds are due to the adiabatic heating of the descending air.

Chinooks and foehns are intensified considerably if there is ascending motion with precipitation on the windward side of the mountain (see Fig. 118). While the air ascends from A to B on the windward side it cools according to the wetadiabatic rate (about 6°C/km). However, when it descends from B to A on the lee side it warms up dryadiabatically (10°C/km). In this manner the lee side benefits from the liberation of the latent heat. The main reason for the warmness in the lee is, however, that the descent in the lee is far greater than the ascent to the windward of the range. On occasions, chinooks and foehns of appreciable intensity are seen to develop without precipitation on the windward side.

The onset of a foehn (or chinook) is marked by a rise in temperature and a drop in humidity. The change is particularly sharp in winter when cold and raw air is present over the lowlands before the warm air arrives. If snow is present on the ground, it melts rapidly. If the snow cover is light, the ground dries out, but where it is deep a heavy thaw sets in, and flooding of rivers may result.

Other Winds. Most of the winds known by local names are parts of general wind systems associated with traveling highs and lows. They have been given names because the air, during its recent history, has acquired some peculiar property (in most cases an unpleasant one), such as excessive dryness, heat, or cold. The mild and caressing breezes are usually taken for granted.

Warm Winds. Best known is, perhaps, the *sirocco*, which is a warm wind that blows from North Africa over the central Mediterranean and southern Italy in front of an advancing low. On the African side the air is dry, but when it arrives in Italy it is often quite humid. Related to the sirocco are the *leveche* in Spain and the *leste* in Madeira and Morocco. The *khamsin* in Egypt is a hot and very dry wind from the desert which blows northward on the forward side of an advancing low-pressure system. The extreme case of a warm wind is the *simoom*, which is so hot and dry that it has often been described as being suffocating. It blows in occasional short bursts over the deserts of Arabia and Africa and is often filled with fine sand.

Cold Winds. The name *blizzard* was originally given to an intensely cold gale filled with drifting snow, which forms in the rear of a strong low-pressure system moving eastward to the east of the Rocky Mountains. Often drainage winds from the mountains add to the strength of the general wind system. In later years the term blizzard has been applied to any high wind accompanied by drifting or falling snow. Such storms are frequent in the antarctic, but here they are accompanied by rising temperature, for the strong winds sweep away the cold and stagnant air which has formed during periods of calm and clear sky.

The *buran* is a cold, northeasterly wind which blows over Russia and central Siberia. When it is filled with drifting snow, it is called a *purga.* Milder varieties of cold winds are the *bise* in southern France, the *levanter* in southern Spain, and the *norte* over the Gulf of Mexico. These are relatively cold, dry, and strong winds from a northerly or northeasterly direction. A mild and very pleasant variety is the *harmattan.* This is a very dry and cool wind which forms in winter when the Sahara cools rapidly. It blows southwestward to the coast, especially to the Gulf of Guinea, and brings a welcome relief to the warm and humid coastal regions.

11

The Major Wind Systems

The purpose of this chapter is to describe what are commonly called the major wind systems of the world. These systems are more or less permanent in the sense that they show up in the mean values for any month, season, or year. On individual days traveling storms may cause considerable distortions, but even then the basic currents are clearly recognizable. Because of their large dimensions the basic currents are very nearly geostrophic, so that the air may be regarded as streaming in isobaric channels in the manner described on page 152. However, near the earth's surface there will be a drift from high to low pressure, caused by friction (see page 156).

The general aspects of the major wind systems will be described in four steps. First, we shall outline the currents that would exist on a smooth and uniform earth. Second, referring back to Chap. 6, we shall account for the modifications caused by the distribution of oceans and continents. Thereafter, we shall consider the influences due to the major mountain barriers, and finally, the thermal-wind relationship (see page 159) will be used to establish a link between the currents near the earth's surface and those aloft.

The Zonal Winds. If the earth's surface were smooth and of uniform composition, the average winds over a long span of time would be arranged in latitude bands, and there would be no variation with longitude. Observations show, however, that there are large variations along any latitude belt, and these are due to the influences of land and sea, mountain ranges, etc. To obtain a first idea of the wind systems of the world, we shall ignore these influences and consider the earth's surface as if it were smooth and of uniform composition.

The system earth-atmosphere is a mechanically isolated system, and since this is so, the total angular momentum must remain constant. The earth and the atmosphere are mechanically connected to one another through friction. However, over a long span of time the one cannot impart momentum to the other, for if this were not so, the rotation of the solid earth would change. This means that there can be no net frictional

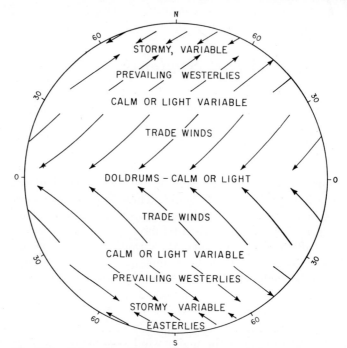

Fig. 119. Schematic picture of the average winds near sea level that would be found if the earth's surface were smooth and of uniform composition.

torque due to the east-to-west and the west-to-east motions of the air. By making use of this requirement, and by working from observations, the average wind systems over a smooth and uniform earth may be outlined as shown in Fig. 119.

In low latitudes the earth moves faster than the air, so that easterly winds are present. The two zones of low-latitude easterlies are called the *trade-wind* belts, and we speak of the northeast trades of the Northern Hemisphere and the southeast trades of the Southern Hemisphere. The trades converge toward the equator, where we find a belt of calm or light and variable winds. This belt is commonly called the *intertropical convergence zone*, and it is sometimes referred to as the *doldrums*.

At about 30° north and south the air moves with the same speed as the earth, and here we find two symmetrical belts with calm or light and variable winds. Farther to the north the air moves faster than the earth so that the winds are from the west. These zones, broadly from 35 to 55° north and south, are called the belts of *prevailing westerlies*. In extreme latitudes (north and south) we find caps of *polar easterlies*. The zones that separate the prevailing westerlies from the polar easterlies are not belts of calm. Here traveling storms are frequent, and the two zones are best described as being stormy, with winds of variable direction and speed.

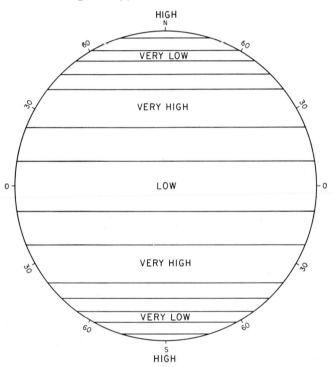

Fig. 120. Schematic picture of the sea-level isobars that correspond to Fig. 119.

The sea-level isobars that correspond to these winds would coincide with the latitude circles, more or less as shown in Fig. 120. There would be a belt of relatively low pressure along the equator, a belt of high pressure at about 30° north and south, a belt of low pressure in subpolar latitudes, and a cap of high pressure at each pole. It is customary to refer to these pressure belts by the following names: the equatorial low-pressure trough; the subtropical high-pressure belts, or the subtropical anticyclones; the subpolar low-pressure troughs, or the cyclone belts; and the polar anticyclones. The winds near sea level would be mainly along the isobars, but there would be a drift from high to low pressure, caused by friction (see page 156). The low-level winds would converge toward the low-pressure belts and diverge out from the subtropical and the polar anticyclones. These motions would imply ascending currents in the convergence zones and descending motion in the divergence zones. While these vertical motions are important in some respects, they are so small that, for practical purposes, the air motion may be said to be horizontal. As we ascend from the earth's surface the frictional influences weaken, and above about 2,000 to 3,000 ft the winds will be very nearly along the isobars.

To obtain some idea of the winds aloft over a uniform earth, we return to the discussion on page 160, where it was shown that a cold sea-level anticyclone weakens with elevation and changes into a low, while the intensity of a warm sea-level anticyclone increases with elevation. Similarly, a warm low will weaken and a cold low will strengthen as we ascend to the higher layers. With these rules in mind, we see that the cold polar highs shown in Fig. 120 will weaken and change into cold upper lows, while the warm subtropical highs will maintain their identity aloft. Because of the poleward decrease in the mean temperature of the columns of air, the poleward slope of the isobaric surfaces will increase with elevation, and so will the strength of the prevailing westerlies. Furthermore, since the temperature is fairly uniform across the equatorial zone, the equatorial easterlies will maintain their identity aloft.

During the annual cycle the pressure belts would shift toward the summer hemisphere. These migrations (see Fig. 196) amount to 10 to 15° latitude.

The diagrams shown in Figs. 119 and 120 should be regarded only as skeleton models. Nevertheless, they will serve as a useful background for the discussion that follows.

Influences of Continents and Oceans. The laws that govern the manner in which the heat is shared by the atmosphere and the uppermost layer of the earth were discussed in Chap. 6. Here it suffices to recall two essential results. First, the conductive capacity of the oceans is very much larger than that of the land masses. For this reason, the annual variation of temperature is very much smaller over oceans than over continents. Second, the annual variation of the incoming radiation (see page 91) is small near the equator and increases toward the poles. As a result, the annual variation of temperature will be small in low latitudes and large in high latitudes. It follows then that the annual variation in the temperature difference between oceans and continents will be small near the equator and large in high latitudes.

To illustrate these influences on the pressure distribution and the winds in the lower atmosphere we consider a schematic distribution of land and sea as shown in Fig. 121. In spring, when the land warms much faster than the oceans, an area of low pressure develops over land while the pressure rises at sea. The processes here are the same as those described in connection with the sea breeze (page 164). However, in the annual cycle, the changes are so slow and the systems so large that the winds are very nearly geostrophic. Moreover, the annual variation penetrates to great heights. Thus, in summer (Fig. 121a) there is a tendency for low pressure to develop over the continents. These are warm lows, and their intensity tends to decrease with elevation.

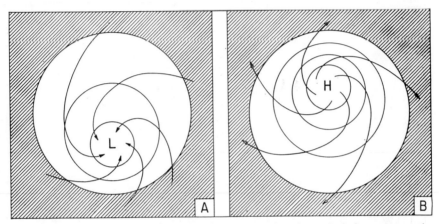

Fig. 121. Schematic picture showing the annual migrations of air between continents and oceans. Hatched areas represent oceans; unhatched areas represent continents. In summer (*a*) the pressure decreases over land, and in winter (*b*) it increases.

In autumn, when the land cools, a high-pressure area develops over land, and the pressure lowers at sea. The temperature difference between land and sea is much larger in winter than in summer, with the result that the continental high in winter is far more pronounced than the continental low in summer. Furthermore, the continental high in winter is distinctly cold, and its intensity decreases rapidly with elevation.

The conditions outlined in Fig. 121 are modified considerably where extensive mountain ranges are present. The nature of these modifications is shown schematically in Fig. 122. North America may be likened to a triangle with its base in the arctic and its apex in the tropics. It is completely open to heat exchanges with the Atlantic but barred by the Rocky Mountains against exchanges with the Pacific. As a result, the cold continental high in winter will be situated just to the east of the mountain barrier. Similarly, the warm continental low in summer is found to the east of the barrier or over the warm plateaus in the south.

The Eurasian continent is rather open to heat exchanges with the Atlantic, and (as was shown on pages 100 to 103) the effect of these penetrates far eastward. On the other hand, the extensive mountain ranges to the south and east form effective barriers against exchange with the Pacific and the southern continents. The continental high in winter is, therefore, displaced far to the east. In summer, the continental low is found in the eastern part of the continent and over the hot deserts and plateaus in the south.

The pressure patterns shown in Fig. 122 are meant to indicate only the effect of oceans and continents. The broad aspects of the real pressure

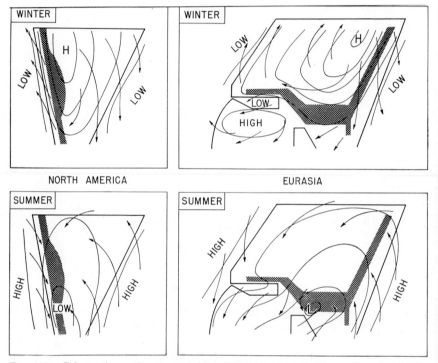

Fig. 122. Schematic continents resembling North America (left) and Eurasia (right). The cross-hatched areas represent major mountain barriers.

distributions come out by superimposing these patterns upon the zonal scheme outlined in Fig. 120. On the whole, we shall find that the annual oscillation shown in Fig. 122 dominates over the continents, while the zonal pattern is present over the oceans in all seasons. In the Southern Hemisphere (which is largely oceanic), no continent extends into subpolar latitudes. As a result, the zonal pattern is overwhelming, and only minor distortions are found over Australia, South Africa, and the southern part of South America.

Mean Sea-level Pressure and Winds in Winter. The mean sea-level pressure over the Northern Hemisphere in February is shown in Fig. 123. The corresponding winds will be mainly along the isobars (low pressure to the left) with a drift toward lower pressure caused by surface friction.

It will be seen that the main features can be accounted for by combining the zonal pattern shown in Fig. 120 with the continental models given in Fig. 122. Referring to Fig. 123, the following may be noted.

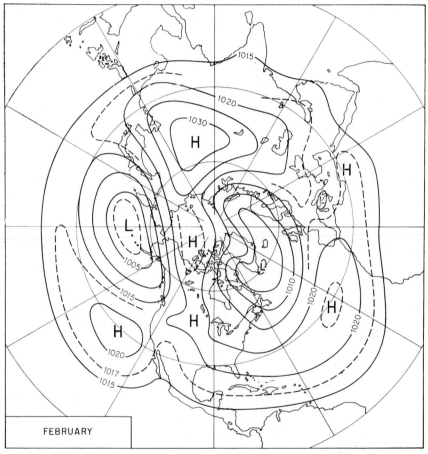

Fig. 123.   Mean sea-level pressure in winter. (*After U.S. Weather Bureau.*)

1. The polar anticyclone is displaced somewhat toward the sheltered side of the Alaskan mountains. These mountains form a barrier against the heat transfer from the Pacific while much heat is brought into the polar region on the European side.

2. The cold continental high over North America occupies a relatively narrow band just to the east of the Rocky Mountains. This is the region which is most sheltered from heat transfer from the Pacific. On its southeastern side the continental high tends to merge with the Atlantic

subtropical high, and there is a tendency for merging with the Pacific high also. Being anchored to the eastern side of the Rocky Mountains, the winter high tends to build a bridge between the polar high and the subtropical belt of high pressure. The effect of the cooling over land is so powerful that the subpolar low-pressure belt, which would be present on a uniform earth (see Fig. 120), is almost completely eliminated.

3. In midwinter the pressure is low over the northern parts of the two oceans. These are the warm regions in high latitudes in winter, and in these areas the subpolar low-pressure belt is intensified. On the Atlantic side the low-pressure area is called the Icelandic low, and on the Pacific side it is known as the Aleutian low.

4. The subtropical high-pressure belt over the oceans is fairly regular, since the underlying surface is more or less uniform. On the European side the belt is interrupted by the Mediterranean, which in winter is a warm area adjacent to colder land.

5. Over Asia the cold air is firmly limited to the south by the Himalayan range and its westward extension toward southern Europe. Along the east coast the mountain ranges afford some hindrance to the eastward spread of the cold air, while on the Atlantic side there is no major obstacle to invasions of warmer air from the Atlantic. As a result of these configurations the cold continental high over Asia (in contrast to North America) is far removed from the west coast. On the whole, it hugs the mountain slopes from the Caspian Sea in the southwest to the Anadyr range in the northeast, and it is so powerful that the subtropical high-pressure belt is completely submerged.

In the Southern Hemisphere the pressure distribution is far simpler than in the Northern Hemisphere. The only cold continent is Antarctica, which is more or less symmetrical around the pole. The belt between 30 and 60° S is almost all ocean, and even between 0 and 30° S the ocean areas predominate greatly. Owing to this uniformity of the underlying surface the pressure systems are similar to the model shown in Fig. 120, and they change but little during the annual cycle. There is a high-pressure area over Antarctica, and an almost uniform belt of low pressure (about 985 to 990 mb) near the polar circle. In about latitude 30° S we find a more or less uniform belt of high pressure (1,015 to 1,020 mb), on the equatorward side of which the trade winds blow. In translating these pressure distributions into winds it must be remembered that the winds in the Northern Hemisphere blow with high pressure to the right, while in the Southern Hemisphere the high pressure is to the left of the wind.

Mean Sea-level Pressure and Winds in Summer. The contrasts between oceans and continents, which are very sharp in winter, are now moderate and, latitude for latitude, the land masses are warmer than the oceans. Also, the temperature distribution is far more symmetrical around

the pole than in winter. As a result we find (Fig. 124) the polar anticyclone situated centrally over the ice field, with a tendency for a belt of
low pressure about 60° N. The subtropical highs are well developed over
the oceans, while the pressure is generally low over the continents. Most
noteworthy is the change from winter to summer over central Siberia,
where the pressure has dropped 20 to 25 mb. At the same time the pres-

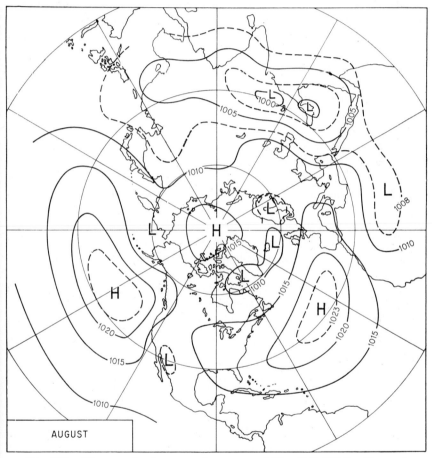

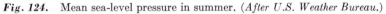

AUGUST

Fig. 124.   Mean sea-level pressure in summer. (*After U.S. Weather Bureau.*)

sure has risen about 10 mb in the Icelandic and Aleutian lows and a few
millibars elsewhere over the ocean areas. These changes reflect the effects
of the annual migration of vast masses of air from continents to oceans in
spring and from oceans to continents in autumn.

A major change has taken place over North Africa, Arabia, and
South Asia. Instead of the subtropical belt of high pressure normal for
the latitude, we find a vast area of low pressure over the heated land

masses. In the Western Hemisphere we find a counterpart in the low over Arizona and northern Mexico.

To the south of the subtropical highs the trade winds are well developed. On the Asiatic side, however, enormous masses of air stream across the equator and over the Indian Ocean and invade South Asia. These are the monsoon winds which will be discussed in a later section.

In the Southern Hemisphere the changes from winter to summer are relatively small. The subpolar belt of low pressure is present throughout the year and so are the subtropical belts of high pressure over the oceans. As the warm season approaches, the pressure lowers over South America, South Africa, and Australia, but the changes are far smaller than in the Northern Hemisphere.

Variation with Height. The general principles that govern the relation between the lower and upper pressure systems were discussed in Chap. 9, and it suffices here to recall the six rules given on page 161.

The pressure distribution at the 10,000-ft level in winter is shown in Fig. 125, and this may be compared with the sea-level distribution shown in Fig. 123. The following points are of particular interest.

1. The polar high (Fig. 123), which has a cold core, has lost its identity at the 10,000-ft level. A reflection of this high may be seen in the wedge of high pressure (Fig. 125) over Alaska.

2. The cold continental high to the east of the Rocky Mountains (Fig. 123) is made up of a very shallow layer of cold air, and it has lost its identity at the 10,000-ft level.

3. The cold continental high over Siberia is also very shallow, and at some distance above the ground the cold air is to the north and the warm air to the south. The axis of the high tilts strongly southward while the intensity decreases. Already at the 10,000-ft level, no indication of the sea-level high is found.

4. The Icelandic and the Aleutian lows have cold air on their northwestern and warm air on their southeastern sides. Their axes tilt strongly northwestward, and only traces of these lows are found at the 10,000-ft level.

5. The subtropical belt of high pressure, which is rather irregular at sea level (Fig. 123), has become fairly uniform aloft. Since the warm air is to the south, the axis tilts southward, and the belt of high pressure at 10,000 ft is found about 10 to 15° to the south of the sea-level position. We note also that the Mediterranean low in Fig. 123 has lost its identity aloft. The cold air is to the north and the axis tilts in that direction. A trace of this low can be seen in the faint pressure trough extending northward. At the same time the warm air over central Africa has caused the high-pressure belt to be displaced far to the south.

Comparing Figs. 123 and 125 we see that the pressure distribution aloft is far simpler than at sea level. On the whole we have an irregular low-pressure area over the pole surrounded by a broad and strong westerly current between about 30 and 70° N. At about 20° N there is a belt of high pressure with light and variable winds, and to the south of

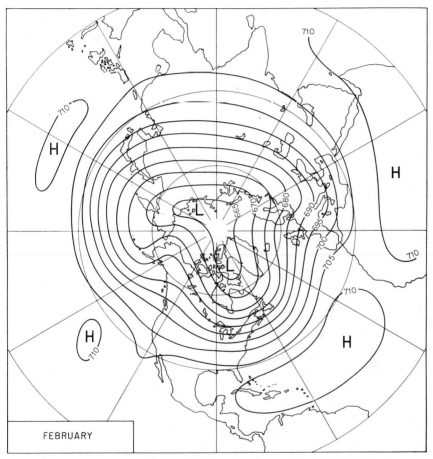

Fig. 125. Mean pressure at the 10,000-ft level in winter. (*After U.S. Weather Bureau.*)

this belt the winds are predominantly from the east. If we ascend to greater heights (say 30,000 ft), we shall find that the westerly current aloft becomes stronger and more circular; the irregularities due to the distribution of oceans and continents weaken rapidly as we ascend above the 10,000-ft level.

In the Southern Hemisphere the winds are essentially the same, except that the irregularities due to oceans and continents are very much smaller.

The conditions at the 10,000-ft level in summer are shown in Fig.

126, and this may be compared with Fig. 124. The temperature contrasts between pole and equator are now much weaker than in winter and the isobars in mid-latitudes are less crowded, indicating weaker winds.

The polar anticyclone in Fig. 124 has a cold core and therefore weakens with increasing height; it can hardly be identified at the 10,000-ft

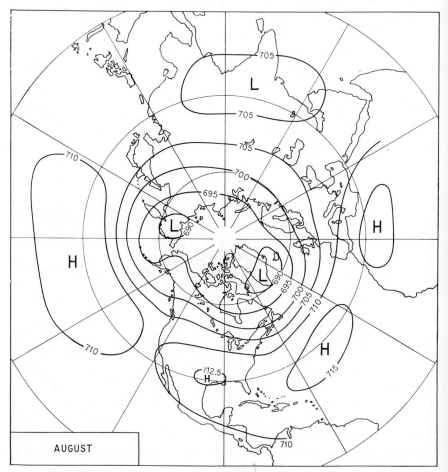

Fig. 126.   Mean pressure at the 10,000-ft level in summer. (*After U.S. Weather Bureau.*)

level. There are indications of low-pressure systems over Greenland and the Anadyr peninsula, but these lose their identities a short distance above the 10,000-ft level.

The belt of high pressure in the subtropics is well developed, except over South Asia, where a reflection of the sea-level low is still present. The very warm sea-level lows (Fig. 124) over northern Mexico and North

Africa have lost their identity and are overlain by high-pressure systems. The rather pronounced sea-level low over Arabia (Fig. 124) has disappeared at the 10,000-ft level; at greater heights it changes into a high.

If we go up to higher levels (say 30,000 ft) we shall find that the irregularities due to continents and oceans have weakened. There is a large polar low surrounded by a broad and almost circular current in mid-latitudes; a more or less continuous belt of high pressure about 25° N, with a broad zone of easterly winds over the equatorial belt.

In the Southern Hemisphere the winds aloft are essentially the same as in the Northern Hemisphere, except that the temperature difference between pole and equator is larger, and the upper winds stronger than in the Northern Hemisphere.

The Jet Stream. Observations show that the winds in the upper troposphere are normally concentrated into relatively narrow bands of strong winds, and such a band is called a jet stream. During the cold season, wind speeds of 100 to 150 mph are often observed at the core of the jet, and in rare cases 300 mph has been recorded. Only high-speed aircraft can make much progress against such winds.

While the average direction of the jet stream is from west to east, the individual jet will normally show a wave-shaped pattern, sometimes with large amplitudes. In examining a sequence of individual charts, one gains the impression that the jet resembles a meandering fast-flowing river between banks of relatively stagnant air. Some such cases will be discussed in a later chapter on cyclones and anticyclones. Here we shall be concerned only with the mean state over a long span of time.

We must now refer to the discussion on page 160, where it was shown that the wind at any level is equal to the sea-level wind plus the thermal wind from sea level to the level concerned. Since the sea-level winds are relatively light, the jet stream is almost entirely a thermal wind; its strength is proportional to the temperature contrast through the whole layer below.

Figure 127 shows the temperature in a mean cross section around the world in winter. We see that the temperature at sea level decreases strongly from the equator to the pole. This decrease is present through the major part of the troposphere, but in the stratosphere the temperature decreases southward from about 60° N. Considering the troposphere below about 30,000 ft, we see that the largest over-all temperature contrast is found about 35° N. While the thermal wind is proportional to the temperature contrast it is also inversely proportional to the Coriolis parameter (see page 160). As a result, we find the strongest winds aloft somewhere to the south of the largest temperature variation.

The mean zonal wind around the world in winter is shown in Fig. 128. On the whole, we may distinguish between three wind regimes. There is a shallow cap of easterlies around the polar high, discussed in the fore-going sections. The trade-wind belt, with easterly winds, begins at about 30° N and extends with increasing depth southward. Both the polar easterlies and the trades are generally light. A broad zone of westerlies is present in mid-latitudes and widens rapidly with elevation. At sea level the strongest winds are found about 45° N, and the axis of maximum wind

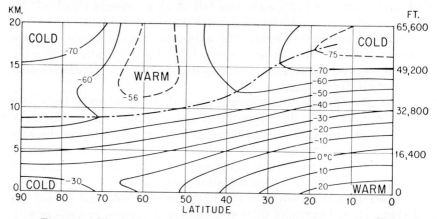

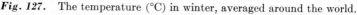

Fig. 127.   The temperature (°C) in winter, averaged around the world.

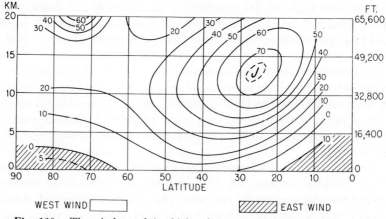

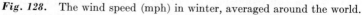

Fig. 128.   The wind speed (mph) in winter, averaged around the world.

speed slants upward to the south to about 40,000 ft in latitude 28° N. The core, indicated by *J*, may be called the jet of the mean zonal current.

In winter, when the sun is below the arctic horizon, the upper arctic troposphere cools rapidly and a strong jet of westerly winds is present in the upper part of the arctic troposphere. This jet appears to form in November; it grows to maximum strength in January, and it disappears when the sun returns in early March.

The conditions in summer are shown in Figs. 129 and 130. The temperature difference between high and low latitudes is now much smaller than in winter, and the winds are weaker. The largest over-all temperature contrasts in the troposphere are found about 50° N, and the jet in

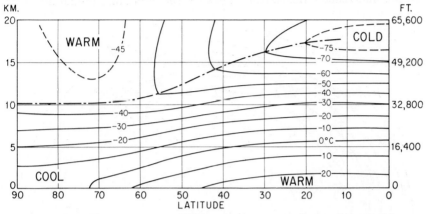

Fig. 129. The temperature (°C) in summer, averaged around the world.

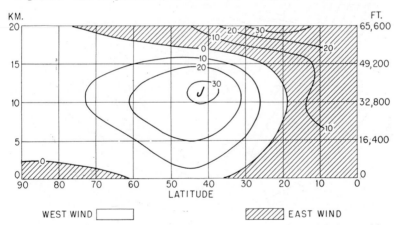

WEST WIND ☐   ▨ EAST WIND

Fig. 130. The wind speed (mph) in summer, averaged around the world.

the mean zonal wind is about 42° N. As the warm season approaches the equatorial easterlies spread northward.

The southward decrease of the temperature in the stratosphere is stronger in summer than in winter. As a result, the westerly winds in the stratosphere weaken rapidly and change into easterly winds at great heights.

The conditions shown in Figs. 128 to 130 refer to the average around the world. The strength of the jet varies, however, considerably with longitude. The mean conditions in winter and summer are shown in Figs.

131 and 132, respectively. The winter jet is strongest near the east coast
of Asia, where the over-all temperature contrasts are largest, and it is
weakest over the eastern Pacific and Atlantic Oceans, where the contrasts
are smallest. In summer, the strongest jet is found along the Canadian
border and reflects the contrast between the warm and humid air in the

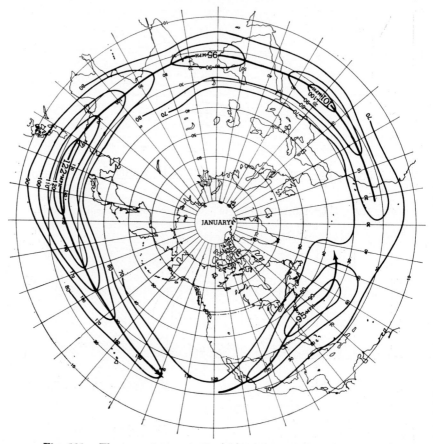

Fig. 131.   The mean jet stream in winter. *(After Namias and Clapp.)*

eastern United States and the much colder air over the Hudson Bay
region. Appreciable winds are found also over the Mediterranean, and
these reflect the difference in temperature between the hot air over
Sahara and the relatively cool air over Europe.

Similar jet streams are present in the upper troposphere of the
Southern Hemisphere. Since large land masses are absent in subpolar
latitudes, the temperature distribution is far more symmetrical around
the pole than it is in the Northern Hemisphere. As a result, the Southern
Hemisphere jet is far more uniform than the northern one.

The Equatorial Belt. On the whole this is the meeting ground for the trade winds from the two hemispheres. The two trade-wind systems meet along a zone which is called the intertropical convergence belt. Here, the winds are generally light, and over large stretches calms prevail. These calms are often called the doldrums. During the annual cycle

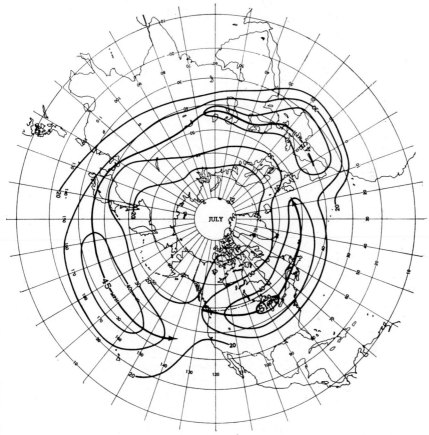

Fig. 132. The mean jet stream in summer. (*After Namias and Clapp.*)

the subtropical anticyclones migrate poleward in the summer hemisphere and equatorward in the winter hemisphere, and the intertropical convergence zone has a similar migration. The positions of the winds in January and July are shown in Fig. 133. The migration is small over the Atlantic and eastern Pacific, and here we find the zone to the north of the equator. The oscillations are quite large over Africa and South America, and it is very large in the Asiatic sector. During the northern summer there is a broad current rooted in the southern high-pressure belt and extending deep into Asia. This is what is commonly called the summer

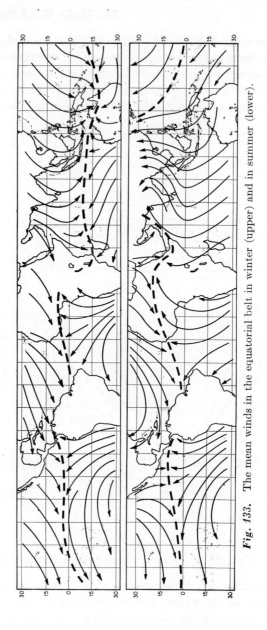

Fig. 133. The mean winds in the equatorial belt in winter (upper) and in summer (lower).

monsoon. During the northern winter an opposite current exists, bringing air from Asia far into the Southern Hemisphere, particularly to the summer low-pressure systems over Australia and South Africa. In South Asia this is called the winter monsoon.

Monsoon Systems. The Indian monsoon is the best-known example of an alternating circulation system which develops in response to the annual variation in the temperature difference between oceans and continents. Since South Asia is situated close to the equator, the monsoon is considerably strengthened by the annual migration of air from the winter to the summer hemisphere, and this migration is somewhat intensified by the annual heating and cooling of Australia.

Considered as a wind system the average Indian monsoon is not very strong. The annual variations in the winds along the fringe of the arctic, along the northwest coast of Europe, and the northeast coast of Asia are stronger than those associated with the monsoon. What has made the Indian monsoon famous is the weather, and particularly the rainfall, associated with it.

In principle the processes associated with the monsoon are the same as those described in connection with land and sea breeze (page 164), except that the time and space scales are very much larger. In detail the monsoon is much modified by the Himalayas and other mountain ranges. In spring, when South Asia warms while the air in the Southern Hemisphere cools, a pressure force is set up which accelerates the air northward. Gradually, an irregular low-pressure area develops over South Asia and reaches a maximum of intensity in July. The monsoon rain begins in April and May in Burma, but is somewhat retarded in India, and this accounts for the high temperatures reached in India in late spring (see Fig. 62). During a three-week period in late May and early June the monsoon sweeps northward into central India. It is accompanied by heavy rain, squalls, and occasional violent storms of the type known as hurricanes in the United States. At the height of the season the average motion is as shown in Fig. 134. The monsoon low is essentially a warm one, so that it weakens with increasing elevation. At levels above about 25,000 ft the monsoon low is overlain by a ridge of high pressure with an easterly current between it and the equator. On its western side the summer monsoon is limited rather sharply by warm and dry air of great depth which comes from the deserts to the west and northwest. This accounts for the sharp transition from the Thar Desert to the neighboring regions with excessive summer rain. To the east the equatorial air sweeps northward as a broad current over Southeast Asia, bringing much rainfall with it.

As the cold season approaches, the continental high over Siberia takes over, and the current reverses its direction. In midwinter (Fig. 135), the average current is from a northerly direction, and the winds converge into Australia and South Africa.

Although the word monsoon is used as a name for the periodic winds in South and Southeast Asia, similar systems exist everywhere where

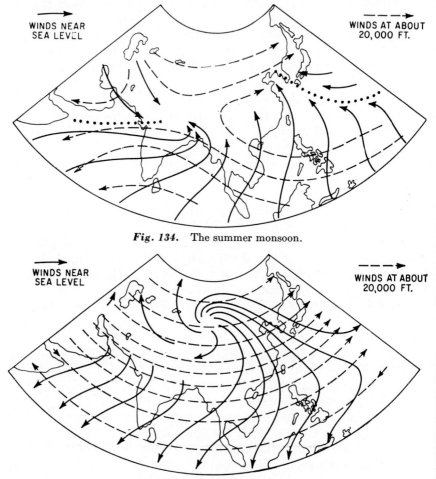

Fig. 134.   The summer monsoon.

Fig. 135.   The winter monsoon.

large temperature differences develop between oceans and continents. In high and mid-latitudes these seasonal winds tend to be overshadowed by the global winds. In low latitudes we find wind systems of the monsoon type in Australia, Central and South Africa, and in South America.

12

Air Masses

In the language of the weather forecaster an air mass is a vast body of air whose physical properties (notably temperature and humidity) are more or less uniform in the horizontal. By *vast* we mean a horizontal extent of a thousand or more miles, and by *more or less uniform* we mean that the changes over a distance of, say, 100 miles within the mass are very much smaller than the changes we experience when we go through the border between two adjacent masses. The border region, which is usually quite narrow (10 to 50 miles), is called a *front* or a frontal zone. This is a region of contrasts in temperature and moisture; it is also a region of contrasts in potential energy, and it is along the frontal zones that part of the potential energy of the air masses becomes converted into the kinetic energy associated with the large traveling storms. These storms are usually called *cyclones*. Particularly in high and mid-latitudes, the weather forecaster is very much concerned with the air masses, fronts, and cyclones. While these entities are interrelated, it is convenient here to discuss them separately.

Life History of Air Masses. It was shown in Chap. 6 that the conductive capacity of the air is so large that a high degree of adaptation exists between the underlying surface and deep columns of air. Furthermore, it was shown in Chap. 11 that the major wind systems have a tendency to be situated either over the continents or over the oceans. Examples are the subtropical highs and the polar continental highs. The air that circulates around such systems will gradually acquire the physical properties of the underlying surface. It is in such regions that the air masses are produced, and we speak of *air-mass sources.*

When an air mass leaves its source region, the balance with the underlying surface becomes disturbed, and the air mass begins to change its structure. This change affects not only the temperature and the moisture content but also the stability along the vertical. For example, when an air mass moves over a warmer surface, it absorbs heat from below and becomes unstable. The result is clouds and weather of the general type discussed in Chap. 7. On the other hand, a mass that moves over a colder surface will surrender heat and become stable; here we encounter weather of the type discussed in Chap. 8. On the whole, the clouds and weather within an air mass depend intimately upon the recent *life history* of the mass.

The life history may conveniently be divided into three parts. We may speak of the source region where the air acquired its basic properties; important, also, are the properties of the surface over which the air traveled after it left its source, and the age, or the time it has spent on its journey. The amount of modification and the depth of penetration will depend upon the contrast with the underlying surface and the duration of the modifying influences.

A typical example of air-mass modification is shown in Fig. 136. Here we see a mass of warm air streaming out of the Atlantic subtropical anticyclone toward England and France. The sea surface is fairly uniform, and the air cools slowly. To begin with, the air contains broken stratocumulus, but as the cooling from below progresses the mass becomes increasingly stable; the cloud layer lowers and thickens into fog, which produces a fine drizzle. The fog over southern England and northwestern France is an advection fog, of the type discussed in Chap. 8. On the other hand, the cold air from Greenland streams right across the warm Atlantic current and changes its temperature at a rapid rate. The heating from below results in instability, vertical overturnings, heavy cumulus clouds, and showers. The area of continuous precipitation is not related to the internal processes of the air masses but is due to warm air gliding up over a wedge of cold air. This is commonly called *frontal weather*, and we shall discuss it in Chaps. 13 and 14.

Air-mass Sources in Winter. A general picture of these source regions can be obtained by considering the broad aspects of the physical properties of the earth's surface and the air currents that sweep over the earth. In Fig. 137 is shown the distribution of the temperature of the sea surface. We note that the temperature is very uniform near the equator. In the mid-latitude belt the transition is rather gradual, and sharp contrasts are found along the edge of the arctic ice fields and along the coasts of northern continents. In particular we must note the concentrated ribbon of isotherms along the border between the Labrador Current and the Gulf Stream. This ribbon extends all the way from the east coast of

Greenland down to the shores of North Carolina. A similar ribbon is present in the Far East and marks the difference between the cold Oyashio and the warm Kuroshio, or Japan Current. These are the Pacific counterparts to the currents in the northern part of the Atlantic Ocean.

Over land we must pay attention to the distribution of snow cover. In Fig. 137 are shown the number of days with monthly mean temperature below freezing. It will be seen that the zone between 0 and 100 days

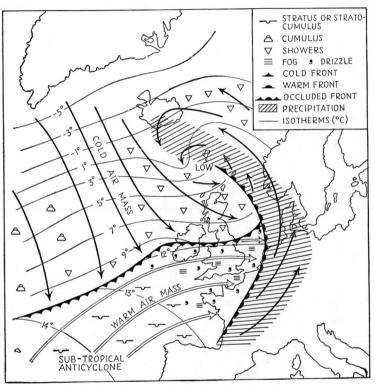

Fig. 136. Example of warm and cold air masses.

is quite narrow. Around the 0°C isotherm there will be snow now and then, but the border of the effective snow cover is found along the −3°C (27°F) mean isotherm during the coldest month. This isotherm is in the belt between 0 and 100 days with frost, and closer to the 0 line than to the 100 line. We see then that there is a sharp transition from ground without snow cover to ground with snow cover lasting more than 100 days. All told, the area of snow cover lasting 3 months or more occupies about 25 per cent of the Northern Hemisphere.

The hatched areas in Fig. 137 identify the snowless regions which are particularly dry. These include the deserts, the steppes, and the savannas with winter dryness. The unhatched continental areas outside the zero line have no snow cover; here rains are relatively frequent and the ground is often wet.

To delineate the regions which are favorable for the formation of distinct air masses and the regions where rapid transformations occur, we

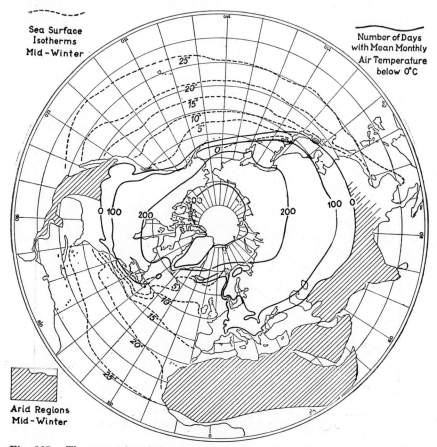

Fig. 137. The properties of the earth's surface in winter. Curves over land indicate the average number of days with mean monthly air temperature below freezing. Curves over oceans indicate the mean sea-surface temperature in midwinter. Hatching indicates regions without snow and with winter dryness.

may superimpose the mean air currents near the earth's surface on Fig. 137. The result is shown in Fig. 138. The streamlines, which here are somewhat generalized, should be compared with the pressure distribution shown in Fig. 123.

A feature of considerable importance is the tendency for the air currents to diverge out of the high-pressure areas and to converge into the low-pressure areas. As a result, the properties acquired by the air in the highs will spread horizontally; the air in the highs will tend to become uniform while air-mass contrasts will be maintained in the low-pressure regions. We must therefore look to the high-pressure areas as the main producers of air masses.

Fig. 138. Air-mass sources in winter. 1, arctic; 2, polar continental; 3, polar maritime, or transitional; 4, transitional; 5, transitional; 6, tropical continental; 7, tropical maritime; 8, equatorial; 9, monsoon.

On the general principles outlined above the Northern Hemisphere may be divided into nine regions, as shown in Fig. 138.

The Arctic Air-mass Source. This is the region of the arctic fields of snow and ice. The properties of the underlying surface are highly uniform; the sun is below the horizon most of the winter, and the area is mainly occupied by the arctic anticyclone (Fig. 123). The winds are generally light; the air remains in contact with the underlying surface for long intervals of time, and the adaptation between air and surface is more or less complete.

On the European side the arctic source region is fairly well separated from its neighbor to the south by the southwesterly winds on the poleward side of the continental high-pressure area. On the American side the separation is less distinct, and the arctic region tends to merge with the polar continental source.

The Polar Continental Source Regions. These are indicated by 2 in Fig. 138. The ground is generally covered by snow, and each of the regions is dominated by a polar continental high-pressure area.

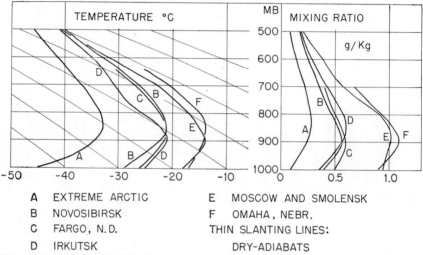

A   EXTREME ARCTIC   E   MOSCOW AND SMOLENSK
B   NOVOSIBIRSK   F   OMAHA, NEBR.
C   FARGO, N.D.   THIN SLANTING LINES:
D   IRKUTSK   DRY-ADIABATS

Fig. 139. Typical distributions of temperature and humidity in arctic and polar continental air masses in winter.

The typical structure of the air masses within regions 1 and 2 is shown in Fig. 139. Since sunshine is either absent or sparse, and since the snow is a good radiator, any air that invades these regions cools rapidly through outgoing long-wave radiation from the ground. The result is a minimum of temperature at the ground and a maximum between 900 and 850 mb (3,000 to 5,000 ft). In the inversion layer, heat is conducted downward, and the temperature at the ground comes out as a balance between loss of heat through radiation and gain through conduction.

The distribution along the vertical of moisture shows a similar trend, indicating that the air surrenders water vapor to the ground.

On the whole the arctic and polar continental air masses are highly stable; the lapse rate in the lower layers is very much smaller than the adiabatic rate, and the predominant cloud forms are layer clouds of the type described in Chaps. 3 and 8.

The Maritime Tropical Source Regions. These are two in number and indicated by 7 in Fig. 138. The air motion in each of these regions is dominated by the subtropical anticyclones shown in Fig. 123. These are highly persistent and situated over ocean regions with fairly uniform temperature. The air is fairly uniform near the surface, but this uniformity does not extend to great heights. In the eastern part of the subtropical highs, there is persistent subsiding motion. A subsidence inversion of the type shown in Fig. 58 is normally present about 1,500 to 3,000 ft above the sea surface to the west of North Africa and also to the west of Southern California and Mexico. The moisture absorbed from the ocean is limited to the surface layer, and above the inversion the relative humidity is very low, generally of the order of 20 to 30 per cent.

In the western part of the subtropical highs there is, on the average, slight ascending motion. Here the lapse rate is steep and the mobility of the air along the vertical is great. As a result, the moisture absorbed from the ocean surface penetrates to great heights. The difference between the air-mass structure in the eastern and western parts of the subtropical highs can best be seen by comparing the rainfall in western North Africa with that of the southeastern part of the United States. For example, while the January rainfall in Marrakech is 0.7 in., Charleston has 3.1 in.

Though the moisture content increases greatly from east to west in each of the tropical air-mass regions, the tropical air masses that arrive in mid-latitudes and invade North America and Europe come from the western part of these regions. These invasions are therefore characterized by high moisture content and much rain. It is through these invasions that the subtropical belt exports much of its heat and moisture to the less-endowed regions farther to the north.

The Tropical Continental Source Region. This region occupies most of North Africa. The land is very dry, and the circulation is anticyclonic but of slight intensity. Subsidence aloft is prominent, and the air is relatively dry through a deep layer. On occasions, air from this region invades the Mediterranean, where it soon becomes moistened. Much of the air that is produced in this source streams southwestward to central Africa, and it does not absorb much moisture until it arrives over the jungle of central Africa.

Regions of Transition. The regions indicated by 4 and 5 in Fig. 138 are typical regions of transition. In the two regions indicated by 5, cold continental air streams southward over warm water and soon becomes transformed into warm and humid masses. In the two regions indicated by 4, arctic and polar continental air of low temperature and moisture content streams first over the cold ocean currents and then over warm ones. These are the regions of extremely rapid air-mass transformation, in which heat and moisture are taken up at tremendous rates. The warming from below steepens the lapse rate and increases the mobility of the air along the vertical, so that heat and moisture are brought up to great heights. These are also the regions with frequent storms.

In the two regions indicated by 3, the mean air flow is mainly along the sea-surface isotherms. When the actual current resembles the mean, a typical maritime polar air mass develops. It is mild and laden with moisture. On occasion, these regions are invaded by cold air from the arctic and the continental source regions, and the two regions 3 then bring about rapid transformations. An example is shown in Fig. 140.

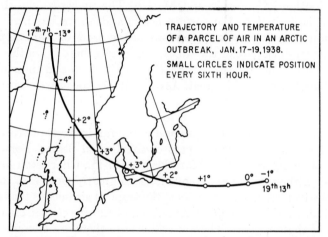

Fig. 140.   Showing the temperature changes of an arctic air mass that moved first over warmer water and then over colder land.

Here a mass of air with temperature −13°C (9°F) was caught in a strong polar outbreak. During the first 12-hr period, the temperature rose 15°C (27°F). As the air came over the more uniform waters of the North Sea, the temperature leveled off, and as it moved into Europe it decreased slowly. Referring back to the discussion in Chap. 6, it is of interest to note that the air adapted itself very quickly to the temperature of the sea surface. On the other hand, as the air moved inland the changes were slow, for over land there is a strong tendency for the land surface to adapt itself to the temperature of the invading air.

The Equatorial Region. On the equatorial side of the subtropical highs the air streams southwestward over warmer water and meets with the trade winds from the Southern Hemisphere. In the convergence zone there is general ascending motion; the lapse rate is steep, and the conduction of heat and moisture up to high levels is lively. Here, we find the equatorial belt of deep clouds and heavy rainfall. The region indicated by 8, which encircles the globe, is called the equatorial air-mass source.

The Monsoon Region. On the Asiatic side the winter monsoon blows as a gentle or moderate wind out of India and Southeast Asia. It is generally dry and mild. In all essentials this region resembles those indicated by 5 in Fig. 138. It is a region in which relatively cool and dry air becomes transformed into warm and humid air.

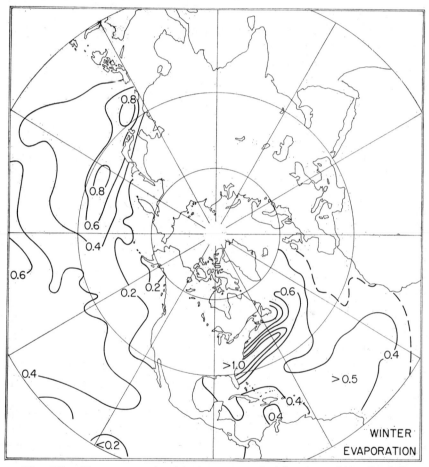

Fig. 141. Mean evaporation (centimeters per day) in winter. (*After Jacobs.*)

Evaporation. The mean amount of water evaporated from the ocean surface in winter is shown in Fig. 141. On the whole, we may identify two zones which contribute greatly to the water supply of the air. In the first place, the trade-wind belts provide much. Although the amounts per unit area are not very great, the total area involved is very large. Much of this water vapor is deposited as rain in the equatorial belt, but a considerable portion is brought northward around the western extremities of the subtropical highs and yielded up as rain in the mid-latitudes. The second belt of high evaporation is found in the mid-latitudes, or more precisely in the regions indicated by 4 and 5 in Fig. 138. Here, cold air streams over much warmer water, with the result that heat and water vapor are absorbed at a rapid rate. On the whole, we may say that the main suppliers of water vapor to the air are the regions indicated by 4 and 5, the southern portions of regions 7, and region 8.

Looking again at Fig. 138, the broad features may be summarized as follows. The regions indicated by 1 and 2 are the main producers of cold air. Much of this air is exported to lower latitudes through the regions 4 and 5; these are the regions of intense evaporation. On the other hand, much warm air is exported from the subtropical belt through the northern parts of the two regions indicated by 7 and through the two regions indicated by 3. In these regions the supply of water vapor is, on the average, small. Much air is exported from the subtropical high-pressure belt to the doldrums by the trade winds, and here we find another belt of high evaporation. On the whole, the liveliest exchange is in the mid-latitudes, and this agrees with the requirements of a balanced budget of heat and moisture which was discussed in Chap. 6.

Air-mass Sources in Summer. During the warmer part of the year the contrasts between high and low latitudes and between oceans and continents are much weaker than in winter. We find, therefore, that the contrasts between the different air masses are smaller than in winter. Nevertheless, distinct air-mass sources can be identified and, as in winter, the factors to consider are the properties of the underlying surface and the circulation patterns in the lower atmosphere.

The Earth's Surface. It will be seen from Fig. 142 that the distribution of sea-surface temperature is essentially the same as in winter, except that the waters in the mid-latitudes are warmer and more uniform. On the other hand, the difference between winter and summer over the continents is very large.

As an indicator of the properties of the land surfaces we may use the mean annual maximum temperature. This, which is the average temperature that would be reached on relatively calm and clear days, is a good measure of the ability of the earth's surface to convert the incoming radiation into surface heat. It will be seen from Fig. 142 that the deserts and the arid regions are characterized by maximum temperature of about 40 to 45°C (104 to 113°F). The vast expanses of grassland and forests farther to the north have a fairly uniform temperature of 30 to 35°C. The difference between these land masses is not very large, and the transition is rather gradual. The major contrasts are found along the fringe of the arctic and along the west coasts in the mid-latitudes.

To delineate the regions favorable for the development of distinct air masses we superimpose the winds near the earth's surface on Fig. 142. On the whole, the Northern Hemisphere may be divided into seven air-mass regions, as shown in Fig. 143.

The Arctic Source Region. This region is well defined; it covers the arctic fields of ice and icy waters and is overlain by an anticyclonic circulation system. The surface temperature is limited by the melting point,

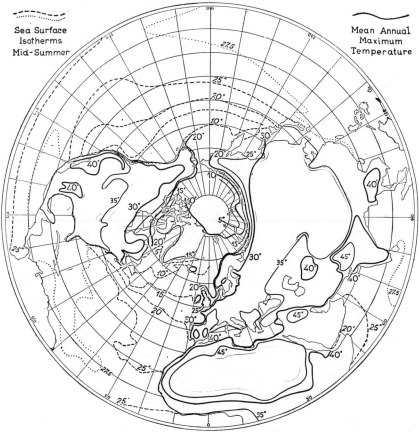

Fig. 142. The properties of the earth's surface in summer.

and the region is surrounded by warm air, particularly on its continental sides. The air mass as a whole is stagnant. Its relative humidity is high, and fogs and low stratus are the predominant cloud forms.

The Tropical Continental Source Regions. These are two in number and indicated by 4 in Fig. 143. Both are characterized by relatively light winds. On the Eurasian side the region contains several large bodies of water, but these are overlain by a high-pressure system and subsiding air aloft. The air column as a whole is relatively dry, and precipitation sparse. Appreciable humidity is found only along the northern borders of the two regions, and here summer showers are fairly frequent.

The Tropical Maritime Source Regions. These regions, which are indicated by 5, are occupied by the subtropical anticyclones. The air masses are essentially the same as in winter, except that the temperature is

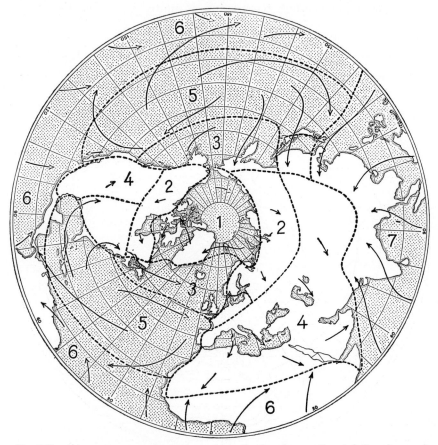

Fig. 143. Air-mass sources in summer. 1, arctic; 2, polar continental; 3, polar maritime; 4, tropical continental; 5, tropical maritime; 6, equatorial; 7, monsoon.

higher. The regions are more extensive and situated farther to the north than in winter.

The Polar Source Regions. The arctic region is separated from the tropical ones by a relatively narrow belt. Within the two regions indicated by 2, polar continental air masses form, particularly when passing high-pressure areas are present. On occasions, air from these sources may spread far southward. The two regions indicated by 3 are the abodes of the polar maritime masses.

The Equatorial Source Region. In summer, the equatorial convergence zone is displaced far to the north. Here there is general ascending motion; the air is moist up to great heights, and heavy clouds and precipitation are typical. On the Asiatic side the summer monsoon, with clouds and rain, penetrates far into the continent.

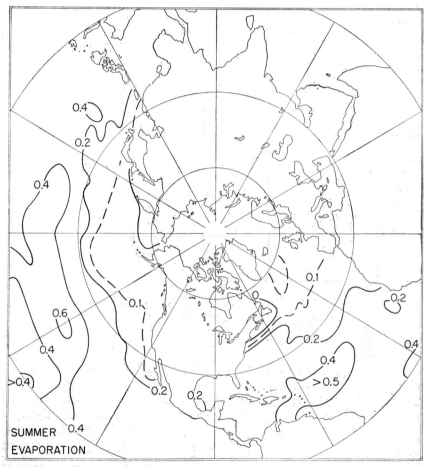

Fig. 144. Mean evaporation (centimeters per day) in summer. (*After Jacobs.*)

Evaporation. The mean amounts of evaporation from the ocean surfaces is shown in Fig. 144. The areas of large evaporation which were present along the east coasts of North America and Asia in winter are absent in the warm season, for the air masses that sweep over these regions are now so warm that little or no evaporation takes place. In fact, the Labrador Current and the Oyashio show slight negative amounts, indicating that the air surrenders water vapor to these cold currents.

Classification of Air Masses. The principal air masses of the Northern Hemisphere may be classified as shown in Table 12.

In addition to this source classification it is customary to refer to the air masses as being either cold or warm. A *cold mass* is one which is colder than the underlying surface, and this designation is used regardless of whether the air temperature is high or low. A cold air mass will absorb heat and moisture from below, the lapse rate will steepen, and heat and moisture will be conducted to higher levels. The typical weather associated with a cold mass is made up of cumulus clouds, showers, and, in severe cases, thunderstorms. Similarly, an air mass which is warmer than

Table 12. Air Masses Classified according to Source Region

Symbol	Name	Winter source (Fig. 138)	Summer source (Fig. 143)	Remarks
A	Arctic	1	1	All seasons
Pc	Polar continental	2	2	Prominent in winter
Pm	Polar maritime	3	3	All seasons
Tc	Tropical continental	6	4	Prominent in summer
Tm	Tropical maritime	7	5	All seasons
E	Equatorial	8	6	All seasons
M	Monsoon	9	7	Dry in winter, wet in summer

the surface under it is called a *warm mass*. Here, heat will be surrendered to the surface. The stratification of the lower layer will be stable, and if clouds form they will be of the layer type. In pronounced cases, fog and drizzle will result.

It is customary to use the letters K and W to indicate cold and warm air masses. These letters are then affixed to the basic symbols given in Table 12. Thus, TmW means a tropical maritime mass which is warmer than the surface over which it streams. Similarly, PcK would signify a polar continental mass which is colder than the underlying surface. Thus, by referring the air mass back to its source and tracing its movement since it left the source, it is possible to account for the broad aspects of the associated clouds and weather.

An Example. The tracing of the life history of air masses is particularly useful over oceans where observations are sparse. Moreover, the moisture supply over oceans is so plentiful that clouds and weather develop readily in response to the influences from the underlying surface.

An example is shown in Fig. 145. Here, a vast mass of polar air streams southward over much warmer water, and rain showers are plentiful. This is a typical cold (K) mass. In the southern portion of the chart we have warm air which originated in the subtropical high-pressure belt. While first moving northward and later eastward, this air was cooled from below. The result is an extensive layer of low stratus and drizzle which is about to invade France and Central Europe. This is a typical

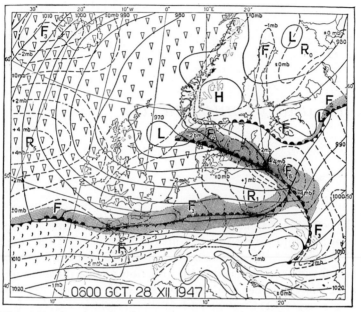

Fig. 145. An example of two air masses with widely different life histories. (*After Berggren.*)

warm (*W*) air mass. We note that the isobars in the warm mass are crowded, and this indicates strong winds. If the winds had been light, a deep fog would have formed.

The two air masses shown in Fig. 145 would be designated *TmW* and *PmK*, respectively. These and similar symbols are the tags that the forecasters use to label the various air masses.

13

Fronts and Frontogenesis

The concepts of air masses and fronts were brought into meteorological literature and forecasting practice about 1920 to 1930; the originators were T. Bergeron, J. Bjerknes, and H. Solberg. Since then, these concepts have found wide acceptance and they are now among the main pillars on which the daily weather analyses are based. If we could draw weather charts on a scale of 1:1 we should find that a front is a relatively narrow zone of transition between two different air masses. In routine analyses it is customary to use charts on a scale of about 1:10,000,000, and on such charts a typical front stands out as a line across which the temperature, wind, and other elements vary in a discontinuous manner.

Some Typical Features. An instructive example of extensive fronts is shown in Figs. 146 to 149. In the first of these we see a trough of low pressure (1,005 to 1,010 mb) extending from the Gulf of Mexico toward Nova Scotia. To the south of the trough line there is a vast mass of maritime tropical air streaming out of the subtropical anticyclone, and to the north, polar continental air streams southward. The front, as indicated in Fig. 146, is the line of separation between two air masses of widely different life histories. Along the front we see that the wind direction varies abruptly; the front lies in a region of strong confluent motion.

Less distinct is a front farther to the north. This zone separates polar continental air (to the south) from an intrusion of arctic air from the north. The confluent motion toward this front is noticeable but not very strong. What we learn from Fig. 146 is that a front is characterized by a shift in the wind direction and a kink in the isobars. This is typical of all fronts.

The temperature distribution associated with these fronts is shown
in Fig. 147. A vast mass of warm air of tropical origin is present to the
south of the southern front. Having spent a long time over a more or less
uniform ocean surface, the tropical mass has become highly uniform and
laden with moisture. The minor irregularities in the temperature within
the mass have been caused by nocturnal cooling over the Caribbean
islands and Florida. These irregularities are present only in the lowest
layer.

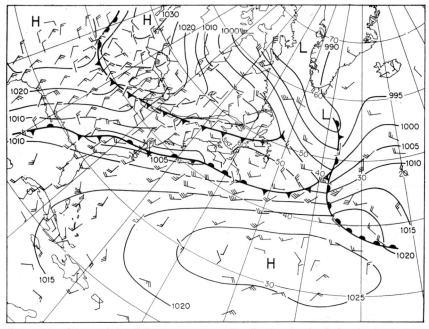

Fig. 146. An example of fronts, pressure distribution, and winds. Jan. 28, 1952,
1230 GCT.

The temperature contrast along the southern front is very large and
varies between 10 and 30°F. While the wind direction (Fig. 146) appears
to be discontinuous, the ribbon of isotherms has a finite width. We may
say that the wind is more nearly discontinuous than is the temperature,
and this is typical of all fronts.

To the north of the southern front we find a long and relatively narrow belt of polar air of continental origin. This air is far less uniform than
is the tropical maritime air. This is a typical feature; the tropical maritime
air masses are far more uniform than other masses.

The northern front separates polar continental air from air of arctic
origin. While the arctic air is fairly uniform in its source region, it
changes rapidly when it moves southward over warmer ground. As a

result, we find a wide ribbon of isotherms along the forward edge of the invading arctic mass of air.

The weather characteristics associated with the fronts are shown in Fig. 148. It will be seen that extensive areas of cloud cover and precipitation are associated with the fronts. While such areas are almost always associated with fronts, the reverse is not true; on many occasions a front may not be associated with an area of precipitation, and, in some cases,

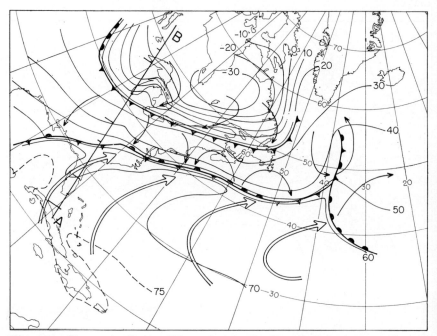

Fig. 147. Fronts, isotherms (°F), and generalized streamlines corresponding to Fig. 146.

the cloud cover may be broken. While overcast sky and precipitation are a frequent occurrence, they are not always present.

Figure 148 shows two extensive areas of completely clear sky. In the western area the motion is down the slope of the mountains. Because of adiabatic heating of the descending air, nocturnal cooling under the cloudless sky is largely compensated for, and the temperature remains relatively high.

The second area of clear sky, over Canada, is over level land. Here, the absence of cloud cover permits the ground to radiate freely toward space, and in the absence of adiabatic heating, a pool of cold air forms. This area, then, acts as a window through which the ground and air in contact with it lose heat at a rapid rate. This cooling affects mainly a shallow layer, with the result that the surface temperatures are not representative of a layer of appreciable depth.

What we learn from the case shown in Figs. 146 to 148 may be summarized as follows: (1) A front is characterized by a sudden change in the wind direction and by a kink in the isobars, the kink pointing in the direction from low to high pressure. (2) A front is often, but not always, associated with an extensive cloud cover from which precipitation falls. The

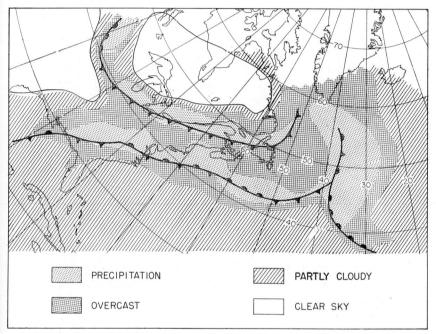

Fig. 148.   Fronts, clouds, and precipitation corresponding to Fig. 146.

precipitation is mainly on the cold side of the front. (3) In pronounced cases the temperature near the ground may be strongly influenced by local conditions, and these may overshadow the representative contrasts through deep layers of air.

Figure 149 shows a cross section through the fronts and air masses along the line *AB* in Fig. 147. In the lowest layer the tropical maritime mass is highly uniform, and the front that separates it from the polar continental air reaches up to great heights. The polar continental air is less uniform, and the arctic mass (which in this case was displaced far to the south) shows strong internal contrasts. In particular, the very low temperatures over the cloudless part of Canada (Figs. 147 and 148) are typical only of a very shallow layer.

The cross section shows that the tropopause is very high over the tropical air mass and low over the polar and arctic masses. On the whole, the features shown in Figs. 146 to 149 are typical, though, in individual cases, the magnitude of the contrasts may vary considerably.

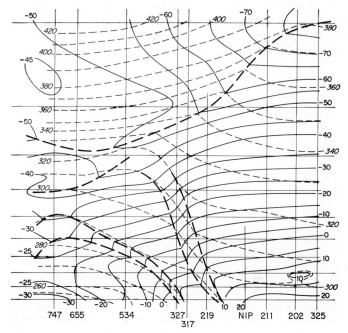

Fig. 149. Vertical cross section along the line *AB* in Fig. 147. Full lines are temperature (°C), and broken lines are potential temperature (°A).

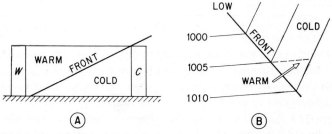

Fig. 150. Illustrating the refraction of the isobars at a front.

Fronts, Pressure, and Wind. Apart from being a zone of rapid transition in temperature, a front is also a zone of rapid change of pressure and wind. To show this we recall the discussion on page 6, where it was shown that the atmospheric pressure is determined by the weight of the air column. Since cold air is denser than warm air, the weight of the column *C* in Fig. 150 will be greater than that of column *W*. The excess weight of the cold wedge under the front will therefore cause the isobars to be refracted as shown in Fig. 150*b*. If the observer stands in the warm air with low pressure on his left, the refraction of the isobars in the cold air will be to the left.

Since the wind is mainly along the isobars, we see that the wind direction will change in the identical manner. If the double-shafted arrow indicates the direction in which the front moves, we see that the following rule holds: If the observer stands with his back against the wind in advance of the front, the wind will shift to his left when the front passes. The wind speed will normally change as the front passes, and it will increase or decrease according to the spacing of the isobars.

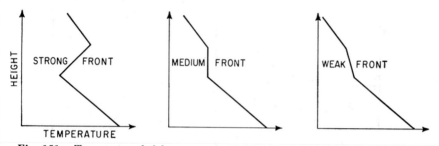

Fig. 151. Temperature-height curves showing strong, medium, and weak fronts.

Thermal Structure of Fronts. The essential features of the vertical structure of fronts were shown in Fig. 149. If we ascend through a frontal zone we shall find temperature distributions of the types shown in Fig. 151. If the front is strongly developed, the temperature will increase through the frontal layer. In the case of fronts of moderate intensity, the temperature will remain more or less constant, and with weak fronts the temperature will decrease through the layer. The important point is that the lapse rate of temperature is smaller within the frontal layer than it is on either side. As was shown in Chap. 6, the mobility of the air along the vertical and the exchanges of heat and moisture increase rapidly with the lapse rate. As a result, we find that the frontal surfaces are effective barriers against such exchanges. For this reason, the heat and moisture taken up by the cold air under the frontal surface will be distributed through the cold wedge, but very little of it will go through the frontal surfaces itself. By and large, the frontal surfaces tend to hinder exchange of heat and moisture between the air masses. The stronger the front is developed, the more effective it is as a barrier against such exchanges.

Classification of Fronts. The fronts are classified according to their motion relative to the warm and cold air masses, and the principal types are shown in Fig. 152. A *cold front* (Fig. 152*a*) is one that moves in such a direction that cold air replaces warm air. Similarly, a *warm front*

(Fig. 152*b*) is a front along which warm air replaces cold air. If there is no appreciable motion the front is said to be *quasi-stationary* (Fig. 152*c*). On occasion, the cold front may overtake the warm front. The warm air between them is then squeezed upward as shown in Fig. 152*d*. This is called an *occluded front* or an *occlusion*.

We shall return to the discussion of these types in the following chapter on cyclones, and we shall see that the fronts constitute essential

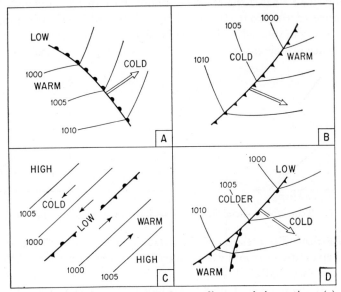

Fig. 152.   Fronts are classified according to their motion: (*a*) warm front; (*b*) cold front; (*c*) quasi-stationary; (*d*) occluded.

links in the large wind and weather systems that dominate the mid-latitudes belt. For the time being we shall be concerned only with the details of the fronts and, in particular, with the circumstances in which they form.

Frontogenesis. To obtain a glance at the processes which lead to the formation of fronts we proceed in the following manner. Consider a body of air which occupies a certain position. This body may be moved from one place to another and it may be made to assume any shape and orientation in its new position by four different motions. First, we may move the body without rotating it or altering its shape and volume. This motion is called *translation*. Second, we may alter the orientation by turning the body around an axis. This motion is called *rotation*. Next, we may expand and contract the volume. This is called expansion (positive or negative) or *divergence*. Finally, we may alter the shape by squeezing, or deforming, the body, and this is called *deformation*.

In the large-scale currents the motion is overwhelmingly horizontal, so that we need consider only the motion in a level surface. The four parts of the total motion are shown in Fig. 153. The direction of the wind in relation to the centers of high and low pressure refers to the conditions in the Northern Hemisphere. In the Southern Hemisphere the words *high* and *low* must be interchanged.

The translatory part of the motion (Fig. 153a) corresponds to a wind blowing between straight isobars of equal spacing. The rotational part corresponds more or less to the gradient wind around centers of high

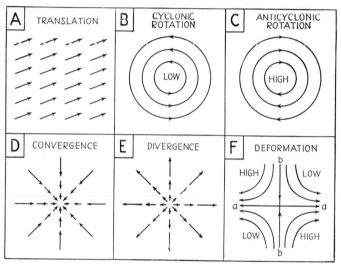

Fig. 153. Principal types of motion.

pressure and centers of low pressure. The contracting or expanding parts (Fig. 153d and e) are not related to any isobar configuration. In the atmosphere these motions are so small that we may ignore them in comparison with the other components. Finally the deformation (Fig. 153f) corresponds to the isobars in the vicinity of the saddle-backed region between pairs of highs and lows.

Now, to explain the essence of the formation of frontal zones we imagine that a bundle of isotherms is superimposed upon each of the motions shown in Fig. 153. We assume that the air is neither heated nor cooled, so that the configuration of the isotherms can be changed only by the motion.

It is immediately apparent that the translation (Fig. 153a) cannot change the distance between the isotherms, for all would move with the same speed. Similarly, the rotation (Fig. 153b and c) would not alter the spacing of the isotherms, for all would rotate equally. However, if a bundle of isotherms is superimposed on the deformation, we see that the distance will change. If the isotherms were more or less parallel to the axis *bb*, they would disperse and the air would become more uniform. On the other hand, if the isotherms were more or less parallel to the axis *aa*, isotherms from either side would be carried toward this axis; as time passes, a large number of isotherms would crowd together, and we say that a discontinuity of temperature forms. This is what we call *frontogenesis*.

The saddle-backed region shown in Fig. 153*f* is called a *col*. The axis *aa* is called the axis of *stretching* or the axis of *dilatation*, and the axis *bb* is called the axis of *shrinking* or the axis of *contraction*.

The movement of the isotherms in the vicinity of a col is shown in greater detail in Fig. 154. The hatched zone represents the maximum

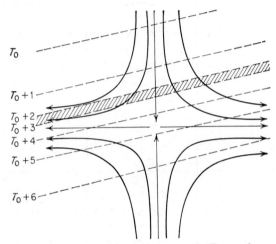

Fig. 154. A clear case of frontogenesis. For explanation, see text.

concentration of isotherms. This zone will be carried downward toward the axis of stretching, and the neighboring isotherms will tend to approach this axis. This is a clear case of frontogenesis. A somewhat different case is shown in Fig. 155. Here the angle between the axis of stretching and the isotherms is larger than 45°. The isotherms will then move faster along the axis of stretching than along the axis of shrinking and, as a result, the isotherms will tend to disperse. However, the point *A* will move toward the center faster than point *B* will move away from it. We see then that the isotherms will tend to rotate; the angle β will decrease, and as soon as the angle becomes less than 45°, the isotherms will begin to approach one another. It is readily understood, therefore, that the cols are favored regions for development of fronts.

Some Frequent Combinations. The flow pattern shown in Figs. 154 and 155 represents pure deformation. In it the axis of outflow is at right angles to the axis of inflow. The flow patterns observed in the atmosphere may be thought of as resulting from superimpositions of the four component fields shown in Fig. 153. However, the divergence is so small that it may be neglected, and the translation adds nothing that is new in principle. The superimposition of deformation and rotation is, however, of some interest.

If we superimpose a weak cyclonic rotation on a field of deformation, we obtain the pattern shown in Fig. 156b. There are still an axis of outflow and an axis of inflow, but these are no longer at right angles to one another. As long as the rotation is weaker than the deformation, the cyclonic rotation will add to the curvature of the cyclonic streamlines (Fig.

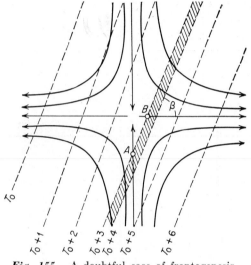

Fig. 155. A doubtful case of frontogenesis. For explanation, see text.

156a) and subtract from the anticyclonic streamlines. The result is a pattern with skew axes. The skewness increases with the rotation, and when the intensity of the rotation equals that of the deformation, we obtain two straight currents, gliding side by side and separated by a shear line along which the velocity is zero (Fig. 156c). If the intensity of the rotation exceeds that of the deformation, we obtain the pattern shown in Fig. 156d. The streamlines are now closed and of elliptical shape. Since the process of frontogenesis depends essentially upon the presence of deformation, we see that the four patterns shown in Fig. 156 will be frontogenetical, provided that temperature contrasts of suitable orientation are present.

If instead of a cyclonic rotation we superimpose an anticyclonic one, we shall find similar patterns, except that these will resemble the motion associated with ridges of high pressure, or elongated anticyclones. Experience shows that these are rarely frontogenetical. We must therefore look for frontogenesis in connection with the cols and the elongated cyclonic systems.

The Principal Frontal Zones. Although the individual fronts are moving, certain regions of the globe are noted for a high frequency of fronts. These are the regions of transition between the principal air-mass sources. The most prominent frontal regions of the Northern Hemisphere in winter are shown in Fig. 157.

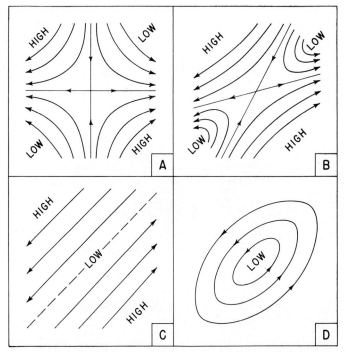

Fig. 156. Combinations of deformation and cyclonic rotation: (*a*) pure deformation; (*b*) deformation and weak rotation; (*c*) deformation and rotation of equal strength; (*d*) rotation stronger than deformation.

The principal frontal zone in the Atlantic region is the *Atlantic polar front*. The temperature contrast is provided by the difference in air-mass properties between the polar continental and the tropical maritime sources (regions 2 and 7 in Fig. 138), and the front tends to be maintained by the opposing currents indicated in Fig. 157.

The Atlantic polar front often extends itself eastward into Europe. It oscillates within wide limits, generally from the West Indies and Portugal in the south to the Great Lakes and Iceland in the north, but it always has a tendency to reestablish itself in the position indicated in

Fig. 157. Disturbances (cyclones) which form along this front account for most of the storms and precipitation over a wide belt from the eastern part of North America, through the North Atlantic, to the northwestern part of Europe.

Next in importance to the Atlantic polar front is the *Atlantic arctic front*. It forms on the border between the arctic source region (indicated by 1 in Fig. 138) and the milder region (3) of the polar maritime air.

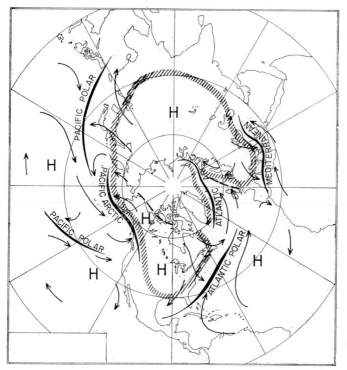

Fig. 157.   The principal frontal zones in winter. The hatched zones indicate the major air-mass contrasts. Arrows are skeletal indications of the winds.

Winter storms which form on this front move generally from Iceland along northern Norway to the Barents Sea; on occasions, such storms may continue eastward along the north coast of Siberia.

Third in importance and persistence is the *Mediterranean front*, which forms on the border between the European cold air and the milder air over the Mediterranean and North Africa. Some of the storms that develop here travel northeastward into southern Russia, while others travel eastward and give much-needed rain over the arid regions of the Near East and as far eastward as Pakistan and northwest India.

On the American side the *Pacific arctic front* often extends itself toward the Lake region, and many of the winter storms which occur between the Rocky Mountains and the Great Lakes develop on this front. In the rear of such storms arctic air may be brought as far south as Texas and northern Mexico. The cold wave shown in Fig. 13 is an extreme example of an outbreak of arctic air.

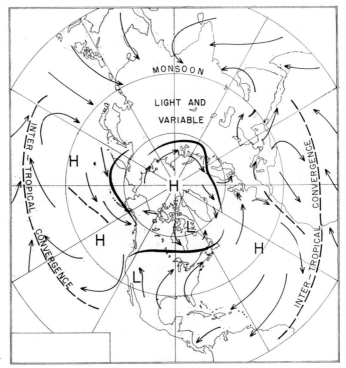

Fig. 158.   The principal frontal zones in summer.

On the North Pacific two high-pressure areas are often present, with the result that one often finds two *Pacific polar fronts*. Normally the one near the coast of Asia is the stronger one. The majority of the storms form along the coast of Asia and travel toward the Gulf of Alaska, but many of them visit the coast as far south as Southern California and the northwestern part of Mexico. These storms account for most of the winter rainfall along the Pacific coast of North America. Fronts from the Pacific which enter North America in winter tend to weaken as they cross the Rocky Mountains, but many of them redevelop to the east of the mountain range. Favorable areas for such redevelopments are the Alberta and the Colorado-Oklahoma regions, and fronts are frequently present there.

During the summer season, the air-mass contrasts are much weaker, and so are the circulation patterns that maintain them. On the whole, more or less permanent frontal zones are found only around the arctic region (see Fig. 158). On occasion cool air and fronts from the northern regions may sweep far southward. In particular, this is true on the Atlantic side. On the Pacific side, the subtropical high is very powerful, and a frontal passage in California is a rare event in summer.

14

Cyclones and Anticyclones

The word *cyclone* is used in meteorological writings to indicate a system of winds blowing around a center of low pressure, and it does not necessarily imply winds of exceptional violence, though such may be present on occasion. Similarly, the word *anticyclone* is used to indicate a system of winds blowing around a center of high pressure. These are the meanings that we shall use here. In India the word cyclone means a revolving storm of exceptional violence, or storms of the type called *hurricanes* in North America and *typhoons* in the Far East. These storms, which are generally called tropical cyclones, will be discussed in the following chapter. When necessary, we shall use the word *extratropical* to indicate that we are dealing with cyclones outside the equatorial belt.

The Cyclone Model. Throughout the history of weather forecasting the extratropical cyclones have received much attention because they are frequent and often bring strong winds and bad weather with them. Toward the end of the First World War, J. Bjerknes investigated the structure of a large number of young cyclones in northwestern Europe and found that their basic structures were essentially the same. This enabled him to construct the so-called "model cyclone," which is reproduced here as Fig. 159.

A remarkable feature is that the distribution of temperature, wind, and weather is discontinuous, rather than continuous, through the cyclones. Bjerknes found that a cyclone is normally made up of two different air masses. One of these is relatively warm and laden with moisture; it is an offshoot of air produced in a subtropical source region. The second is colder and has originated in some polar air-mass source. In the young cyclone, the warm air extends northward as a tongue between vast masses of cold air. The separation between the two air masses is normally sharp, and since it represents the southern border of the polar air masses, it was called the *polar front*. Along the front, the temperature and the wind change abruptly, and so does the weather.

The vertical structure of the model is of considerable interest. A cross section to the south of the low-pressure center is shown in the lower part of Fig. 159. The cold air forms a wedge of gentle slope under the

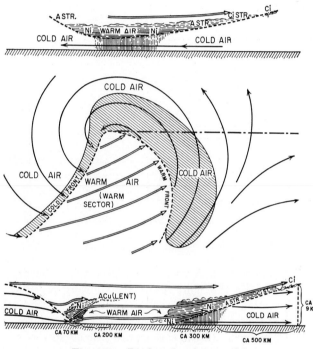

Fig. 159.   Bjerknes' cyclone model.

warm air. A similar section to the north of the sea-level center is shown in the upper portion of the figure. Here, the cold air forms a trough filled with warm air.

Air from the warm sector (see Fig. 159) streams up over the cold wedge and cools adiabatically while it ascends. This accounts for the extensive cloud system and area of precipitation in advance of the warm front at the ground. Likewise, in the rear of the cyclone, the cold air pushes in under the warm air and here, too, we find a belt of clouds and rain. The first approach of a cyclone of this type is indicated by fast-moving cirrus clouds (see Fig. 27), which change into cirrostratus (Fig. 28) and thicken into altostratus (Fig. 31) and nimbostratus with precipitation. As the warm front passes, the rain ends, and the warm sector is normally characterized by a low layer of clouds, sometimes accompanied by drizzle. As the cold front approaches, high clouds appear again and soon thicken into nimbostratus with rain or snow.

The precipitation associated with the cold front is often mixed with showers. A typical example of rainfall associated with the passage of a cyclone composed of moisture-laden air is shown in Fig. 160. We note the steady increase of the rain intensity until the warm front passes shortly after 5 A.M. Thereafter, there is a period of about 3 hr with small amounts of drizzle falling from low stratus and fog in the warm sector. Shortly

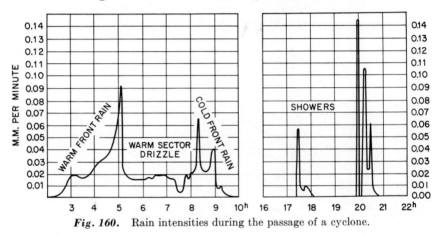

Fig. 160.   Rain intensities during the passage of a cyclone.

after 8 A.M. the cold front arrives with variable rain intensity. In comparison, the diagram on the right shows the showery precipitation that fell from cumulonimbus clouds in the deep cold air mass that followed in the rear of the cyclone. Here the precipitation is discontinuous, with large peaks and dry spells. In the case shown, the air in the warm sector had originated in Atlantic subtropical high and moved northeastward to the west coast of Norway (60° N). On its journey, the warm air had been cooled from below and become filled with low stratus. In the United States, warm-sector drizzle is rare except when warm air from the Gulf of Mexico invades the continent during the cold season.

Bjerknes' work was a major step toward a better understanding of the large-scale weather processes. In the first place, the model explains the broad aspects of the weather systems associated with extratropical cyclones. Secondly, the model shows cold and warm air arranged side by side, and this is equivalent to a difference in potential energy. Bjerknes visualized the kinetic energy of the storms to derive from the stored potential energy, and he suggested that the development of the storms was brought about by cold (and heavy) air pushing under warm (and

lighter) air, thus lowering the center of gravity of the whole system.
These ideas have proved most fruitful in practical as well as theoretical
meteorology.

It is of interest to note that Bjerknes' model was produced about
1918, before upper-air observations were available. Since the radiosonde
came into general use (about 1940) much additional knowledge has accumulated. Nevertheless, the basic aspects of the model have withstood
the passage of time.

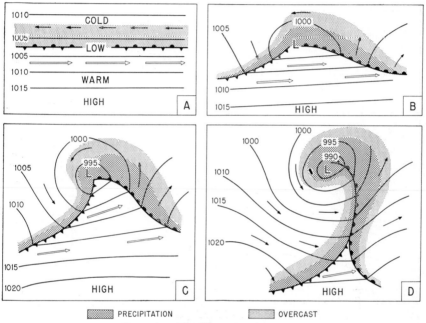

PRECIPITATION   OVERCAST

Fig. 161.   The life cycle of cyclones.

Life Cycle of Cyclones. Soon after the cyclone model came into
being, it was found that the cyclones (and the associated fronts and air
masses) undergo a typical life cycle, and these processes were clarified to a
considerable extent by T. Bergeron, J. Bjerknes, and H. Solberg.

The typical life cycle of a cyclone is shown in Fig. 161. In the initial
state (Fig. 161*a*) a warm and a cold air mass are present side by side, and
separated by a quasi-stationary front. Whether the currents are of the
same or of opposite direction makes no difference; what matters is the
presence of the shearing motion of the type shown. It will be seen that
the initial state resembles Fig. 156*c*. In the next stage (Fig. 161*b*) a wave
has formed on the front, and a center of low pressure is developing at the
apex of the wave. This is the *nascent cyclone,* and the process is commonly
called *cyclogenesis.*

The young and developing cyclone is shown in Fig. 161c. This corresponds to Bjerknes' model (Fig. 159). During the further development, the cold front overtakes the warm front (Fig. 161d); the system is said to *occlude*. As the occlusion process continues, the warm air is lifted to higher and higher levels. Thus, initially, cold and warm air are present side by side, while in the final stage, the colder (and heavier) air is situated under the warmer air. We see then that the center of gravity of the whole system

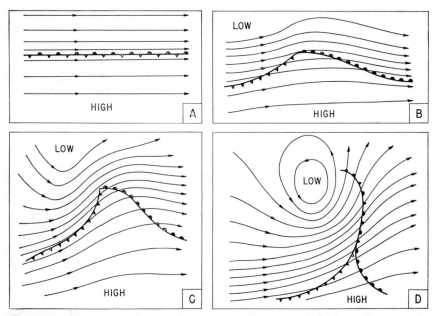

Fig. 162.   Sea-level fronts and the contours of an upper isobaric surface (say 500 mb) over a cyclone in various stages of development.

has lowered; potential energy has been set free, and this gives an important contribution to the kinetic energy as represented by the winds around the cyclone center.

The flow patterns aloft over a sea-level cyclone in the various stages of its development are shown in Fig. 162. To interpret these diagrams we must refer back to the discussion of the thermal wind (page 160) and the manner in which the upper and lower pressure configurations are related to the mean temperature of the air. In Fig. 162a the largest over-all temperature contrast is found in the border region between the cold and the warm air masses. In this zone, the thermal wind will be strong, and the wind at the upper level will be dominated by the thermal wind. The jet stream in the upper troposphere will be situated over this zone.

When the frontal wave forms (Fig. 162b) the current aloft begins to change, and as the sea-level cyclone grows (Fig. 162c), cold air is brought southward in the rear and warm air is brought northward in advance of the center. The flow aloft becomes wave-shaped, with a ridge in advance and a trough in the rear. As the cyclone occludes (Fig. 162*d*) the amplitude of the upper wave increases, and if the temperature contrast is large, an upper cold low forms in the rear of the sea-level low.

Although the models shown in Fig. 161 and 162 are somewhat idealized, they bring to light the essential structures of the various stages of the life cycle of an extratropical cyclone.

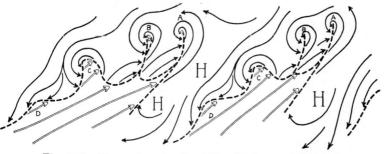

Fig. 163.   The cyclone family. (*After Bjerknes and Solberg.*)

The Cyclone Family. The early works of Bjerknes, Bergeron, and Solberg showed that an extratropical cyclone rarely appears alone. Most frequently, three or four such cyclones form a series, and this was called a *cyclone family.* The first or leading member of the family would be an old occluded cyclone; the next would be partly occluded, and the trailing member would be an incipient cyclone wave. The family can be represented by joining Fig. 161*a* to *d*, in reverse order, more or less as shown in Fig. 163. The leading cyclone would dissipate gradually while new ones form on the trailing front. As a result, the family as a whole would move more slowly than each member. On the whole, the first member would be in high latitudes, and each of the following members would take a more southerly path. In the rear of the last member, cold air from the polar and arctic source regions would stream far southward to the subtropics. Such invasion of polar and arctic air masses is called a *polar outbreak;* it brings up the rear of the cyclone family and builds up a major anticyclone. A typical example is shown in Fig. 164. Here the young low to the southeast of Newfoundland is the last member of a cyclone family on the Atlantic. In the rear of the family there is a strong outbreak of arctic and polar continental air, which is banked by a high over Canada. While the cyclone family moves northeastward, the high, or the polar-outbreak anticyclone, moves southeastward, thus maintaining the strong current of cold air. As the cold air moves over the Atlantic, it absorbs heat and moisture, and soon becomes transformed into a warm, humid, and unstable mass.

Cyclone families are frequent over the oceans. Over North America and Eurasia cyclone families are far less regular, but here, too, the tendency for cyclones to appear in series is distinctly noticeable.

The circulations associated with cyclones and anticyclones bring about a large-scale exchange of heat between low and high latitudes. A typical example is shown in Fig. 165. Here, the warm air that is about to invade the Great Lakes came from the Gulf of Mexico, and as the low

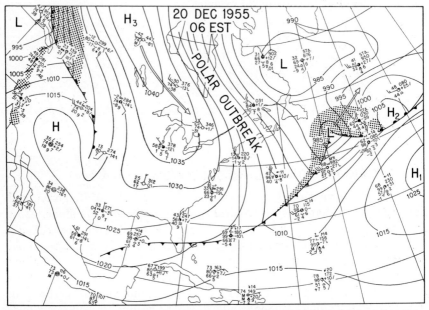

Fig. 164. The low to the southeast of Newfoundland is the last member of a cyclone family on the Atlantic. It is followed by a major outbreak of arctic and polar continental air. H_1 is the western extremity of the subtropical anticyclone. H_2 is a small high within the cyclone family, and H_3 is a polar-outbreak high.

moves northeastward, the warm air will spread over the southeastern part of Canada. At the same time, the very cold air in the rear of the low will push southward and replace the warm air over the western Gulf.

The exchange of heat and moisture is brought about not only by the individual cyclones and anticyclones, but also by the cyclone family as a whole. It will be seen from Fig. 163 that warm air from the subtropics moves northeastward and ascends in the occluding cyclones. In the process vast amounts of sensible heat are brought northward. At the same time, much of the latent heat supplied by evaporation in low latitudes is yielded up in condensation when the warm air ascends over the frontal surfaces. The counterpart to this northward transfer of heat is found in the rear of each cyclone and, more pronouncedly, in the rear of

the cyclone family as a whole. Here, vast masses of cold air from the
northern regions travel over a warmer surface and absorb much heat and
moisture. It is through these horizontal exchanges that the extreme temperature contrasts which radiation alone would produce (see Chap. 6)
become much reduced.

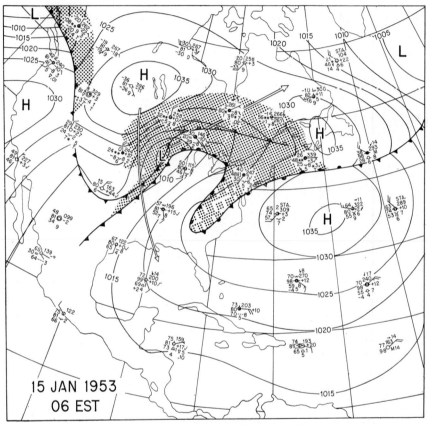

Fig. 165.   For explanation, see text.

Waves Aloft. The presence of cyclone families at low levels is
strongly reflected in the pressure distribution in the middle and upper
troposphere. On the general principles given in pages 160 to 163 we find
an upper cold trough in the rear of the cyclone family and an upper warm
ridge of high pressure over or to the east of the leading member of the
family. Such large-scale ridges and troughs are shown schematically in
Fig. 166. They reflect the circumstance that the polar outbreaks are made
up of deep layers of cold air, while the cyclone family as a whole is made
up of warmer air.

The wave-shaped pressure patterns aloft, as shown in Fig. 166, are called *long waves*. In the case shown there are four major troughs, extending from (1) Labrador toward Florida, (2) northern Scandinavia toward the Mediterranean, (3) central Siberia toward Burma, and (4) Alaska toward the central Pacific. These are the positions normally preferred. On individual occasions, the number of upper long waves may vary from three to six, but the atmosphere has a strong tendency to revert to a

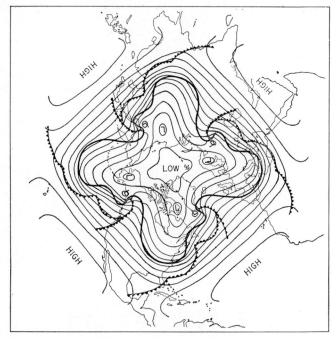

Fig. 166.   Schematic chart showing four cyclone families at sea level over four long waves aloft. (*After Palmén.*)

pattern with four major waves. Although somewhat simplified, Fig. 166 may be taken to represent the typical features of the circulation pattern aloft during the cold season.

The long waves aloft are often called *Rossby waves*, after Rossby, who first investigated their properties. Rossby found that the speed C of these waves could be represented by the formula

$$C = U - \frac{2\Omega \cos \varphi}{4\pi E} L^2$$

Here U is the mean zonal wind aloft, Ω is the angular velocity of the earth (page 150), φ is the latitude, E is the mean radius of the earth, and L is the length of the wave. From this formula, we see that the wave speed decreases with the square of the length. Very long waves are stationary or move very slowly. In general, we find that the long waves travel with a speed of about 2 to 5° longitude a day.

While the long waves reflect the over-all temperature difference between the front and rear of a cyclone family, each cyclone within the family has a short wave aloft associated with it, more or less as shown in Fig. 166. Since these waves are short, they travel fast. On the average, we find that the short waves move about 10 to 18° longitude a day. Referring back to the discussion in Chap. 11, we may say that the circulation aloft consists basically of a huge and stationary circumpolar vortex. Upon it is superimposed a system of slow-moving long waves, usually four in number. On top of these long waves travel faster short waves. If we examine the short waves in detail, we find that they carry smaller disturbances with them. We may remind ourselves of these superimpositions by quoting Jonathan Swift, through Augustus de Morgan: "Great fleas have little fleas upon their backs to bite 'em, And little fleas have lesser fleas, and so ad infinitum" and, also, L. F. Richardson's much later version: "Big whirls have little whirls that feed on their velocity, And little whirls have lesser whirls, and so on to viscosity."

Anticyclones. While the cyclones show a high degree of uniformity in their patterns of formation, growth, and decay, the anticyclones are far more irregular in behavior as well as in shape. Often the anticyclones appear as sluggish and passive systems which fill the spaces between the far more vigorous cyclonic systems. On occasion an anticyclone may undergo a distinct development and acquire appreciable intensity, but such developments are almost always associated with cyclone development in the neighboring regions. Considered as wind systems, the anticyclones never acquire intensities comparable with those of well-developed cyclones.

According to their structure, movement, and general behavior, the anticyclones may be divided into four classes.

1. *The Subtropical Highs.* These are large, elongated, and very deep anticyclones situated in the subtropics. They are so persistent that they stand out clearly in the mean pressure distribution for any month, season, or year, and they are rarely absent on any individual occasion. They are either stationary or move very slowly. The general structure of these anticyclones was discussed in connection with Figs. 123 and 124.

2. *The Polar Continental Highs.* These anticyclones are prominent over northern continents in winter. Being made up of cold air, they rarely make their influence felt above about 8,000 ft above sea level. The average structure of these anticyclones was discussed in connection with Figs. 123 and 124. In North America, the favored region for the initial development of such anticyclones is Alaska and western Canada to the

east of the Rocky Mountains. Most of these anticyclones move southeastward and then eastward toward the Atlantic Coast. As soon as they come over the warm waters of the Atlantic, they lose their identity and become absorbed in the subtropical anticyclone.

3. *Highs within the Cyclone Series.* Anticyclones with small horizontal extent are sometimes present between the individual members of the cyclone family. Often these highs are mere wedges of high pressure (see Fig. 165) which glide along the border of the much larger subtropical anticyclones. In most cases these wedges bring clearing weather with them.

4. *Polar-outbreak Highs.* The last member of a cyclone family, or any cyclone which acquires great intensity, will build up a rear which draws deep masses of cold air toward low latitudes. A case of this type was shown in Fig. 165. As the cold air pushes southward, the front dissolves; the cold air absorbs much heat from the warmer waters, and after two or three days the high has been transformed into a subtropical anticyclone.

It is useful to bear in mind that the individual cyclones and anticyclones are not made up of the same air at different times. They are pressure configurations through which the air moves.

The Geographical Distribution of Cyclones. If we examine the figures for various areas around the world, we shall find that there is a strong preference for cyclones to occur in the higher mid-latitudes. In the Southern Hemisphere, there is a sharp peak in the frequency at about 60° S, and there is little difference between summer and winter. In the Northern Hemisphere, there is a strong maximum in the frequency at 60° N in summer and about 50° N in winter. This seasonal shift of about 10° latitude is typical also of the migrations of the subtropical anticyclones and the equatorial convergence zone.

In the Southern Hemisphere, the belt of maximum cyclone frequency is continuous around the world. In the Northern Hemisphere, the zonal arrangement is much disturbed owing to the influences of continents and oceans. In Fig. 167 is shown the percentage frequency of cyclone centers in winter. To interpret these charts, it is necessary to bear in mind the manner in which the centers were counted. In the first place, a center was included in the count only if the pressure difference from the center to the rim of the cyclone exceeded 5 mb. Second, a center was included only if it maintained its identity for at least 24 hr. As a result of these requirements, weak and transient cyclones have been excluded. Third, the count was made once a day. The numbers in Fig. 167 give the percentage frequency within areas of 100,000 km², or about 40,000 sq miles.

On the Pacific side, we note a broad band of high cyclone activity extending from Southeast Asia to the Gulf of Alaska. Most of these cyclones form on the Pacific polar fronts shown in Fig. 157. During the cold season, these storms acquire great intensity. Most of them travel northeastward and accumulate in the Gulf of Alaska, and this accounts for the high frequency in this region. Some of the storms, and particularly those which form on the mid-Pacific polar front (Fig. 157), take a more southerly track and visit the coast as far south as Southern California.

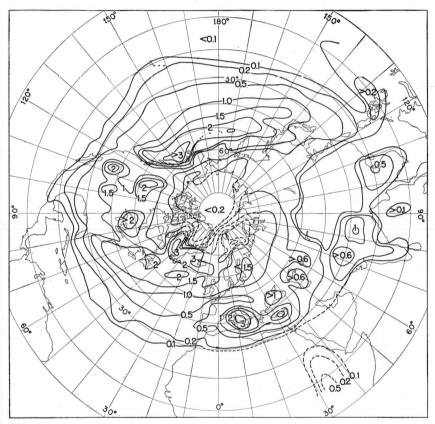

Fig. 167.   Percentage frequency of cyclone centers in winter.

Few of the Pacific cyclones are able to cross the Rocky Mountains, but many of them redevelop to the east of the mountain ranges. In fact, we may distinguish between three regions in which such redevelopments occur frequently.

First, we note the high frequency to the east of the Sierra Nevada. On the whole, these cyclones are weak. A second favored region is the one to the east of the Colorado Rockies; because of their place of origin they are often called *Colorado cyclones*. Many of these develop to great intensity and become dominant in the central and eastern part of the

United States. The favored direction of movement is northeastward toward the Great Lakes. The third region of high cyclone activity is to the east of the Canadian Rockies, and the storms that form here are often called *Alberta storms*. Many of these become strong, and while moving eastward, they bring much cold air southward over the Great Plains. In pronounced cases, cold waves and blizzards follow in their rears.

There is a fourth region of high frequency in North America during the winter, namely, that of the Great Lakes. This is a highly complex region. In the first place, many disturbances form here because the water is much warmer than the land. Second, the tracks of the Alberta and Colorado storms converge toward the Lakes. In addition, a few storms form over the Gulf of Mexico and move northward, with the result that the Lake region receives storms from many sources.

On the Atlantic side, the conditions are similar to those on the Pacific Ocean. Storms develop frequently on the Atlantic polar front (Fig. 157). The most favored region is the coast of Virginia and the general area to the east of the southern Appalachians. It is customary to speak of *Cape Hatteras storms*, or *east-coast storms*. These move more or less along the Gulf Stream, develop to great intensity, and tend to stagnate in the vicinity of Iceland or over the waters between Greenland and Labrador. Many cyclones form or redevelop on the Atlantic arctic front and move eastward to the Barents sea, as far east as Novaya Zemlya. Some of them continue along the entire coast of Siberia.

In Europe, we find a secondary maximum of cyclone frequency over the Baltic. Here open water is surrounded by cold land, and we encounter conditions similar to those over the Great Lakes. The effect of open water adjacent to colder land is clearly seen everywhere along the fringe of the arctic, and also in the Mediterranean region, where two pronounced maxima are present. Noteworthy also are the maxima of cyclone frequency over the Black Sea, the Caspian Sea, and the Aral Sea. Here, too, we find open water surrounded by cold land. Most of the Mediterranean cyclones form on the Mediterranean front (Fig. 157). Some of these travel northeastward into Russia, while others move, mostly as weak disturbances, across the Near East and give much-needed winter rain as far east as Pakistan and northern India. It is due to the action of these cyclones that the winter rainfall, typical of the Mediterranean climate, extends eastward toward the Himalayas.

The frequency of cyclones in summer is shown in Fig. 168. We now find an irregular belt with high frequency surrounding the arctic and a second belt over the warm continents in subtropical latitudes. While the northern belt is made up of cyclones with fronts and weather systems, the southern belt is entirely different. The large maximum over Southern California, Nevada, Arizona, and northern Mexico reflects the presence of a more or less permanent *heat low* over warm land. This is overlain by a high-level anticyclone with strong subsidence, and, as a result, clouds and weather are absent. The same is true of the heat lows over northern Africa and Arabia. The large frequency of lows over India and Southeast Asia reflects the presence of the summer monsoon (see page 187). Here rain is plentiful.

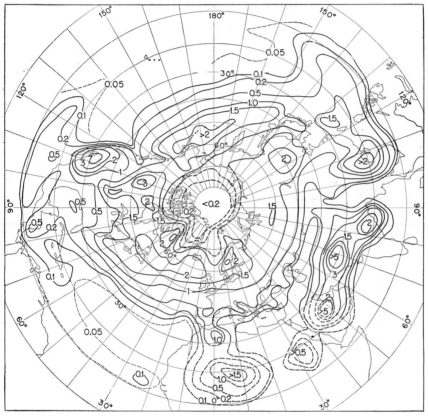

Fig. 168.   Percentage frequency of cyclone centers in summer.

Another interesting feature is the presence during the warm season of a belt of cyclones in low latitudes over the oceans. These are tropical disturbances or storms which travel from east to west on the border of the trade-wind belt. Some of these develop into tropical cyclones (hurricanes or typhoons), and we shall discuss them in the following chapter.

The Geographical Distribution of Anticyclones. The most prominent feature in winter (Fig. 169) is the belt of subtropical anticyclones over the oceans, with a maximum frequency off the subtropical west coasts. The dominance of anticyclones on the eastern part of the

North Pacific is impressive. Here, and to the west of Morocco, cyclonic systems are very rare.

Over North America, the frequency is very high over the broad plateau of the Rocky Mountains. The general area of Nevada, Utah, and Idaho has anticyclonic systems more frequently than any other region in the world. The frequency is relatively high from Alaska to the Great

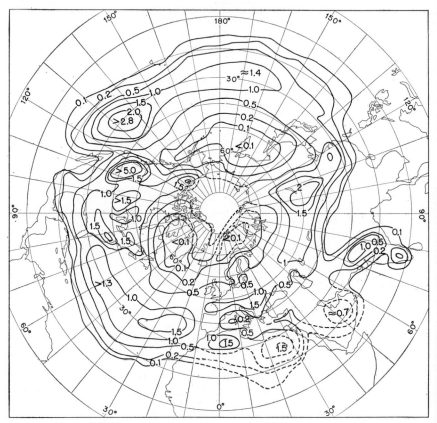

Fig. 169.   Percentage frequency of anticyclone centers in winter.

Plains. These are cold and shallow highs of the polar continental type. Noteworthy is the low frequency over the Great Lakes. As explained above, this region favors cyclone developments, and most of the anticyclones that move across the continent shun the Lakes. The frequency is high also near the Atlantic Coast. Most of these are polar continental highs which become stagnant as they approach the warm waters of the Atlantic.

On the Eurasian side, we find a belt of high frequency from western France to China, with a maximum in the Baikal region, which is the preferred place for the Siberian anticyclone. On the European side, too, we note the low frequency over inland water bodies surrounded by cold land, and over the bays on the fringe of the arctic fields of ice and snow.

During the warm season (Fig. 170) the belt of subtropical anti-cyclones is situated farther to the north than in winter. The frequency is

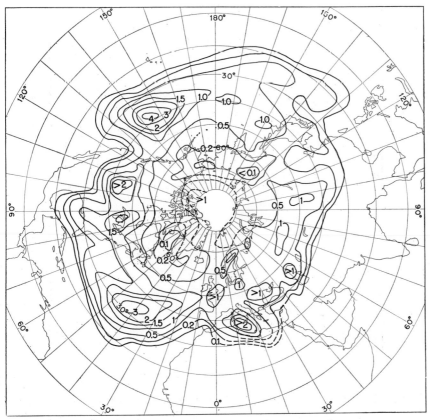

Fig. 170. Percentage frequency of anticyclone centers in summer.

very high over the eastern Pacific and low in the western part, where the summer monsoon is active.

Over North America, we find two maxima. The one over Kansas and Nebraska consists of a number of weak highs. Many of these drift east-ward and stagnate over the cool waters of the Great Lakes. Thus, the Lakes, which have a maximum of cyclone frequency in winter, have a maximum of anticyclone frequency in summer.

On the European side, we find, on the whole, maxima over inland water bodies, which, particularly in early summer, are cooler than the surrounding land masses.

Regimes of Cyclones and Anticyclones. It is of interest to compare the frequencies of cyclones and anticyclones, and a convenient way is to work out the rate of alternation. A measure of this rate can be obtained as follows. If C is the frequency of cyclones and A is the frequency of anticyclones, we say that C/A is the rate of alternation if A is greater

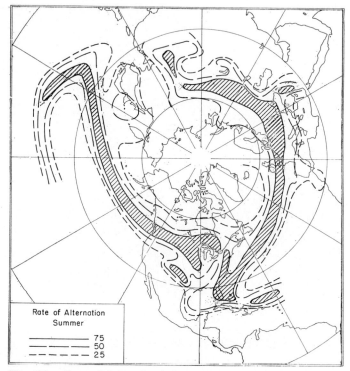

Fig. 171.   Rate of alternation in summer. For explanation, see text.

than C; if C is greater than A we take the ratio A/C. If the rate of alternation is unity (or 100 per cent) cyclones and anticyclones are equally frequent, and if the rate is less, one or the other predominates.

The rate of alternation in summer (June to August) is shown in Fig. 171. The most striking feature is a well-defined narrow lane of high rate of alternation on the Pacific Ocean, beginning in the equatorial belt to the southeast of Guam, extending first northwestward, then recurving between 20 and 25° N, and continuing across the Pacific into North America. On the Atlantic side, the conditions are essentially the same. On both oceans, the southern branch of the lane reflects tropical disturbances and storms which move northwestward and recurve northward around the western part of the subtropical anticyclones. In the mid-latitudes the lanes reflect traveling anticyclones and cyclones of the extratropical type.

The conditions in winter (December to February) are shown in Fig. 172. The tropical branches are now almost absent. Instead, there are two polar branches, indicating disturbances coming out of the continents and joining with the chain of cyclones and anticyclones over the oceans. A new feature is a lane with high rate of alternation over the Mediterranean,

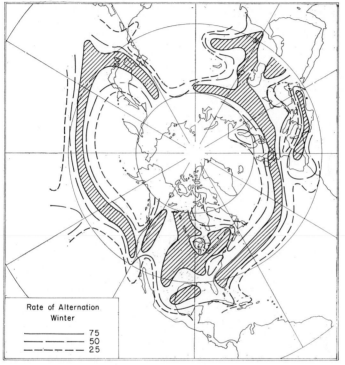

Fig. 172. Rate of alternation in winter. For explanation, see text.

reflecting disturbances that form on the Mediterranean frontal zone shown in Fig. 157.

The lanes shown on these charts represent the dividing zones between regimes which are predominantly cyclonic or anticyclonic. On the poleward side, cyclones are frequent and rain is plentiful, except in the lee of mountain ranges. On the equatorial side, anticyclonic systems predominate, and here rain is sparse. On the whole, the frequency of cyclones and anticyclones and the regularity with which they occur have a marked influence on what we call the climate.

15

Tropical Disturbances, Storms, and Hurricanes

The vast area occupied by the intertropical belt has weather regimes which differ essentially from those of the mid- and high-altitude zones. Distinct air masses and cyclones with fronts are hardly ever present. The air is generally unstable and laden with moisture; much of the rain falls as showers and thunderstorms are frequent, particularly over land. Traveling wind systems are present, but most of these are small and weak as compared with their counterparts in the mid-latitudes. However, once in a while, a devastating revolving storm develops. In the days of sailing ships, the tropical mariner had two main dreads: the calm of the doldrums and the fury of the hurricanes. We may remind ourselves of the former by quoting Coleridge:

> Day after day, day after day,
> We stuck, nor breath nor motion,
> As idle as a painted ship
> Upon a painted ocean.

The secrets of the hurricanes have been difficult to unravel, for they form and live out most of their lives over oceans and are better avoided by ships. From Chesterton:

> I tell you naught for your comfort,
> Yea, naught for your desire,
> Save that the sky grows darker yet
> And the sea rises higher.

No one who has heard the winds and the waves of a hurricane hammering at a ship or a home is likely soon to forget.

A Classification. To obtain a first glance at a fully developed hurricane, we may look at Fig. 173. This is a rather rare case of a storm at the peak of its strength situated over land; it is also a storm of unusual intensity. From the inset barogram, we see that the pressure at Miami dropped about 75 mb, and the drop was somewhat larger along the path of the storm. Since the atmospheric pressure is very nearly equal to the

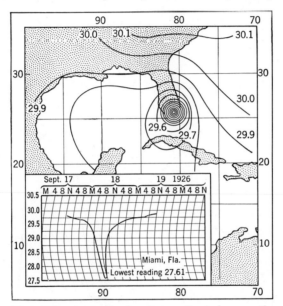

Fig. 173. A strong hurricane situated over the southern tip of Florida. The inset barogram shows the pressure trace as the hurricane passed Miami. Pressure is here given in inches of mercury. (*After Trewartha.*)

weight of the air column, we find that the total pressure drop was equivalent to a removal of 2,000,000 tons of air/sq mile. It is evident that tremendous forces are involved.

Another interesting case is shown in Fig. 174. This is the time of the year when the monsoon is beginning to recede. It will be seen that the typhoon to the north of the Philippines draws in air from Asia, from the southwest monsoon, and from the broad belt of tropical easterlies. The details of the outside currents are of some importance. In the first place, we note some minor waves superimposed upon the easterly current. These are called *easterly waves.* Second, we note lines along which the wind shifts abruptly, and these are called *shear lines.* Third, in the middle part

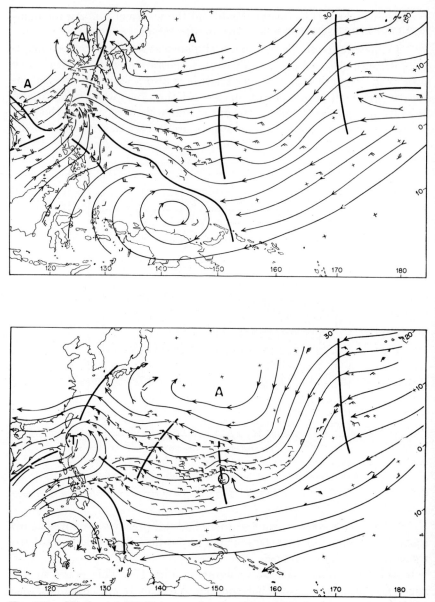

Fig. 174. Winds at 1,000 ft (upper chart) and at 10,000 ft above sea level (lower chart). A typhoon is situated southeast of Formosa. In the broad easterly current across the Pacific are several minor waves and an indication of a closed low. (*After Riehl.*)

of the lower chart, we observe a small *low* which is about to form in connection with a wave trough. These minor disturbances are important, partly because much bad weather is associated with them and partly because tropical storms of great intensity may develop from them.

On account of the great variety of intensities, tropical disturbances and storms have been classified as indicated below. The reader should, however, bear in mind that there are no sharp dividing lines and that a strong disturbance may develop from a weaker one. Nevertheless, the classification is useful for easy reference and particularly for public information.

1. *Easterly Waves.* These are wave-shaped streamlines superimposed upon the easterly winds in the trade-wind belt. The distinguishing feature is that there is a trough of low pressure poking northward into the isobars of the trade winds, but no definite center of low pressure.

2. *Tropical Depression.* This is a center of low pressure around which the winds are generally less than 25 mph. Such lows are quite frequent near the intertropical convergence zone and less frequent in the trade-wind belt. Many of these lows live out their lives as minor disturbances, but some develop into major storms.

3. *Tropical Storm.* This is a definite low-pressure center surrounded by winds in the range from 25 to 75 mph.

4. *Hurricane.* This is an intense low-pressure center surrounded by winds in excess of 75 mph. Violent storms of this type are called *cyclones* in India, *typhoons* in the Far East, *baguios* in the Philippines, and *willy-willies* in Australia. For convenience, we shall refer to them as *hurricanes*, which is the name used in North America and the Caribbean islands.

Easterly Waves. In Fig. 175, the sequence of the winds up to 20,000 ft and the clouds and weather associated with the passage of an easterly wave are shown. To begin with (on the left), the winds are more or less uniform from the east-northeast and the sky is fair with scattered flat or modest cumulus clouds. The trade-wind inversion is low, with moist air under it and dry subsided air aloft.

While the wave trough advances, the winds above the surface layer swing to a more northerly direction; the inversion rises sharply and the clouds grow in depth. As the wave trough passes, showers develop, often with scattered thunderstorms. The showery and squally weather continues for some time, but as the wave progresses westward the trade-wind inversion lowers and the sky becomes fair again.

The easterly wave may be translated into sea-level isobars as shown in Fig. 176. To the north we find a dominant subtropical anticyclone, and to the south we have the equatorial trough of low pressure. In the air that moves northward, to the east of the trough line, there is horizontal convergence. This results in upward motion and bodily lifting of the air (see

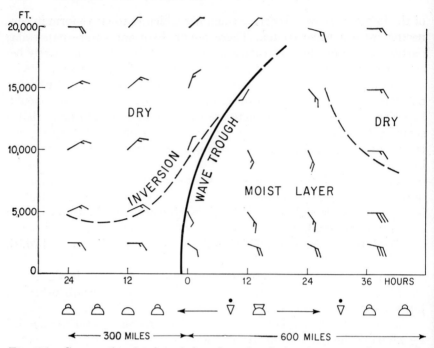

Fig. 175.   Cross section showing winds and weather during the passage of an easterly wave.

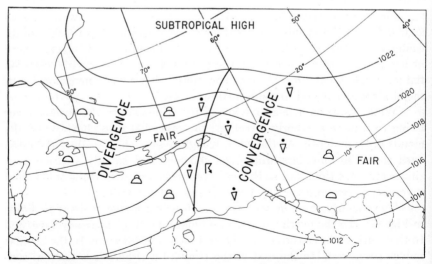

Fig. 176.   Sea-level isobars and weather associated with an easterly wave.

page 111); the inversion rises and weakens, the lapse rate steepens, and the moist layer becomes deep. It is here that we find the deep cumulus clouds and the showery precipitation.

In the air that has passed through the trough, there is divergence and subsiding motion; the inversion re-forms and lowers, and the moist layer becomes shallow.

Easterly waves are frequent, particularly during the northern summer, throughout the trade-wind belt, broadly as indicated in Fig. 177. In the Asiatic sector, the wind systems are controlled by the monsoons, and here we often find disturbances in the form of centers of low pressure superimposed upon the prevailing winds.

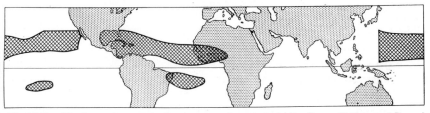

Fig. 177. Regions where easterly waves are frequent. (*After Berry, Bolley, and Beers.*)

A weak low-pressure center is often present at the equatorial end of the trough of an easterly wave. On occasions, such a center may develop into a tropical depression, storm, or hurricane.

Tropical Depressions and Storms. Tropical disturbances and depressions are very common throughout the humid low latitudes, but most of them are rather inconspicuous when considered as pressure configurations. The wind systems are poorly developed and the velocities are usually light. The movement of such weak lows is often erratic, and sometimes they hover in one place for several days.

The importance of these lows lies mainly in the circumstance that they produce much rainfall. While scattered showers are frequent in the tropics, there has been a tendency to overestimate their importance as producers of great amounts of rain. Much of the rainfall in the wet zone that straddles the equator comes from relatively weak lows. It is unfortunate that the network of observing stations over the tropical oceans is so sparse that many of these lows escape detection.

Some of these lows develop intensities which entitle them to the rank of storms. In particular, this is true in the warm season. A favored region for the development of such lows and storms is the Bay of Bengal. Here, low-pressure centers of appreciable intensity often form in the monsoon trough (see Fig. 134) and move north and northwestward into India. Others form over the Arabian Sea and move northward. A considerable portion of the monsoon rainfall comes from these superimposed systems.

Tropical depressions and storms are frequent in the general vicinity of the Philippines, and these drift in the eastern branch of the summer monsoon to the north and northwest. Similar lows and storms are found also in the West Indies, and they drift northwestward toward the Gulf of Mexico or the Atlantic Coast. Such lows and storms are a constant source of worry to the forecasters whose function it is to issue hurricane warnings, for observations are sparse over the oceans and the signs are not always clear.

During the cold season, the polar front may be displaced far to the south, particularly in the regions to the south of the east coasts of North America and Asia. During this season, one sometimes finds cyclones with fronts over the Southwest Pacific and in the West Indies as far south as 15° N. But the winter storms in these low latitudes are rarely strong. The violent storms, known as hurricanes or typhoons, occur mostly in the warmer part of the year when fronts are absent in low latitudes.

Life Cycle of Hurricanes. Captains of sailing ships in the tropics were constantly watching the changes in the wind, the clouds, and the swell in order to locate minor disturbances, for they knew that devasting storms could flare up out of humble beginnings. Later researches, notably by T. Bergeron, G. E. Dunn, E. Palmén, C. E. Palmer, and H. Riehl, have shown that what we call a hurricane always develops out of a pre-existing disturbance, such as an easterly wave, a shear line, or a tropical depression. The initial development is usually highly localized, so that the beginning hurricane occupies only a small portion of the mother system. Both sailors and scientists agree that the life cycle of a hurricane can be divided into four stages.

1. *The Beginning.* The origin of a hurricane can be traced back to a diffuse and fairly large area of low pressure, sometimes connected with a wave trough or a shear line. The winds around the low-pressure area are modest; cumulus clouds and showers are numerous, but there is no organized system of clouds and weather. Such low-pressure areas may be present for several days before the development commences, and often none takes place.

On occasion, one observes that the winds begin to strengthen around the center. The increase is strongest to the right of the direction in which the center is moving, that is, normally on the poleward side of the center. The central pressure is above 1,000 mb; the winds over a limited area are moderate to strong but below hurricane force. The clouds begin to organize themselves into a coherent system, and dense cirrus begin to drift forward, broadly in the direction of the movement of the center. At the same time, swell begins to form and spread out from the storm.

2. *The Growth.* Some incipient cyclones die out before they acquire maturity, and others travel long distances without much growth. During

such periods, the sailors and the meteorologists watch anxiously, for a sudden development is always possible. When it starts, the pressure falls rapidly over a small and almost circular area; winds of hurricane force form a tight band around the center; the radius of this band is only 20 to 40 miles. The clouds are now well organized and show a strong spiraling structure, more or less as shown in Fig. 178. In this stage, the hurricane acquires an *eye.* This is a small and almost circular area coinciding with

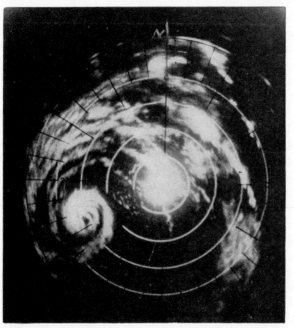

Fig. 178. Showing inward spiraling clouds in a hurricane. (*Courtesy Dr. P. M. Austin and U.S. Weather Bureau.*)

the area of lowest pressure. Here the winds are light and variable, clouds are absent or scattered, and the sea shows a confused pattern of crossing waves.

3. *The Mature Stage.* The central pressure has stopped falling, and the maximum winds are no longer increasing. Instead, the storm area expands horizontally and vast masses of air are drawn into the whirl. While the storm expands to a radius of 200 miles or more, its symmetry becomes less pronounced, for the area of strong winds and bad weather build out to the right of the direction in which the storm is moving.

4. *The Decaying Stage.* In their developing and mature stages, most storms move westward and away from the equator. The majority of them decay when they come over land or when they recurve northward over

oceans. Even after the winds have become weak, heavy rain may continue. On occasion a tropical storm which enters the mid-latitude belt may redevelop and become an intense cyclone resembling the extratropical variety.

Weather, Winds, and Waves. The weather that accompanies a hurricane can best be described as torrential rainfall from heavy clouds. Rainfall is absent or light in the center (the eye) of the storm, and it is very heavy in the inner part of the ring of strong winds. Rainfalls of 6 to 10 in. in 24 hr are common. On or near slopes of hills and mountains, much larger values have been recorded. In Baguio, in the Philippines, a typhoon gave 6 ft 4 in. of rain in 24 hr, and at Silver Hill, Jamaica, more than 8 ft fell in 4 days.

The amount of rainfall that is observed at any station depends greatly on the speed with which the storm moves by, and this accounts for much of the variation in the observed amounts. A slowly moving storm will pile up much rain, while a fast-moving one will give relatively small amounts.

The names hurricane and typhoon are well chosen, for in Carib and Chinese they signify *big wind*. As a matter of classification, the lower limit of hurricane winds is put at 75 mph; however, little is known about the strongest winds that may occur. The reason is that few anemometers survive the passage of a strong hurricane. Good estimates indicate that winds well over 200 mph have occurred.

Hurricanes in the growing and mature stages may exist for several days. Because of their long life and large dimensions, they are far more destructive than tornadoes and other severe storms. Much of the damage is due to wind pressure on structures. In coastal regions (and few hurricanes go far inland) most damage is caused by inundations. It has been estimated that about three-fourths of all loss of human lives in tropical storms has been caused by flooding and by the hammering of the waves that accompany the storms.

The inundation by sea water is of two kinds. In the first place, wind-driven currents pile up water along the coast. This effect is strongest where there are bays or concave coast lines which prevent the piled-up water from escaping. This accumulation of water may begin while the center of the storm is far out at sea (200 to 500 miles), and the total rise may exceed 10 ft. The second contribution to the inundation is due to a rise in the sea level near the center of the storm, and this rise may amount to 15 or 20 ft. The most devastating floods occur when both causes combine. In addition to inundations by sea water, we have the effect of the rainfall.

On top of the general rise of the sea level caused by hurricanes, we have the swell generated by the winds. In extreme cases, such swell waves may be 40 ft high. The wind energy concentrated in the hurricane causes a system of swell waves to spread out of the storm area, more or less as shown in Fig. 179.

The swell moves with a speed (somewhat less than 1,000 miles/day) which is three or four times greater than the speed of the storm center. Now, the swell generated in the rear right quadrant will move forward in the direction of the movement of the storm. These waves will be under

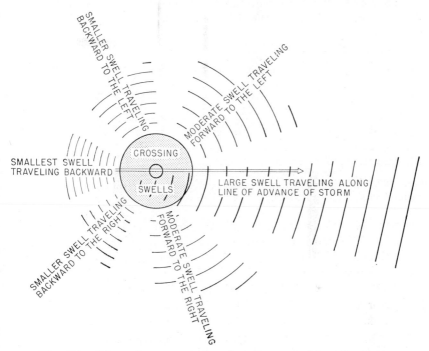

Fig. 179. Schematic representation of swell generated by a hurricane.

the influence of the strong winds for a long time, and we say that the *fetch* is large. To the left of the storm track, the waves are under the influence of the wind for a relatively short time, and we say that the fetch is small. The energy that goes into the swell increases with the fetch, with the result that the swell generated on the right of the storm becomes prominent. This swell travels a long way; it may be observed as far as 1,000 miles away from the storm center, and this provides a warning. The direction from which the swell arrives points toward the place where the swell was generated. The warning is, however, not very precise, for it provides no information on the behavior of the storm since the swell left it. Nevertheless, the arrival of the swell is a useful early alert to the man on the bridge, the harbor master, and the beach dweller.

On top of the smooth swell, we have the wind waves churned up by the hurricane. These are short, sharp, and fierce waves which, when added to the swell, cause extreme roughness. A ship caught in a hurricane is worn down by the action of the sea rather than by the direct action of the wind.

Origins and Tracks. In Fig. 180 are shown the main regions where hurricanes occur and the average, or generalized, tracks they follow.

In the first place, we note that the hurricanes avoid the belt close to the equator. This is due to the circumstance that there is no Coriolis force

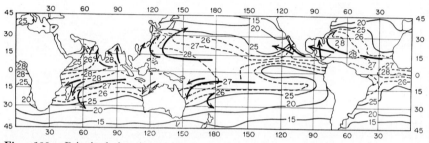

Fig. 180. Principal hurricane tracks and sea-surface temperatures during the warmest season. (*After Palmén.*)

(see page 149) at the equator, and some such force is needed to work up the spin of the motion around the low-pressure center. Without such a force, the air would be accelerated toward the center of low pressure and the center would fill up.

Second, we note that the hurricanes begin over oceans with temperatures over about 27°C (about 80°F). It is now recognized that such high surface temperatures are necessary to produce a steep lapse rate through a major part of the troposphere, and a steep lapse rate is necessary to maintain the vertical circulation in a hurricane.

Third, we note that all hurricanes begin at sea, and there is a strong tendency for them to dissipate over land. The reason is thought to be as follows. Over land, the rain cools the surface and produces a stable lapse rate in the lowest layer. At sea, such cooling is insignificant because the rain is churned into the sea water which, because of its very high conductive capacity (see page 95), supplies heat in generous amounts to the air.

Most hurricanes form in the belts between 8 and 15° from the equator, for the Coriolis force is here sufficiently strong to cause the winds to spin around the center of low pressure. Within these zones, the preferred regions are the ocean areas where the sea-surface temperature is high.

Although these conditions are necessary, they are by no means sufficient to produce a hurricane. On the whole, hurricanes are rare phenomena which develop out of a preexisting disturbance only when some

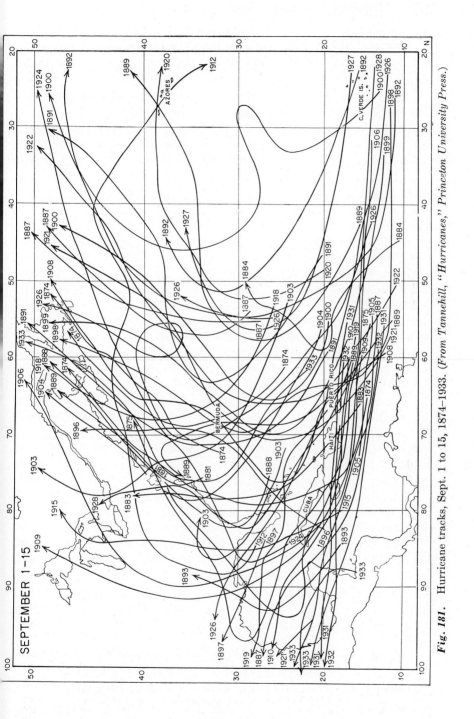

SEPTEMBER 1-15

Fig. 181. Hurricane tracks, Sept. 1 to 15, 1874–1933. *(From Tannehill, "Hurricanes," Princeton University Press.)*

triggering mechanism is present and sufficient to set up a vertical circulation through a major part of the troposphere. It is likely that the triggering mechanism must be sought in the upper troposphere, but little is known about these processes.

On the whole, the beginning hurricanes move westward, develop, and recurve northward (Fig. 180). In particular, this is true where the subtropical anticyclones are well developed. Over the north Indian Ocean, the storms are superimposed upon the summer monsoon, and a northward motion is prominent. In individual cases, the tracks may be irregular, showing loops or bends. The tracks of West Indian hurricanes at the height of the season are shown in Fig. 181. Those which move westward, into Texas and Mexico, soon disintegrate. On the other hand, those which recurve northward show a greater ability to survive. Some of these are caught in extratropical disturbances and redevelop into large storms.

Hurricane Seasons. Over the years, many data on the number of storms in various regions have accumulated. The counts are not uniform, and it has often been difficult to determine whether or not a storm qualified as a hurricane in the meaning given on page 239. However, the data given in Table 13 should be broadly representative of the frequencies if we are prepared to accept some borderline cases.

On the North American side, we find high frequencies from August to October, and the period December to May is free of hurricanes. In the Far East, hurricanes (typhoons) may occur in any month, but there is a strong preference for late summer and early autumn. The annual variation on the north Indian Ocean is more complex. The hurricane (cyclone) season may be said to begin with the approach of the summer monsoon, and a first maximum is reached in late June or early July. During the height of the monsoon, the frequency is relatively low, but it increases again when the winter monsoon takes over.

The data for the Southern Hemisphere are rather meager, but it is clear that the largest number of hurricanes occur in late summer and early autumn.

The South Atlantic stands out as the only ocean which is spared the ordeal of hurricanes. Referring back to Fig. 180, we see that the sea-surface temperature is rather low in latitudes suitable for the generation of hurricanes. Noteworthy also is the fact that the intertropical convergence zone (see Fig. 133) remains to the north of the equator throughout the year. As a result, tropical lows (from which hurricanes could form) are rarely found over this ocean.

Hurricane Warnings. The damage wrought even by a single hurricane is very large, and not all of it can be measured in terms of dollars. For example, the famous hurricane which struck New England in September, 1938, was responsible for nearly 400 million dollars' worth of property

Table 13. Average Number of Tropical Cyclones of Hurricane or Near-hurricane Strength

Regions (see Fig. 180)	Jan.	Feb.	Mar.	Apr.	May	June	July	Aug.	Sept.	Oct.	Nov.	Dec.	Year
North Atlantic	0	0	0	0	0.1	0.4	0.6	1.6	2.4	1.8	0.4	0	7.3
West of Mexico	0	0	0	0	0.1	0.2	0.7	1.0	1.9	1.0	0.1	0	5.7
Western North Pacific	0.4	0.2	0.3	0.4	0.7	1.0	3.2	4.2	4.6	3.2	1.7	1.2	21.1
Bay of Bengal	0.1	0	0.2	0.2	0.5	0.6	0.8	0.6	0.7	0.9	1.0	0.4	6.0
Arabian Sea	0.1	0	0	0.1	0.2	0.3	0.1	0	0.1	0.2	0.3	0.1	1.5
Madagascar, etc.	1.3	1.7	1.2	0.6	0.2	0	0	0	0	0.1	0.2	0.8	6.1
Northwest Australia	0.3	0.2	0.2	0.1	0	0	0	0	0	0	0	0.1	0.9
South Atlantic	0	0	0	0	0	0	0	0	0	0	0	0	0
South Pacific						Highest frequency, December to March							

damage. All told, more than 2,000 boats and nearly 14,000 dwellings were either destroyed or severely damaged. Worse still, it claimed the lives of more than 500 persons and injured another 1,750.

Science knows no technique which can be used to prevent, direct, or modify storms of such immensity. All that can be done is to predict their arrival and take precautions against avoidable losses. Special hurricane-warning services are now established in many parts of the world. Ships and island stations send in reports several times a day; where possible, radiosonde balloons are sent up to measure the conditions aloft, and aircraft equipped with radar and other instruments patrol the critical ocean areas. In this manner, the brewing storms are identified in the early stages of their development. Once a potential storm has been located, aircraft reconnaissance keeps track of its movement and reports its growth. The movement of a hurricane depends greatly on the large-scale pressure systems in distant regions, and much work goes into the charting of their behavior. As a result of all this, the public receives early general alerts as well as short-range and detailed specific warnings, which enable those concerned to take possible precautions.

By any standard, the hurricane-warning service can claim spectacular success. For example, during the 5-year period 1926–1930, there were 161 hurricane fatalities for each 10 million dollars of property damage in the United States. The corresponding figure for 1931–1935 was 81; for 1936–1940, 26; and for 1941–1945, it was 4.

We cannot hope to eliminate loss of life altogether, for effective precautions are not always possible. For example, hurricane Audrey, which struck the coast of Louisiana in June, 1957, took more than 500 lives, mainly because precautions were difficult to take by the poorly developed communities on the low and marshy lands of Cameron County. Nor can we hope to eliminate damage to property, but even in this area, progress is noteworthy. Millions and millions of dollars have been saved by preparing for the arrival of storms by removing ships and evacuating aircraft and other expensive equipment from the threatened areas. While a hurricane is a rare event, the watch and worry are continuous, and no system of bookkeeping is able to show the reduction of deaths, destruction, and hardship which results from our hurricane-warning service. Though exact figures are hard to come by, the hurricane forecaster would seem to be entitled to go over the quotation on page 236 and replace "naught" by "a good deal," and "save that" by "approximately when."

16

Temperature Regimes

The general principles that govern the sharing of heat between the earth and the atmosphere were discussed in Chap. 6. It was shown there that the mobility of the ocean waters and of the atmosphere is a factor of primary importance. In discussing the distribution of temperature over the face of the earth, we must pay particular attention to the horizontal motions, for it is through them that the maritime influences are carried far into the continents. In the atmosphere the horizontal exchanges are brought about partly by the mean air currents, which were discussed in Chap. 11, and partly by the traveling cyclones and anticyclones, which were discussed in Chap. 14. In the oceans traveling disturbances are of little importance, and it suffices to consider the mean ocean currents.

The Influence of Ocean Currents. The essential features of the ocean currents are shown in Fig. 182. Near the equator the sea-surface temperature is so uniform[1] that the ocean currents bring about very little exchange of heat. The largest contrasts are found in mid- and high latitudes.

On the North Atlantic a dominating feature is the Gulf Stream and its extension toward the Norwegian Sea and the Barents Sea. Here, vast masses of warm water are transported from low to high latitudes, and this reduces the meridional temperature contrast that otherwise would exist.

The density of sea water depends upon the temperature and the salinity. Although the Atlantic water is warmer than the melt water near the polar ice, its salinity is so high that it is heavier than the water that it

[1] The sea-surface temperatures in winter and summer were shown in Figs. 137 and 142.

encounters near the ice edge. As a result, the Atlantic current ducks under the icy water and supplies the polar basin with vast amounts of heat. Much of this heat is conducted through the ice (see page 102), and as a result, the winter temperatures over the polar ice fields are not excessively low.

The counterpart to the warm Atlantic current is the so-called Labrador Current, which transports cold water of low salt content out of the arctic. It starts in the Arctic Ocean and extends southwestward to the Grand Bank and the New England coast, and it makes its influence felt

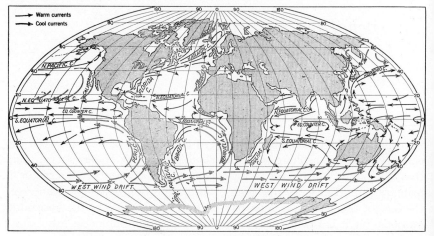

Fig. 182. The main ocean currents of the world. (*After Schott.*)

as far south as the coasts of the Carolinas. In late spring and early summer icebergs are plentiful as far south as the Grand Bank.

It will be seen from Fig. 182 that the Atlantic current has an equatorward branch along the west coast of Portugal and Morocco. Particularly during the warmer part of the year, when the prevailing winds are from the north, the upwelling of cold water along these coasts creates a strong temperature contrast between the coastal waters and the adjacent land areas.

On the North Pacific Ocean the current system is essentially the same as on the North Atlantic. In particular, we note the North Pacific, or Japan, Current (also called the Kuroshio), which brings much warm water toward the Gulf of Alaska; the cold polar current (the Oyashio) along the east coast of Asia; and the cool California Current.

In the Southern Hemisphere the cold polar current is mainly from west to east, but distinct branches are found along the west coasts of South Africa and South America. In the Northern Hemisphere, where the land masses extend into high latitudes, the effect of ocean currents may be summarized as shown in Fig. 183. To the north of about 40° N we find cold east coasts and mild west coasts. In particular, this is true in winter. On the other hand, to the south of about 35° N we find warm east coasts and cool west coasts, and here the difference is most pronounced in summer.

The Mean Sea-level Temperature. The long-term mean temperatures for January and July are shown in Figs. 184 and 185. As explained in Chaps. 1 and 5 the temperature of the air varies with elevation, such that a mountain station will normally have a lower temperature than a

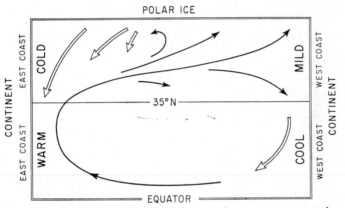

Fig. 183. A sketch showing the influence of ocean currents on the temperature along east and west coasts in the Northern Hemisphere.

station situated in the lowlands. If we were to map the temperature distribution along the earth's surface, the charts would be exceedingly complex. To eliminate the complexities due to the elevation of the terrain, the temperatures shown here have been reduced to sea level, using appropriate lapse rates. As a result of this reduction the long-term mean temperature at any given place may differ somewhat from the reduced temperature, but the reduction to a common level is convenient for describing the broad features of the world-wide temperature distribution.

In January (Fig. 184) the temperature is uniformly high (a little over 80°F) near the equator. On the whole, the temperature decreases toward the poles, showing that the meridional variation of the net radiation (see Chap. 6) is a dominating factor.

The influences due to the distribution of oceans and continents are clearly indicated. These differences are quite small in low latitudes and very large in high latitudes. For example, the 70°F isotherm runs fairly smoothly around the world, broadly along the 20th parallel. On the other hand, the freezing isotherm (32°F) dips down to about 35° N in east Asia, to about 40° N in North America, and rises to almost 70° N along the coast of Norway.

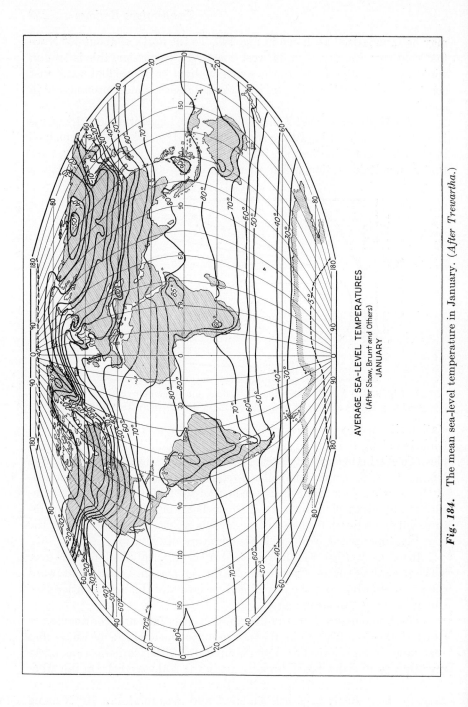

AVERAGE SEA-LEVEL TEMPERATURES
(After Shaw, Brunt and Others)
JANUARY

Fig. 184. The mean sea-level temperature in January. (*After Trewartha.*)

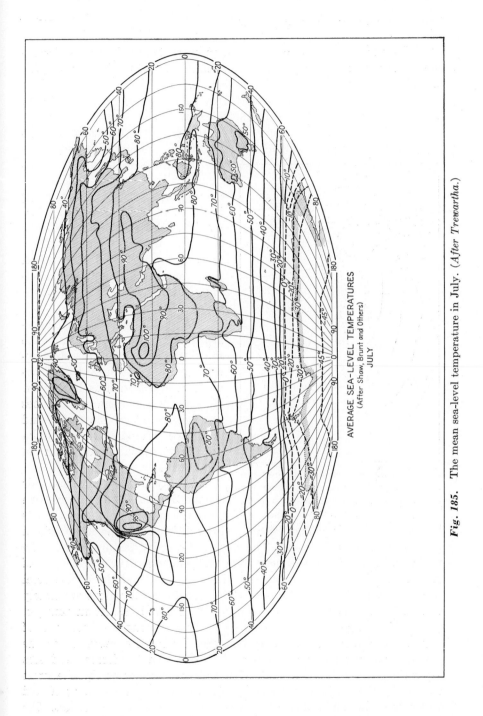

AVERAGE SEA-LEVEL TEMPERATURES
(After Shaw, Brunt and Others)
JULY

Fig. 185. The mean sea-level temperature in July. (*After Trewartha.*)

The effects of warm and cold ocean currents are also large. For example, the mean January temperature in Scotland is a little over 40°F, while in the same latitude on the coast of Labrador it is −10°F. The northward displacement of the isotherms is largest in the Atlantic region, where the warm ocean current penetrates far into the arctic.

The influences of the prevailing winds and of the traveling cyclones and anticyclones are also evident. For example, in Western Europe, where

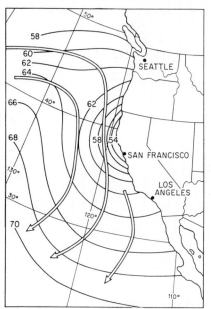

the prevailing winds are from the ocean and where the traveling cyclones move eastward, the freezing isotherm is found far inland, while on the American side, in the same latitude band, it is found well off the east coast. In this latter region the prevailing winds and the traveling disturbances bring cold continental air eastward.

On the Pacific side the temperature distribution is essentially the same as in the Atlantic sector, except that the northward displacement of the isotherms is smaller. Here the warm ocean current does not penetrate into the arctic, and the winter temperatures in Alaska are very much lower than in Scandinavia.

Fig. 186. Mean sea-surface temperature and predominant wind along the west coast of North America in August. The persistent north winds cause upwelling of cold water along the coast.

In July (Fig. 185) the ice fields around the North Pole have warmed up to the melting point, and there is little difference between oceans and continents in high latitudes. The most noteworthy features during the northern summer are the very high temperatures over the deserts of North America, North Africa, Arabia, and Asia, and the cool coastal regions of California and Morocco. These cool coastal regions are closely related to the ocean currents shown in Figs. 182 and 183. As an example, a map of the sea-surface temperature in August along the west coast of North America is reproduced in Fig. 186. During the warm season the prevailing winds along the coasts of Oregon and California (and also along the coasts of Portugal and Morocco) are from the north. The stress exerted by these winds on the ocean surface results in upwelling of cold water, and this maintains a low air temperature along the coasts. The layer of cool air is relatively shallow and it is often filled with low stratus or fog. The California summer fog (see page 142) is an example. Above the cool and moist layer we find warm and dry air. In Fig. 187 is shown the annual variation of temperature at San Francisco and at the nearby station Mount Tamalpais. It will be seen that the summit of Mount Tamalpais, which overlooks San Francisco from the other side of the Golden Gate, has a much higher temperature than San Francisco, which is under the influence of the cool coastal waters. Similar, but less extreme, conditions prevail along the coasts of Portugal and Morocco.

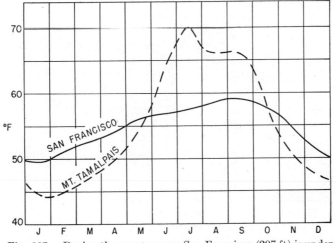

Fig. 187. During the warm season San Francisco (207 ft) is under the influence of the cool coastal waters, while Mount Tamalpais (2,375 ft), which is above the temperature inversion, has higher temperature.

In the Southern Hemisphere the temperature distribution is relatively simple. None of the continents penetrates into the higher mid-latitudes, and the difference between oceans and continents is small in all seasons.

The Annual Range of Temperature. By the annual range of temperature is meant the difference between the average temperature during the warmest and coldest months. This difference is shown in Fig. 188. Around the equator the range is less than 5°F, and there is little difference between land and sea. Over the arctic fields of snow and ice the summer temperature is limited by the melting point, and here we find an annual range of about 70°F. The largest ranges are found in the central and northern parts of Siberia (110°F) and Canada (80°F). Lesser maxima are present over Sahara, Argentina, South Africa, and Australia. Figure 188 illustrates very clearly the combined effect of latitude and continentality on the distribution of temperature through the seasons.

Fuel Consumption. The amount of fuel needed to heat a unit volume of a building depends on (1) the thermal properties of the building materials, (2) the surface-to-volume ratio of the building, and (3) the outside temperature. For a large sample of buildings, such as is represented by a city or a large rural area, it has been found that the fuel consumption can be determined very accurately by the outside temperature. While the oilman delivers so many gallons of oil, the companies schedule their distribution of fuels according to an index, the unit of which is a *heating degree-day*. If the daily mean air temperature is 65°F or higher,

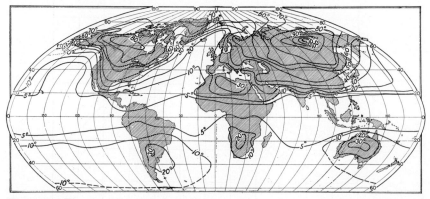

Fig. 188. The annual range of temperature. Note the difference between low and high latitudes and between oceans and continents. (*After Trewartha.*)

the index is zero. If, on a certain day, the mean outside temperature is 40°F, the index is 25, and this is taken as a measure of the fuel consumption for that day. The fuel consumption for a week, a month, or a season is proportional to the number of days with mean temperatures below 65°F and the amount of temperature drop below that limit. In working out the index, days with mean temperature above 65°F are not counted.

In Fig. 189 is shown the distribution of the heating degree-days in the United States. Shortly after the end of the month the U.S. Weather Bureau calculates the heating degree index for a large number of stations, and this provides a good estimate of the fuel consumption in the different areas.

Frost. There are certain temperatures which, in one sense or another, are recognized as being critical. One of these is the freezing point of water, or 32°F. If the temperature sinks below this limit water will freeze and plant life may become endangered. For general purposes the frost-free season is determined by the first and last dates of the year on which the minimum temperature sinks below 32°F. The distribution of the frost-free period is shown in Fig. 190. It is of interest to note that even the southern deserts are not entirely free of frosts.

In mid-latitudes frosts are of chief significance in spring and autumn, and the dates marking the beginning and end of the frost-free period may vary considerably around the mean dates. In subtropical regions, such as Florida, California, etc., occasional winter frosts are the main concern because of the active growth of sensitive and high-cost crops during that season. A single frost has been known to cause damage amounting to over 50 million dollars. On the poleward side of the mid-latitudes belt, occasional summer frosts cause much damage to cereal crops.

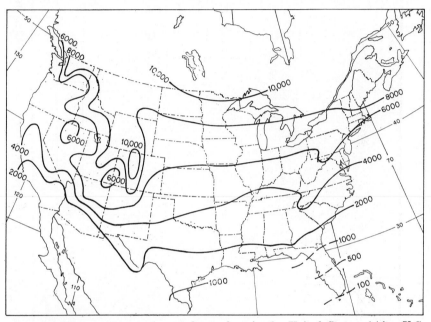

Fig. 189. The average number of degree-days in the United States. (*After U.S. Weather Bureau.*)

Since most plants can withstand a mild frost of short duration, the term *killing frost* is used to denote "a frost of sufficient severity to be generally destructive to the staple products of the locality." An example of a killing-frost record is shown in Fig. 191.

Normally the length of the period without killing frost varies considerably about the mean value, and if the agricultural production were planned according to the mean length, frequent killings would result. It is necessary, therefore, to plan with a period which is shorter than the mean. On the other hand, it would be unprofitable to base the planning on a perfectly safe period. As a compromise it is customary to allow a certain risk, and the *effective* (or available) *growing season* is taken to be the period within which killing frosts would not occur in 4 out of 5 years.

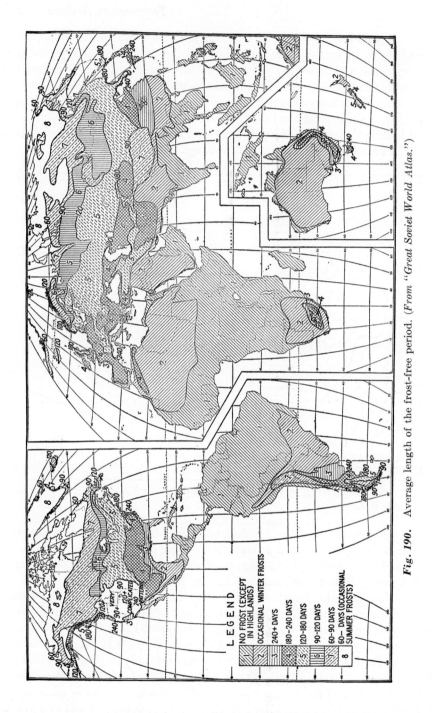

Fig. 190. Average length of the frost-free period. (*From "Great Soviet World Atlas."*)

LEGEND

1 NO FROST (EXCEPT IN HIGHLANDS)
2 OCCASIONAL WINTER FROSTS
3 240+ DAYS
4 180–240 DAYS
5 120–180 DAYS
6 90–120 DAYS
7 60–90 DAYS
8 60– DAYS (OCCASIONAL SUMMER FROSTS)

The distribution of this season in the United States is shown in Fig. 192. Where the season is long a great diversification of crops is normally possible, and where the length of the season is less than 90 days, agricultural production is severely limited.

The temperature at which a killing frost sets in varies with the type of crop, and the occurrence of such frosts depends much upon the local configuration of the terrain.

The conditions favorable for initiating a frost in the marginal seasons may be outlined as follows. An invasion of chilly polar air is necessary to create a situation which is generally favorable. When this is followed by

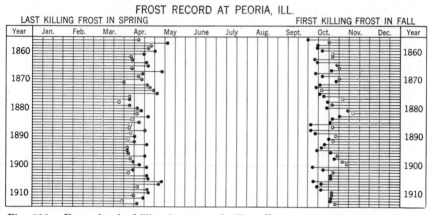

Fig. 191. Example of a killing-frost record. (*From "Atlas of American Agriculture,"* U.S. Dept. of Agriculture.)

calm and clear nights, the ground and the air in contact with it cool further by outgoing radiation. The cooled air seeps down the slopes and gathers in the depressions of the terrain. Such depressions may suffer severe frosts while the adjacent hills are free. An example is shown in Fig. 193. It will be seen that the temperature at the foot of the hill dropped to about 25°F while temperatures between 50 and 55°F were recorded on the slope 225 ft higher.

Most field crops in mid-latitudes are annuals which are planted so late in spring that frost damage is of little concern during the early growth. If sown in autumn, active growth does not commence until the danger of spring frosts is passed. Field crops of this type are normally harvested before there is any danger of autumn freeze.

The problems of frost warnings and frost prevention become most acute in connection with sensitive and valuable crops which occupy restricted areas. Examples are garden crops, orchards, and other fruit crops of the perennial type. Where frost is a hazard, the risk may be minimized by planting the crops on the slopes of hills so that the cooled

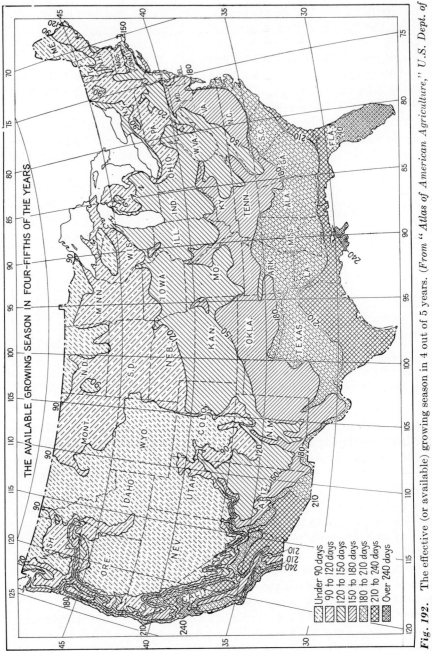

THE AVAILABLE GROWING SEASON IN FOUR-FIFTHS OF THE YEARS

Under 90 days
90 to 120 days
120 to 150 days
150 to 180 days
180 to 210 days
210 to 240 days
Over 240 days

Fig. 192. The effective (or available) growing season in 4 out of 5 years. (*From "Atlas of American Agriculture," U.S. Dept. of Agriculture.*)

air drains out. Particularly favorable are the windward slopes near coasts or lakes, for in such places the air will take up heat from the water bodies.

Damage to sensitive crops within limited areas may be prevented by artificial means. Smudging has been used, with varying success, to reduce the outgoing radiation. Far more successful in preventing the temperature from falling below critical limits are the orchard heaters. Preventive covers made of paper, straw, or cloth are often used as protection against loss of heat. In the cranberry areas of Wisconsin and New England the

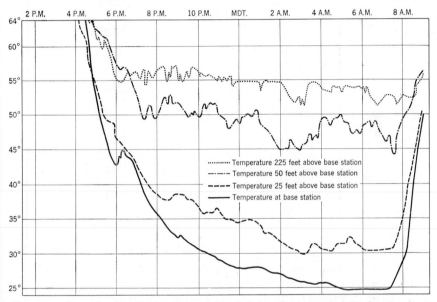

Fig. 193.   Records of temperature at various heights along a steep hill, showing frost at the base station with warm air above. (*From U.S. Weather Bureau.*)

bogs are usually flooded if a killing frost is expected. On account of its far greater conductive capacity (see Chap. 6), the water cools much more slowly than the land surface, and this reduces the frost hazard.

Temperature and Plant Growth. Another critical temperature limit may be placed at about 40 or 42°F. This is the temperature needed for most seeds to germinate and for plant life to begin to function. The effectiveness of temperature in promoting growth is often called the *temperature efficiency,* and it is measured as the number of days with mean temperature above 40°F and the amount of rise above that limit.

The basic temperature varies with the type of crop. While peas begin to germinate at 40°F, sweet corn requires about 50°F. As a rule, the rate of maturing increases with the rise of temperature above the basic value, provided, of course, that the soil contains a sufficient amount of water.

It is customary to use a *growing degree-day* as a unit. For example, in the case of peas, each Fahrenheit degree above a daily mean temperature of 40°F is a growing degree-day, and in the case of sweet corn the basic number is 50°F. Thus, to a daily mean temperature of 60°F corresponds 20 growing degree-days for peas and 10 for sweet corn.

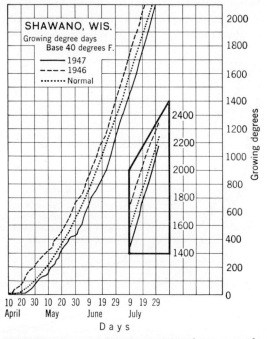

Fig. 194.   An example of a growing-degree record. (*From U.S. Weather Bureau.*)

An example of a growing degree-day record is shown in Fig. 194. Data of this type are very useful for planning planting and harvesting, particularly where perishable crops are involved. Using the normal curve in Fig. 194, we see that if 1,600 units were required for a crop to mature, July 9 would be the optimum date for harvesting. In individual years the date may differ somewhat from the normal, but the harvest can usually be scheduled with fair accuracy by plotting the current temperatures in a diagram of the type shown.

17

Precipitation Regimes

The overwhelming part of the water that falls upon the earth comes from clouds which form in ascending air currents. In such currents the air comes under lower pressure and cools by expansion, and this leads to condensation of water vapor and the formation of clouds. When the clouds become sufficiently deep, precipitation (rain, snow, etc.) falls out in the manner described in Chap. 4. Over the globe as a whole the ascending currents must be compensated for by descending, or subsiding, motions. A rainfall chart (see Fig. 195) will therefore reveal the regions where ascending and descending currents predominate. In spite of the complexities shown on the chart, certain systematic features are clearly indicated. In the first place, we notice abundance of rain in the equatorial zone, moderate to large amounts in the mid-latitudes belts, and relatively dry regions in the subtropics and around the poles. Secondly, we note that there is a tendency for the subtropical west coasts to be dry while rain is plentiful along the east coasts in the same latitude. In high latitudes, on the other hand, the west coasts are generally wetter than the east coasts. Thirdly, we see that rain is abundant on the windward side of mountain ranges and sparse in the lee of such ranges.

The Zonal Pattern. If the earth's surface were perfectly uniform, we should find that the long-term average rainfall would be arranged in rather distinct zonal bands. During the annual cycle, the zones of vertical motion and the corresponding belts of rainfall would migrate somewhat toward the hemisphere where summer prevails. These zonal bands are illustrated very schematically in Fig. 196. Although highly simplified, the diagram is useful for indicating the general nature of the zonal arrangement.

1. *The Equatorial Belt.* The central part of this belt is occupied by the doldrums, or the so-called intertropical convergence zone. Here the trade winds from both hemispheres converge, giving rise to general upward motion. Much of the rainfall in this belt comes from the traveling disturbances and storms discussed in Chap. 15, though showers and thunderstorms contribute a great deal, particularly over the land areas.

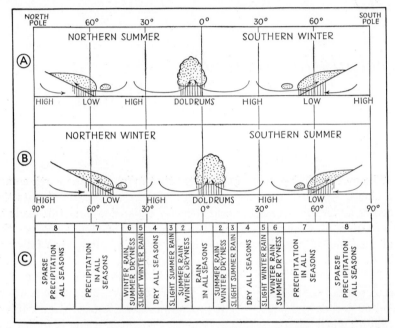

Fig. 196. Schematic cross section through the atmosphere showing the main zones of ascending and descending motion: (*a*) during the northern summer; (*b*) during the northern winter; (*c*) the main zones of precipitation.

During the annual cycle, the doldrums move toward the summer hemisphere, more or less as shown in Fig. 196. As a result, we find a central belt (indicated by 1) with rain in all seasons. Farther away from the equator, we find two more or less symmetrical zones (indicated by 2) which receive much rain during the summer and scanty rains in winter. Still farther away from the equator we would find two belts (indicated by 3) in which there would be some rain in summer but very little in the other seasons. These two zones would mark the extreme poleward influence of the annual migration of the intertropical convergence zone, and the belts indicated by 1, 2, and 3 in Fig. 196 would indicate various degrees of the equatorial rainfall regime.

2. *The Subtropical Belts.* On a uniform earth these belts would be under the influence of the subtropical anticyclones. Subsiding motions and air with low relative humidity would be typical, though rain would fall occasionally. During the annual cycle the high-pressure belts would migrate north and south as shown in Fig. 196, causing summer dryness on the poleward side and winter dryness on the equatorward side of their mean positions.

3. *The Mid-latitudes Belts.* In both hemispheres traveling cyclones and fronts and unstable air masses would be frequent. Precipitation would

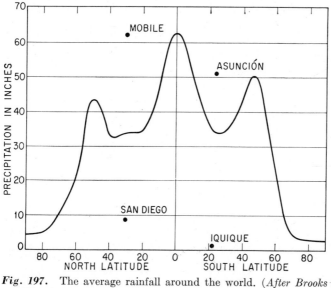

Fig. 197. The average rainfall around the world. (*After Brooks and Hunt.*)

be plentiful in all seasons, except along the equatorward borders (the zones indicated by 5 and 6), where dryness would prevail during the summer seasons when the subtropical highs are displaced poleward.

4. *The Polar Regions.* Here the temperature is so low that the air holds little moisture. Traveling cyclones are rare, particularly in summer, and the amounts of precipitation are small in all seasons.

The zonal scheme outlined above is, of course, much modified by the distribution of oceans and continents, by mountain ranges, etc. However, it will be seen from Fig. 197 that it is able to account for the broad features of the distribution of precipitation around the world. First, the poverty of precipitation in the polar regions and the abundance in the equatorial belt are striking, and quite pronounced are the maxima in the cyclone belts in the mid-latitudes. When the mean around the world is taken, one finds fairly large amounts (about 35 in.) in the subtropics.

However, these belts contain areas of excessive dryness as well as areas with abundance of rainfall (see Fig. 195). The variation within the zone is seen clearly by comparing San Diego, California, with Mobile, Alabama, and Iquique, Chile, with Asunción, Paraguay, as is done in Fig. 197. On the whole, we shall find that within the subtropical belt, rainfall

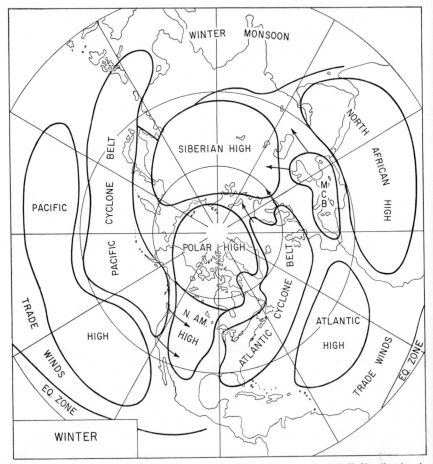

Fig. 198.   The predominant motion systems which affect the rainfall distribution in winter. Summarized from the hemispheric charts in Chaps. 11 to 15. MCB indicates the Mediterranean cyclone belt.

is plentiful along the east coasts and sparse along the west coasts and in the interior of extensive continents.

   Influences of Oceans and Continents. To account for the broad aspects of the distortions of the zonal rainfall patterns (compare Figs. 195 and 197), we must refer back to the discussions of the major wind systems, the air masses, fronts and cyclones, and the tropical disturbances and storms. Of particular interest are the data presented in Chaps. 11 to 15. A skeletal summary of these data is given in Figs. 198 and 199 for the Northern Hemisphere. Throughout, frequent references must be made to Fig. 195. On the whole, we may distinguish between four major precipitation regimes in the Northern Hemisphere.

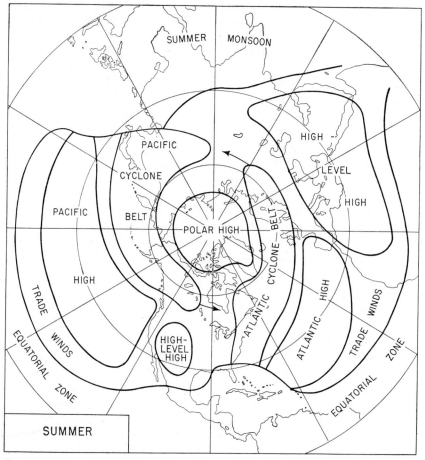

Fig. 199. The predominant motion systems which affect the rainfall distribution in summer. Summarized from the hemispheric charts in Chaps. 11 to 15.

1. *The Equatorial Regime.* As explained in the foregoing section, this regime oscillates in an annual cycle around the equator. Over the Atlantic and eastern part of the Pacific, the oscillation is rather small and rarely exceeds 10° latitude. The main effect of oceans and continents is to cause large oscillations in regions where seasonal wind systems of the monsoon type prevail. Most pronounced is the Indian monsoon. During the northern winter (Fig. 198), cool and dry air from the interior of the continent

streams southward, and rain is sparse over land. After the air has moved some distance over the warm tropical and equatorial waters, showery rain becomes frequent. Thus, while India as a whole has winter dryness, rain is plentiful in the East Indies and neighboring regions.

During the northern summer (Fig. 199), the monsoon is from the south and rainfall is heavy over India and Southeast Asia as far north as the southern coast of Japan. The largest amounts are found where the prevailing winds are intercepted by mountain ranges (see Fig. 195). The summer monsoon accounts for the major part of the annual rainfall in India, Burma, and neighboring regions.

The annual migration of the equatorial rainfall regime is appreciable also in the Western Hemisphere. During the southern summer, rainfall is heavy in the central part of South America. As the northern summer approaches, the equatorial regime spreads northward and makes its influence felt over the north coast of South America, the Caribbean, and Mexico. Toward the end of the summer season, tropical disturbances and storms are frequent and these add to the rainfall. Similar conditions exist in the Far East, except that the season there is longer (see Chap. 15).

2. *The Pacific Cyclone Belt.* During the northern winter there is a broad belt with frequent cyclones, fronts, and unstable air masses, extending from the Philippines toward the Gulf of Alaska. Here storms of great intensity are frequent and give rise to much precipitation. Most of the winter storms accumulate in the Gulf of Alaska, and winter rainfall is quite heavy along the Pacific Coast north of about 40° N. A few storms and trailing fronts drift eastward to the south of this latitude, and these account for the winter rainfall in California and in the northwestern part of Mexico.

Some of the winter storms from the Pacific move into North America, but they weaken as they cross the Rocky Mountains. Quite frequently these cyclones redevelop to the east of the range, either in Alberta or in the Oklahoma-Colorado region. These storms do not produce much precipitation until they have moved so far eastward that they begin to draw warm and moist air from the Gulf of Mexico or the North Atlantic. On the whole, winter precipitation is sparse over a broad belt in the lee of the Rocky Mountains.

During the northern summer, the Pacific cyclones and fronts are relatively weak. The cyclone belt (see Fig. 199) is displaced farther to the north. At the same time, the Pacific high dominates much of the ocean area. As a result, summer rainfall is very sparse along the west coast to the south of the 50th parallel. Some of the summer storms from the Pacific move into northern Canada, and when the cool Pacific air becomes heated over the warmer land areas, showers and occasional thunderstorms develop.

On the whole, the southwestern part of the Pacific cyclone belt has most rainfall in the warm season when the monsoon is active. The northeastern part has most rainfall in winter when the cyclonic storms are numerous and strong. Along the west coast of North America, the southern limit of the rain belt moves northward in summer and southward in winter, and here we find a pronounced annual variation.

3. *The Atlantic Cyclone Belt.* The conditions on the North Atlantic are very much the same as those on the North Pacific. In the cold season (Fig. 198), the cyclone belt cuts through all latitudes from Florida to northern Norway. Some of the winter storms develop in the Gulf of Mexico and move northward to the Great Lakes, causing much precipitation in the eastern states. On the European side, occasional cyclones and trailing fronts occur as far south as Portugal and Morocco. Here, as in California, winter is the rainiest season. Some of the Atlantic winter storms move to the north of Norway and give some precipitation along the north coast of Russia. But by the time the air arrives in these high latitudes, it is so cold that it holds little moisture. Moreover, these coastal regions are under the influence of the Siberian high most of the time, and precipitation is sparse. A few Atlantic storms redevelop over the North and the Baltic Seas and move eastward into central Russia, and these account for much of the winter precipitation in western and central Russia.

During the summer season (Fig. 199), the Atlantic cyclone belt extends from the east coast of North America across the Atlantic and Scandinavia and far into the Eurasian continent. Most of these cyclones are weak disturbances. However, as the cool Atlantic air is brought inland and warmed by the land masses, showers and occasional thunderstorms develop. On the whole, the Atlantic cyclone belt has much precipitation in all seasons except to the east of the Scandinavian mountains, where most of the precipitation falls as showers during the warmer part of the year. On account of the northward displacement of the Atlantic anticyclone belt, the summer is a relatively dry season in Spain and northwest Africa. Here the rainfall regime is similar to that of California.

4. *The Mediterranean Regime.* During the cold season (Fig. 198), a frontal zone (see page 215) develops over the Mediterranean as a result of the contrast between the cold air over Europe and the warmer air to the south. Cyclones of appreciable intensity develop frequently, particularly over the western Mediterranean. Some of these move northeastward and give winter precipitation over the Balkans, Asia Minor, the Black Sea, and the regions to the northeast. Other cyclones, mostly weak disturbances, move through the Near East, and these give much-needed winter rainfall over a wide and arid belt of the Near East and eastward toward Afghanistan and Pakistan. During the warm season, the Mediter-

ranean front is absent and there is very little rainfall except such as falls in occasional showers.

5. *The Dry Regions.* The regions of little precipitation (see Fig. 195) coincide broadly with the areas occupied by anticyclonic systems in which subsiding motion prevails and with areas which are sheltered by mountain ranges. The largest region of pronounced dryness is made up of North Africa and Arabia. A second region is the central part of Asia to the north of the main mountain system. Other extensive regions are central Australia and the west coast of South Africa. In South America, we find a west-coast desert in low latitudes and an east-coast desert in high latitudes. The former of these is protected by the Andes against the rain-bearing winds from the Atlantic side and it is situated under the persistent subtropical anticyclone of the South Pacific. Here rainfall is very sparse in all seasons. The desert in southern Argentina is situated in what we may call the cyclone belt of the Southern Hemisphere, but it is protected by the southern Andes against the rain-bearing winds. Here we see most clearly the tremendous influence which the distribution of land, sea, and mountain ranges exerts on weather and climate.

The deserts of North America are of rather limited extent. During the cold season (Fig. 198), small amounts of rainfall come from occasional disturbances which move in from the Pacific. During the warm season, the desert area is protected by a high-level anticyclone (Fig. 199) which, most of the time, is situated over the heat low over northern Mexico, Arizona, and Nevada. On occasion, this protection is absent, and summer showers occur now and then.

6. *The Arctic Region.* In winter, stray cyclones from the Atlantic and Pacific regimes will visit the arctic fields of snow and ice, but the air is then so cold that it holds little water vapor. In summer, the polar icecap is under an anticyclonic regime and cyclones are very rare. The precipitation is light in all seasons, and the annual amounts are about the same as those typical of moderate deserts in low latitudes.

Examples of Seasonal Variations. To illustrate the seasonal variation of rainfall and its relation to the rainfall regimes, we consider a belt extending from the equator to the north-polar region through Africa and Europe (Fig. 200).

At New Amsterdam, which is about 2° N, there is much rainfall throughout the year. We notice a sustained maximum from May to October and a peak in December. Such variations are due to the movement of the equatorial convergence zone, seasonal shifts in the prevailing winds, etc. At many equatorial stations, there are two distinct maxima, and at others, there may be a relatively dry season. On the whole, however, rainfall is abundant, and where there is a dry season, it is usually so short that it has not much effect upon vegetation.

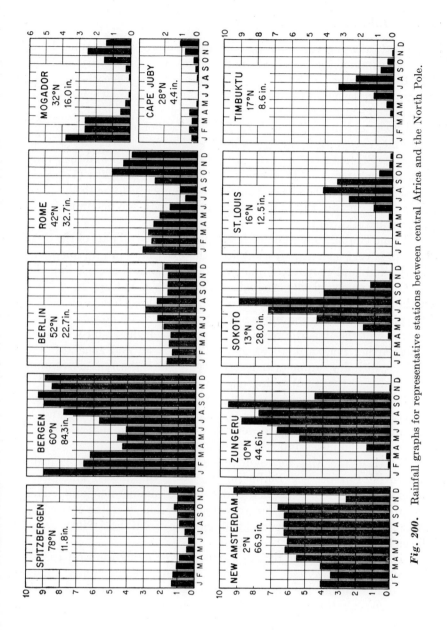

Fig. 200. Rainfall graphs for representative stations between central Africa and the North Pole.

Next, at Zungeru, which is about 10° N, there is a pronounced maximum in summer (high-sun maximum), with a distinctly dry spell from late October to early April. The maximum occurs when the equatorial regime is displaced northward, and the minimum occurs when the regime is displaced southward. Here we can speak of an annual cycle, with distinctly wet and dry seasons. The conditions at Sokoto (13° N) are about the same, except that the wet season is shorter and the dry season is longer. At St. Louis (16° N), the dry season is still longer and the summer peak is much reduced. Proceeding northward to Timbuktu (17° N), we find that the wet season has shrunk further, and only 3 months have rainfall in excess of 1 in. But here, too, we find the high-sun maximum typical of the equatorial regime.

From Timbuktu, we go northward into the central part of the desert. Rainfall is very sparse, and what little there is comes in rare bursts, falls on dry sand, and evaporates quickly. Here the annual cycle is indistinct.

On the poleward side, we find a reversed cycle. At Cape Juby (28° N, on the coast of Sahara), the annual amount is less than 5 in., and the wet spell occurs when the sun is low in the sky. We are now on the southern fringe of the Atlantic regime with summer dryness and winter rain. Going farther poleward, to Mogador (32° N), we find generally larger rainfalls, with dry summers and wet winters. Here, the January rainfall is comparable to that of Washington, D.C.

Going northeastward to Rome (42° N), we find typical Mediterranean conditions. The summer is dry though not rainless, and late autumn and winter are quite wet. Here the winter rainfall is about the same as the summer rainfall in Washington, D.C.

North of the Alps we begin to encounter the real Atlantic regime. In Central Europe (see Berlin in Fig. 200), the annual amounts are moderate and there is a distinct tendency for a summer maximum. This is due primarily to summer showers which develop over the heated land areas. Cyclonic disturbances and trailing fronts from the Atlantic occur in all seasons.

The typical Atlantic regime is encountered along the west coasts of Scotland and Norway (see Bergen, 60° N). Here, we find annual amounts in excess of 80 in. This is comparable to the annual rainfall in most parts of the equatorial belt (see Fig. 195). In the Atlantic cyclone belt, the largest amounts are observed during the colder part of the year, for it is during these months that the cyclones are most active. In comparison, spring and early summer are relatively dry, but even the driest month in Bergen is as wet as the wettest month in Washington, D.C.

The Atlantic regime continues northward, but when we come to Spitzbergen, the annual amounts are very small. Being situated on the fringe of the Atlantic cyclone belt, Spitzbergen has a winter maximum.

The temperature in these high latitudes is, however, so low that the air holds little water vapor, and the amounts of precipitation are low in all seasons.

In Northern Europe (Fig. 201), the winter maximum of rainfall is limited to the coastal regions. Almost the entire stretch from the west coast of Europe to the east coasts of Asia has most rainfall during the

Regions with more rain
in winter half year than
in summer half year
(after Kendrew)

Fig. 201. In Europe and North Africa the coastal regions have most rain in the winter half of the year. (*Reproduced from Trewartha.*)

warm season, when summer showers are most active. In southwest Europe, the Atlantic and Mediterranean regimes merge, and the latter regime continues as far east as the western branches of the Himalayas.

Rainfall Regions in North America. Particularly in the mountainous areas, the rainfall for any month, season, or year may vary appreciably over short distances. We shall here ignore such variations and try to account for the broad aspects of the various types of rainfall distributions. On the whole, we may distinguish between seven regions, as shown in Fig. 202. The rainfall graphs shown in Figs. 203 to 209 will serve to illustrate the various types.

Region 1 covers the Pacific coast from the northernmost part of California to the south coast of Alaska, and it includes the Cascade

Range. The precipitation comes mainly from the Pacific cyclone belt, and the amounts vary in an annual rhythm. To the south of the Canadian border, the summer is quite dry, but the amounts increase rapidly northward. Typical rainfall graphs for this region are shown in Fig. 203. In the northern part of the region, the largest amounts occur in late autumn rather than in winter.

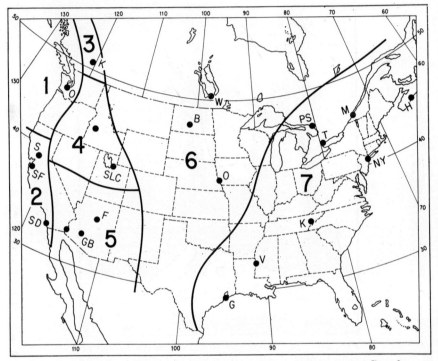

Fig. 202.   In broad outline, the United States and the adjacent part of Canada may be divided into seven rainfall regions. Their typical characteristics are shown in Figs. 203 to 209. (*Summarized from Kendrew.*)

Region 2 is the Pacific coast south of about 40° N, and it includes the great valley of California and the western slopes of the Sierra Nevada. As in region 1, most of the rain falls in winter (see Fig. 204), but the annual amounts are smaller and there is a distinctly dry period in summer, varying in length from 2 to 4 months. The rainfall here is due mainly to Pacific cyclones which drift eastward in low latitudes during the cold season.

Region 3 is a narrow strip which represents the transition between the coastal region with a strong winter maximum and the interior with a pronounced summer maximum. Kamloops (Fig. 205) may be taken to represent this region. The annual amount is small, and there is some indication of maxima in winter and summer. The windward upper slopes of the mountains are certain to have a pronounced winter maximum since the depth of the snow cover in late winter and early spring is very large.

Region 4 is the northern part of the United States Rockies, and its typical rainfall features are shown in Fig. 206. In most of this region, the

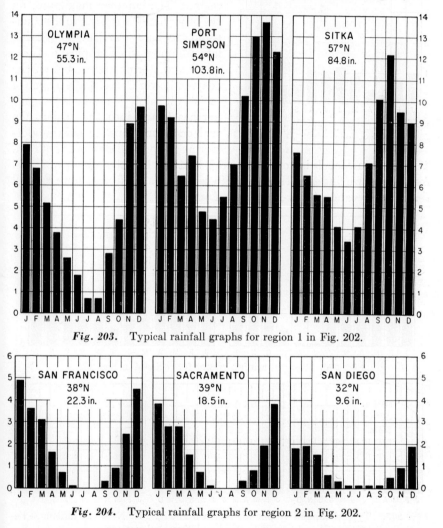

Fig. 203. Typical rainfall graphs for region 1 in Fig. 202.

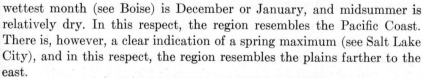

Fig. 204. Typical rainfall graphs for region 2 in Fig. 202.

wettest month (see Boise) is December or January, and midsummer is relatively dry. In this respect, the region resembles the Pacific Coast. There is, however, a clear indication of a spring maximum (see Salt Lake City), and in this respect, the region resembles the plains farther to the east.

Region 5 includes the driest area of the continent. The rainfall graphs in Fig. 207 show two distinct processes at work. The maximum of rainfall during the cool season is due to winter cyclones which drift in from the Pacific; it may be regarded as an extension of the California rainfall regime. The summer maximum, on the other hand, is related to the equatorial regime. Particularly during late summer, when tropical disturbances and storms are present off the coast of Lower California, a tongue of moist air aloft sometimes extends northeastward into the region. On such occasions, showers and thunderstorms give variable amounts of rain. The air at low levels is normally so dry that much of the rain evaporates. As a result, we find that the mountain region (Flagstaff) has more rainfall than the lowlands (Gila Bend and Yuma).

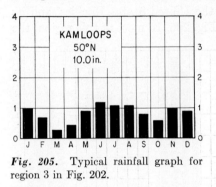

Fig. 205. Typical rainfall graph for region 3 in Fig. 202.

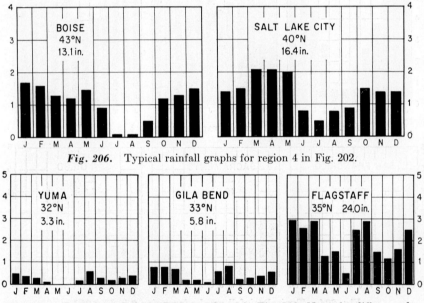

Fig. 206. Typical rainfall graphs for region 4 in Fig. 202.

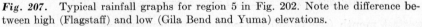

Fig. 207. Typical rainfall graphs for region 5 in Fig. 202. Note the difference between high (Flagstaff) and low (Gila Bend and Yuma) elevations.

Region 6 is very uniform and covers an enormous area to the east of the Rocky Mountains. It extends from northeastern Mexico to the Canadian tundra. Appropriately, it may be called the Plains precipitation regime, and its essential features are shown in Fig. 208. Winter is everywhere dry, with monthly precipitation amounts less than 1 in. From April to June the rainfall increases rapidly. Although fronts and cyclones are fairly frequent, much of the precipitation comes from showers and thunderstorms. In the central part of the area, more than half the rain comes in the months May to August. This concentration of the rain during the agricultural season is of considerable value. In the northern part of the region, the summer maximum is delayed till July, and autumn is rainier than spring. In part, this delay is due to the circumstance that

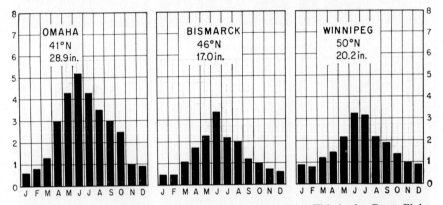

Fig. 208. Typical rainfall graphs for region 6 in Fig. 202. This is the Great Plains region.

the ground is frozen in winter, so that the spring rise in temperature occurs later.

Region 7 is under the influence of the Atlantic cyclone regime, and rainfall is plentiful throughout the year. On the whole, the driest month has more than 2 in. and the wettest month may have as much as 6 in. of rainfall. In the north, there is very little annual variation (see Toronto, Montreal, and New York in Fig. 209), for here the frequency of cyclones varies but little through the year. Along the New England coast and in Nova Scotia and Newfoundland, there is a distinct winter maximum because of the greater cyclone activity in that season. In the remainder of the area, the annual maximum shifts considerably, but, on the whole, the rainfall is adequate throughout the year.

Rainfall Variability. It is important to bear in mind that the long-term mean amounts of precipitation for a month, season, or year give little information on the regularity with which rain may be expected. In particular, this is true in the regions where the average amounts are small. For example, at Doorbaji, in the Thar Desert, where the annual amount is about 5 in., a rare storm gave 34 in. in 2 days. At Iquique, in northern Chile, 4 years passed without rain, while the fifth year gave 0.6 in., so that the five-year average turned out to be 0.12 in. It is clear

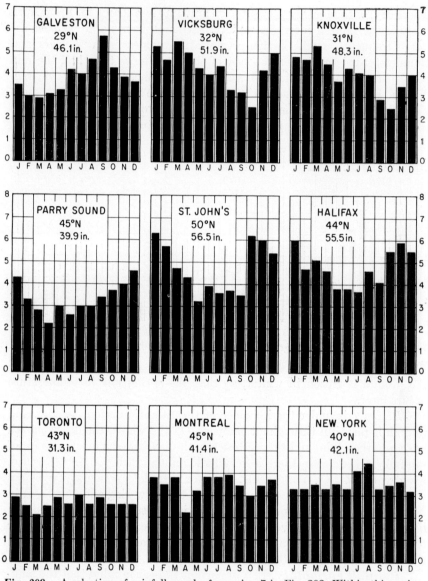

Fig. 209. A selection of rainfall graphs for region 7 in Fig. 202. Within this region rainfall is generally adequate in all months.

that such averages are of little practical value. In addition to the mean values, it is useful to have tabulations of the frequency of occurrence for various intervals of amounts. Particularly during the growing season, it is far more beneficial to have frequent small amounts than occasional heavy bursts.

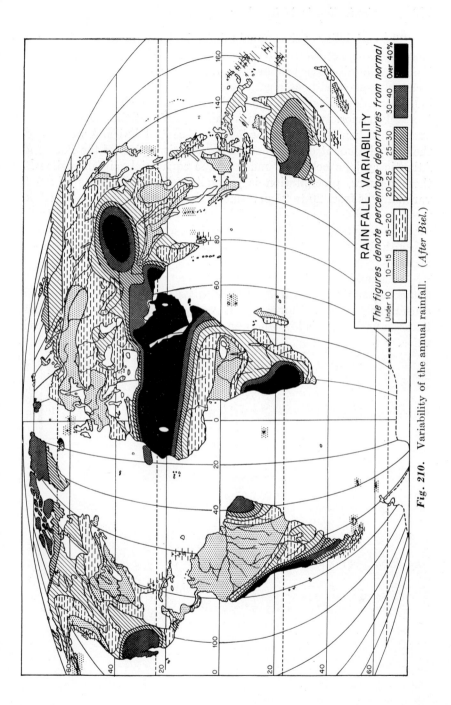

Fig. 210. Variability of the annual rainfall. (*After Biel.*)

The variability of the annual rainfall is closely related to the average amounts. The distribution over the land areas is shown in Fig. 210. Here the variability is defined as the ratio of the mean of all deviations from the mean (averaged without regard to sign) to the mean itself. A low ratio indicates a high degree of dependability, and a high ratio indicates an erratic behavior. It will be seen from Fig. 210 that the ratio is very low over the British Isles and in the interior of central Africa. A variability in the annual amount of less than 15 per cent is typical of the Pacific and Atlantic cyclone belts and much of the equatorial rainfall regimes. In these regimes, precipitation is generally reliable. In areas where the variability is from 20 to 25 per cent, the reliability is much reduced, and prolonged droughts may occur. Values in excess of 40 per cent are typical over the deserts of Africa, Arabia, and Asia, and also along the west coast of South America. In the interior of these deserts, the variability is very high.

It should be noted that Fig. 210 refers to the variability of the annual amounts. The variability for the seasons or months may differ considerably from that for the year. As a general rule, however, one finds that the variability is low where the average amounts are high, and vice versa.

18

World Climates

The word *climate* is derived from the Greek word *klima*, which means slope or incline, and in the context it refers to the inclination of the sun's rays relative to the earth's surface. The Greek savants were quite familiar with the hot and arid lands of Arabia and North Africa, the warm and relatively moist countries of Southern Europe, and the cold boreal regions. It was natural, therefore, to generalize and place emphasis on the inclination of the sun's rays (or latitude) in referring to types of weather regimes.

Climatology. It has been customary to say that the climate of a place or a region is the weather averaged over a long span of time. But what we commonly call weather is made up of a large number of elements, such as temperature, humidity, cloudiness, sunshine, rainfall, wind, and so forth. Each of these can be expressed in terms of numbers, but we cannot add or otherwise combine these numbers and obtain a measure of the weather. Without considerable qualification, it has little meaning to speak of the average weather.

The difficulties in the way of combining observations into groups which represent climatic regions are enormous. Some simple examples will illustrate the point. First, Peiping and the Scilly Isles have almost the same annual mean temperature (about 54°F), but the annual range differs widely; at Peiping it is 56°F, while in the Scilly Isles, it is only 18°F. The annual mean temperature is here no link at all, for the climates of the two places differ greatly, not only because of the annual range of temperature, but also because of differences in rainfall, humidity, cloudiness, etc. Second, San Francisco and Winnipeg (see Figs. 204 and 208) have about the same annual rainfall, but the former has a dry summer and the latter a dry winter. It is evident, therefore, that annual mean values are of little use in characterizing climates. Third, Cairo, Egypt, and Galveston, Texas, have almost identical mean temperatures in every month, but the former has only 1 in. of rainfall, most of which falls in winter, while the latter has 46 in., well distributed over all seasons. In addition to the differences in rainfall amounts and seasons, there are vast differences in cloudiness, humidity, winds, etc.

Even if we restrict our attention to the two most important elements, temperature and rainfall, it would clearly be impossible to combine the data into some general measure which would characterize the climates without appealing to some human activity to which the data are to be applied.

While strict definitions are desirable, they are sometimes better avoided, particularly where human activities and preferences are involved. To obtain a general impression of what the word climate may be taken to mean, we turn to chap. 11 of Deuteronomy and read:

For the land, whither thou goest in to possess it, is not as the land of Egypt, from whence ye came out, where thou sowedst thy seed, and wateredst it with thy foot, as a garden of herbs: but the land, whither ye go to possess it, is a land of hills and valleys, and drinketh water of the rain of heaven: a land which the Lord thy God careth for: the eyes of the Lord thy God are always upon it, from the beginning of the year even unto the end of the year.

And it shall come to pass, if ye shall hearken diligently unto my commandments which I command you this day, to love the Lord your God, and to serve him with all your heart and with all your soul, that I will give you the rain of your land in his due season, the first rain and the latter rain, that thou mayest gather in thy corn, and thy wine, and thine oil. And I will send grass in thy fields for thy cattle, that thou mayest eat and be full.

Later in the same chapter, we hear of droughts and the consequences of droughts.

In this cogent description of the climate of Canaan, we hear of hills and valleys, or such topographic features as affect the weather; we hear of meteorological conditions to the extent that they are important to plant and animal life and to human habitation. We obtain a clear picture of the climate of a land where rainfall is periodic and marginal, and may often fail.[1] Nothing is said about what we now call temperature, probably because heat and cold are not restrictive in this area; rainfall is the overwhelming climatic factor.

[1] The reference to "the first rain and the latter rain" may suggest the existence, at that time, of two maxima, one early and one late in the rainfall season (November to April). Such maxima are clearly evident in the rainfall records of Asia Minor and southeastward to Bagdad, but there is little evidence of them in modern Palestine. Whether the rainfall regimes have changed since Biblical times is not known.

In the scheme of the ancient Greeks, the climates were divided into latitude zones according to the elevation of the sun, and we may speak of a solar (or radiation) classification. If the composition of the earth's surface were uniform, this would probably be adequate. However, as we have stressed repeatedly in the foregoing chapters, the distributions of oceans, continents, mountain ranges, etc., exert profound influences. Any description of the distribution over the face of the earth of meteorological averages must therefore lean heavily on physical geography and oceanography. But when it comes to the description of climates, we must go a step further. The essence of climatology is to combine the various meteorological elements in such a manner that some useful information results. The word *useful* can refer only to some human activity, and since, basically, these activities are centered around the production and acquisition of food, it is natural to seek such combinations of temperature, rainfall, etc., as are meaningful in terms of plant and animal life, agriculture, and related fields of endeavor.

This thought is not new. It is inherent in the quotation from the Bible given above. It was vaguely revived in the writings of von Humboldt (1769–1859), who may be said to be the father of modern climatology. It was developed into a world scheme of classification of climates by Köppen (1846–1940), to whom meteorologists as well as geographers will remain indebted. In our time, an additional classification, in which evaporation and transpiration have been incorporated, has been proposed by Thornthwaite. In the following, we shall give a brief account of Köppen's classification and its application to the world as a whole. Our choice is determined by the circumstance that the observations needed to describe Köppen's classification are more readily available.

Since descriptions of climates must be scaled to practical uses, we may speak of several kinds of climatology. In marine climatology the emphasis is on the factors that affect navigation, such as prevailing winds, storminess, swell and surf, visibility, etc. In bioclimatology, we are concerned with the meteorological factors which affect growth and health. There are numerous other fields which require special treatment of the data. In this chapter, we can deal only with the skeletal aspects of the main climatic regions of the world. For detailed treatments of the subject, the reader is referred to the books listed in the Recommended Reading.

Köppen's Classification. A glance at Fig. 211 conveys the impression that Köppen's classification scheme is a shorthand notation in which the various climatic regions are indicated by combinations of letters. To interpret the chart, we shall first explain the meaning of the symbols and later indicate how the limits between the various regions have been determined.

First, the world is divided into a few main zones, and these are designated by the following letters:

A = tropical rainy climates
B = dry climates
C = temperate rainy climates
D = cold snow-forest climates
E = polar (snow) climates

In this broad outline, the letters serve only as a numbering system, starting at the equator and ending at the poles.

Next, each of the main zones is subdivided according to temperature and rainfall, their seasonal variations, and their effects on natural vegetation. The subdivisions are indicated by adding a letter to the principal symbol. This leads to 11 principal climatic types, as shown in Table 14.

Table 14. *The Eleven Principal Climatic Regions in Köppen's Classification*

Main zones	Symbols	Subdivisions
A. Tropical rainy climates	1. *Af* 2. *Aw*	Tropical rain forest Savanna
B. Dry climates	3. *BS* 4. *BW*	Steppe Desert
C. Temperate rainy climates	5. *Cw* 6. *Cf* 7. *Cs*	Warm, with dry winter Warm, moist in all seasons Warm, with dry summer
D. Cold snow-forest climates	8. *Df* 9. *Dw*	Snow forest, moist in all seasons Snow forest, dry winter
E. Polar (snow) climates	10. *ET* 11. *EF*	Tundra Perpetual snow and ice

The second letter in each of the symbols is the initial of a German word. Thus, f (*feucht*) is used to indicate that the climate is moist (adequate rainfall) in all seasons. The letters w and s are used to indicate that there is a dry season in winter (w) or in summer (s). The annual variation of rainfall is of particular importance in the more or less rainy zones (A, C, and D), and the symbols f, w, and s are normally not used in the zones B and E. The symbol S (in zone B) is used to indicate that the climate is of the steppe type, and W is used to indicate desert (*Wüste*).

Referring again to Fig. 211, it will be seen that the Cf and Df climates span wide latitude belts within which the vegetation varies considerably. Similarly, the deserts and steppes (BW and BS) reach from very warm to quite cool regions. These variations indicate that the classification given in Table 14 is rather coarsely graded, and there is a need for further subdivisions. A finer differentiation is indicated by adding certain letters to the symbols in Table 14. In the first place, the letters a, b, c, and d are used within the zones C and D with the following meanings:

a = with hot summer
b = with warm summer
c = with cool, short summer
d = with very cold winter (in D only)

In the high mountains of the mid-latitudes one finds climates of the polar type, and the letter H is added to distinguish them from those of the polar regions. Thus, ETH signifies a tundra climate due to high elevation. We find large areas of such climates (see Fig. 211) in central Asia and in South America, and there are small islands of these climates in many places elsewhere.

In the arid regions (BW and BS) the following letters, which stand for German words, are added to the basic symbols:

h = hot (*heiss*)
k = cool (*kühl*)
n = frequent fog (*Nebel*)

Thus, BWn indicates a desert with frequent fogs. Such deserts are found along subtropical west coasts.

In detail a number of additional distinctions may be made, but we shall not discuss them here. The boundaries between the various regions in Fig. 211 have been determined over land and extended over the oceans to emphasize continuity. Obviously, the names of the climatic regions are meaningless over the oceans.

The interested reader may wish to journey over the map shown in Fig. 211 and try to interpret the climatic symbols. Interesting journeys would be from the Canal Zone along the east coast of North America to Greenland, and from Liberia along the west coasts of North Africa and Europe to Spitzbergen. On these journeys one would learn to appreciate the difference between east and west coasts through all latitudes. A third interesting journey would be to retrace Marco Polo's route from Italy to Cathay. On this journey one would experience vast differences due to elevation and distance from the oceans.

Boundaries and Characteristics. In the broad belt around the equator the temperature is high throughout the year and plant life depends essentially upon the availability of water. Here we find barren lands where the rainfall is insufficient, and we may speak of a *rainfall control* of the climate. At the other end of the scale, in the polar regions, the temperature is low in all seasons, and here we may speak of a *temperature control*. It is true that precipitation is sparse in extreme latitudes, but this is due mainly to the circumstance that the temperature is so low that the air holds little moisture. Between these extremes we find vast regions where plant life depends on both temperature and rainfall, and their seasonal changes. We are thus led to consider the combinations of rainfall and temperature which determine the borders of the main climatic regions, and, in doing so, we must think of the borders as wide lanes through which the neighboring regions merge.

It is convenient to begin in the arctic and proceed to the equator. In the Southern Hemisphere the conditions are largely the same, except that the tundra and the snow-forest climates do not exist because the midlatitude continents do not extend poleward into suitable latitudes.

Frost and Tundra Climates. An obvious and well-defined limit is the border of the area within which the mean temperature of the warmest month does not rise above the melting point of ice. Thus the 32°F isotherm during the warmest month marks the border between the frost climate (*EF*) and the tundra climate (*ET*).

Another important limit is the border of the area within which the subsoil remains frozen in summer. In the shallow layer which thaws in the warm season, conditions for plant life are severely limited. The vegetation consists mainly of coarse grasses, lings, and mosses. Where the soil is suitable, brilliant saxifrages and other loosely rooted plants brighten the landscape, and in the marshy areas sedges are prominent. Important is a lichen, commonly known as the reindeer moss, which provides much of the food for the herds of reindeer along the arctic coast of Eurasia and the caribou in northern Canada.

On the whole, the tundra is treeless, except along the southern border, where dwarf birches and scruffy conifers begin to appear. The southern limit of the tundra climate is fairly well placed where the mean temperature of the warmest month barely reaches 50°F (10°C). This is the limit between the tundra and the snow-forest climates used by Köppen. Actually, the frozen subsoil in eastern Siberia, northwestern Canada, and Alaska extends farther to the south, but here the thawed layer is so deep and the summer temperature so high that marginal forests are maintained. The original meaning of the word tundra (Lappish) is *barren land*, and does not necessarily imply treelessness or frozen soil. However, in climatology the region of the tundra climate is generally taken to be the treeless belt of lands adjacent to the Arctic Ocean, and the 50°F isotherm of the warmest month is a better limit than the southern border of the permanently frozen subsoil (permafrost).

Snow-forest Climates. These climates occupy vast regions of northern Eurasia and North America. Like the tundra climate, it has no counterpart in the Southern Hemisphere (see Fig. 211). On the poleward side, it merges with the tundra, and the 50°F isotherm during the warmest month is taken as its poleward border. On the southern side and toward the coasts, it is limited by what Köppen calls the *effective snow cover*. Once in a while, snowstorms may occur far to the south, but such snows soon disappear and leave no lasting impression on the vegetation. Köppen found that the southern limit of the effective snow cover is fairly well determined by the zone along which the mean temperature of the coldest month is about −3°C (27°F). On the poleward side of this line, the duration of the snow cover soon increases to 100 days or more, and the winter temperature may be very low (see Fig. 184). On the other hand, the summer temperature may be very high, and it is within the snow-forest climate that we find the largest annual range of temperature (see Fig. 188).

The vegetation typical of this climate requires a long winter rest and a fairly high summer temperature. The annual variation of precipitation is no great concern provided that the amounts are sufficient during the growing season. Most of the regions indicated by *Df* in Fig. 211 have fairly dry winters, but the winter dryness leaves little impression upon the vegetation. Only in eastern Siberia does the winter dryness become critical.

The snow-forest climates (*Df* and *Dw*) are divided into four subtypes, according to the following temperature criteria:

a—The temperature of the warmest month is above 72°F (22°C).

b—The temperature of the warmest month is below 72°F, with at least 4 months above 50°F (10°C).

c—Only 1 to 4 months have a temperature over 50°F, and the coldest month is above −36°F (−38°C).

d—The coldest month is below −36°F.

The mildest variety is found in North America along a narrow belt from northwestern Ohio to the eastern border of Wyoming. Although the western part is fairly dry in winter, precipitation is generally adequate, and this region is designated by *Dfa* in Fig. 211. We find a counterpart in China, but here the winter dryness is pronounced and the spring rains are late. This climate is indicated by *Dwa*. Within these mild varieties of the snow-forest climate, the summer temperatures are high, rainfall is generally adequate in the growing season, and the frost-free period is so long that agriculture with considerable diversification is possible.

The coldest variety is found only in the Lena Basin of northeastern Siberia adjacent to mountain tundra. Here the conditions for agriculture are severely limited. The remainder of the snow-forest climate is divided between the temperature groups *b* and *c*. The former (*Dfb* and *Dwb*) has at least 4 months with temperature above 50°F, and the warmest month is generally in the range from 62 to 72°F. Although the winter temperature may be low, the length of the winter is moderate. Along the northern border, late spring and early fall frosts are hazards to farming, and agriculture is somewhat specialized. Within the *Dfb* and *Dwb* climates as a whole, we find mixed forests, extensive grasslands, and considerable agricultural activity. In particular, this is true of the European *Dfb* region. By and large, the northern border of the *Dfb* climate represents the northern limit of fruit farming.

By far the largest part of the snow-forest climate is the *Dfc* regions. These include the vast belts of forests of hardy conifers. Grasslands are common along the southern border; farming contributes to the livelihood of the population, but the main produce derives from the forests.

Temperate Rainy Climates. These climates occupy the continental parts of the mid-latitude zone, where the maritime influences are strong. On the whole, the *C* regions are under the influence of the belts of high cyclone activity discussed in Chap. 17. On the European side, the *C* region spans a wide latitude belt, and it extends eastward over the Mediterranean and the Near East.

In the eastern part of North America, the continental influences are stronger and the belt is narrower. Along the west coast the *C* region is limited to the coastal strip, for the Rocky Mountains prevent the maritime influences from spreading eastward. In the Southern Hemisphere, the *C* belt is fairly uniform; it touches the south coasts of Australia and Africa, and it spreads northward along the west coast of South America.

On the poleward side, the *C* climate is limited by the presence of snow cover, and here the limit may be drawn along the 27°F (-3°C) isotherm for the coldest month. On the southern, continental side, it merges with the dry climates, and here the limit is drawn where the rainfall drops below certain critical limits. These will be discussed later. Along the east coasts of North America and Asia, the *C* climate merges with the tropical rainy climate.

The major part of the *C* region has adequate rainfall in all seasons, and this is indicated by *Cf*. Along the coast of California, in the Mediterranean, and in the Near East, the cyclone activity is in winter, and here the summers are so dry that vegetation is affected. These regions are indicated by *Cs*. Similar regions are present in the Southern Hemisphere (see Fig. 211).

Next, the *C* region is divided according to temperature, and this is indicated by the letters used in connection with the *D* climate, except that *d* is not used.

The coldest variety is the *Cfc* type, which occupies some narrow coastal strips in high latitudes. Most of these are wind-swept, and vegetation is sparse. The largest area is occupied by the *Cfb* type, which covers much of Europe, the west coast of Canada, and a narrow strip in the Far East. Within this climate the vegetation is highly varied; mixed forests and highly diversified agriculture are typical. A warm variety is the *Cfa* climate in the United States (see Fig. 211). Although snow and frost sometimes occur, the growing season is long. In the eastern part, rain is plentiful in all months, and in the western part, there is a strong tendency for rain to occur in spring and early summer. On the whole, agricultural production is highly diversified and the yield is high. A counterpart to this climate is found in Japan. In much of China and neighboring parts of Asia a similar climate exists, but here the dryness caused by the winter monsoon is so intense that the climate is designated as *Cwa*.

Perhaps the most interesting climate is that of the Mediterranean region, which is characterized by warm and dry summers and wet winters. In the lowlands this qualifies as a *Csa* climate, but a cooler variety (*Csb*) is present at higher elevations, and in the high Alps we find a snow-forest climate. The typical vegetation in the Mediterranean region consists of a large variety of evergreens and flowering bushes and shrubs. Forests are rare, except in the mountains. The produce includes olives, figs, almonds, wines, and citrus fruits. On the whole, there are two blooming seasons. The first comes in fall, when the temperature is still high and rains begin to wet the ground. Midwinter is colorless, for the vegetation is heat-demanding, and the temperature is then generally low. The second blooming season is in spring, when the temperature rises while soil moisture and rainfall are still adequate.

A counterpart to the Mediterranean climate is found along the coast of California, but here the cool coastal waters (see Chap. 16) keep the summer temperature down, and the climate qualifies as a *Csb* type. Similar climates exist in Chile, at the southern tip of Africa, and along the south and east coasts of Australia.

Dry Climates (*BS and BW*). From a study of the relation between rainfall, temperature, and vegetation, Köppen found a very simple relation between the annual mean temperature and the annual rainfall which determines the border between a steppe and the neighboring moist climates. If r is the rainfall in inches and t is the temperature in °F, the border is found where

$$r = 0.44t - 8.5$$

We see that the higher the temperature, the greater is the rainfall that can be tolerated. The reason for this is that if the temperature is high, evaporation is lively and less water is left in the soil to maintain plant life.

In regions where the rainfall is strongly seasonal, other formulas are used. These are

$$r = 0.44t - 3 \quad \text{(rainfall maximum in summer)}$$
$$\approx 0.44t - 14 \quad \text{(rainfall maximum in winter)}$$

The borders shown in Fig. 211 have been drawn according to these formulas.

Furthermore, Köppen found that the border between a steppe (*BS*) and a desert (*BW*) can be placed where the rainfall is one-half the amounts given by the above formulas.

The vegetation typical of the steppes is low-growing and shallow-rooted grasses. Small thorny trees or bushes are found in places, and cacti and similar plants are common in the drier areas. The fertility of the steppe regions varies considerably with the soil. Least fertile are the steppes where evaporation has been so strong that salt has accumulated in the soil. Quite fertile are the steppes of the southern Ukraine and the prairie in North America. Over much of the Great Plains, we find high-grade short grass, and here we have one of the most extensive and finest of the earth's semiarid natural grazing lands. Part of this region has been brought under the plow, but rainfall is sparse and unreliable, and crop failures are frequent. Where additional water can be provided by irrigation, the agricultural yield is high. Along the drier border of the steppe regions, vegetation is sparse and of little value, except where oases or streams supply water.

Tropical Rainy Climates. In most continental regions, the tropical rainy climate (*A*) is limited by steppes (*BS*), and here the border is determined by the foregoing formulas. In the wetter parts of the world, such as the Far East and the Caribbean, there is a gradual transition to the warm variety of the temperate climate (*Cfa*). Here the border is sometimes indistinct, but, on the whole, it can be placed where the temperature of the coldest month does not sink below 64°F (18°C).

The *A* climate is divided into two grades. The wetter is the rain-forest climate (often called the jungle), and the drier is the savanna climate. The distinction between them is the amount of rain that falls in the driest month. If the rainfall in this month is 2.4 in. or more, the rainfall is adequate to maintain a tropical rain forest, and the climate is designated by the symbol *Af*, *f* meaning that the rainfall is adequate in all seasons. This is the climate of the typical equatorial rain forest. Such forests are often exceedingly dense; we find them in the equatorial belts of South America and Africa.

In contrast, the savanna climate has no forests, though the land is fertile and trees may be numerous. The symbol for a savanna climate is *Aw*, *w* meaning that there is a relatively dry period in winter, with rainfall less than 2.4 in. in the driest month. However, this criterion does not suffice to separate the rain forests from the savannas in all cases. If the annual amount of rainfall is very large, the rain forest can tolerate more dryness during the dry season. Climates with rain forests in spite of a dry season are indicated by the symbol *Am*, *m* meaning *mixed*. The limits are shown in Fig. 213. For example, if the rainfall in the driest month is 2.0 in., we have a savanna if the annual rainfall is less than 50 in.; if it is more, we have a rain forest (*Am*). If the rainfall in the driest month exceeds 2.4 in., the annual total does not matter.

The vegetation typical of the savannas varies through the whole range from that of a wettish steppe to the border of a rain forest. Throughout the *Aw* climate, grasses and trees are predominant. In certain regions one finds narrow forest strips along rivers and river beds, surrounded by wide expanses of grass, mostly of the coarse and tall variety. The trees of

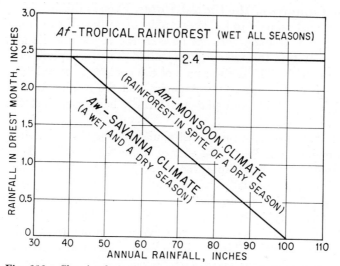

Fig. 213. Showing how the tropical rainy climate is divided into savanna (*Aw*), rain forest without winter dryness (*Af*), and rain forest in spite of winter dryness (*Am*).

the savanna are relatively low and usually of the deciduous type, though all trees may not be leafless during the dry season. However, it is during the drought season that the savanna stands out most clearly from the neighboring rain forest.

The typical rain forest represents the most vigorous and luxuriant vegetation on earth. The number of species is very large, and they are so well intermingled that none predominates. There is no dominant period, and each tree sheds its foliage as new leaves grow; a seasonal rhythm is almost completely absent. Seen from the air, the tropical forest looks like a vast expanse of monotonous brownish green. Walking through it, one finds trees of great height and with few lower branches, but with upper branches and leaves so dense that little light comes through. The typical *jungle* conditions, with an almost impenetrable undergrowth, are found mostly along rivers and coasts, on steep slopes, where sufficient light comes to the forest floor, and in virgin forests which spread over abandoned clearings.

With the rapidly increasing population, the eyes of the world are always on lands suitable for expansion. The arctic wastelands offer much area, but meager opportunities for livelihood. The steppes have much to offer as far as soils are concerned, but the possibilities are limited by the availability of water. The tropical rain forests have abundance of moisture and heat, but here the problem is to control rather than to promote growth.

The Climates of the United States. Even in this brief description, attention must be paid to the geographical features. North America may be linked to a triangle with its base in the arctic and its apex in the subtropics. Within this triangle, the United States occupies a belt broadly from 25 to 50° N. The eastern part of the country is completely open to influences from the arctic, the Atlantic, and the tropics. In the western part, high mountains and plateaus form a barrier against the Pacific weather systems.

In broad outline, we may distinguish among three divisions. In the eastern region, broadly to the east of a line from central Texas to the western part of North Dakota, the country is rather flat and the climatic divisions depend essentially upon latitude. Minor modifications are caused by the Appalachian range, but the elevations here are not sufficiently large to create typical mountain climates. In the west, we have high plateaus and mountains, and here elevation, rather than latitude, is a dominant factor. The third main division is a narrow strip along the Pacific Coast, where the maritime influences provide a strong measure of uniformity and also moderate the differences between summer and winter. Though the United States covers a latitude range of only 25°, all climatic types are represented, except those typical of the polar icecap and the tropical jungle. In comparison with Europe, the United States is rich in climatic contrasts.

If Köppen's classification and criteria are applied to the large amount of data available in the United States, one obtains the picture shown in Fig. 212. The tropical savanna climate (Aw) reaches into Florida, and here the climate is very close to the wetter Af type. The other extreme is found in the high mountains, notably in Colorado, where a tundra climate (ET) is present.

In the complex pattern over the Rocky Mountains, the steppes (BS) are prominent, and they rule supreme over the western plains from the Gulf Coast to beyond the Canadian border. The true desert (BW) is found only in the immediate lee of the high Sierras and in the southwestern interior. On the high ranges, which are more exposed and wetter, the moister types (C and D) form numerous belts and islands.

In various degrees, summer dryness prevails along the entire west coast. The moderating influence of the Pacific provides a fairly uniform temperature, and the main variation in vegetation is due to the northward increase along the coast of the length of the wet season.

The southeast is exceedingly uniform, with a climate of the warm *Cfa* type. The advantage of having an extensive subtropical coast, with warm winters and adequate rainfall, can be seen in everyday life throughout the country, and it is, perhaps, most noticeable in the great variety of fruits and vegetables which are available in all seasons.

The eastern half of the country is open on its northern side to winter invasions of cold air masses, and above a line from Pennsylvania to Kansas these influences are strong and frequent. The length of the frost-free season shrinks rapidly northward, and the climate changes rather suddenly from the highly productive *Cfa* to the rather restrictive *Dfb* type.

The wide range of climatic types offers unusual opportunities for varied agricultural activities and also for studying the relation between climates and crops. A wealth of information on such relationships has been published by the U.S. Weather Bureau and the Department of Agriculture.

The effects of climate are reflected in many ways in human activities and health. In the northern and central tiers of states to the east of the Rocky Mountains, the annual variation in temperature is large and the weather is highly variable, particularly during the cold season. Although cold waves and hot spells may be unpleasant, the climate as a whole is invigorating and tends to stimulate activity. It is within this belt as a whole that we find the highest per capita output, as reflected in statistics on factory production.

Though the general level of health is high, certain illnesses are typical of this region. Diseases of the respiratory organs are prevalent in winter, probably as a result of the raw cold and the sudden changes in humidity and temperature. Diseases of the nervous and circulatory systems are fairly common, and so is rheumatism. During hot spells in summer, diarrheal disorders are not uncommon; sunstroke and heat prostration occur occasionally, and many people are affected by hay fever.

The mountain districts in the Northeast offer relief from the summer heat. Many of these are almost free from hay fever and are generally beneficial for people who suffer from bronchial and similar disorders. The Adirondacks are well known as a health resort, partly because of the success that has been achieved by open-air treatment of tuberculosis. The Atlantic Coast is favored as a resort for persons suffering from nervous debility, anemia, and other troubles. But along the New England coast occasional chilly fogs and damp easterly winds are disadvantageous for patients suffering from lung illnesses, and the climate is too stimulating for patients with very low vitality. On the whole, the level of health and production is high in the *D* climate and in the northern part of the *C* climate (see Fig. 212) to the east of the Rocky Mountains.

Many invalids and convalescents seek relief during the cold season by moving to the warmer *Cfa* climate of the South. Districts with favorable climate are Virginia, North and South Carolina, Georgia, and the Florida peninsula. On the whole, these regions are favorable for persons suffering from nose, throat, and lung diseases, rheumatism, nervous troubles, and overwork. The mountains of Virginia, the Carolinas, and Georgia offer many advantages, for they are sufficiently high to moderate the summer heat and far enough to the south to escape winter colds. In the southern tier of states to the east of the Rockies, the summer heat and moisture are generally oppressive; the climate is not invigorating, and the levels of health and per capita output are noticeably lower than in the northern regions.

The mountain and plateau regions in the West have altitudes sufficiently high to produce typical mountain climates. Much sunshine, low relative humidity, and large diurnal variations in temperature are typical features, and strong cyclonic storms are rare. Colorado has become famous for high-altitude treatments of pulmonary tuberculosis; even in winter much of the time can be spent in the open. The highlands of New Mexico are also favored places for sanatoriums. Over the lowlands and farther to the south, the summers are long and hot, and the dusty winds are unwelcome. The winters in Arizona are exceedingly pleasant.

The climate of the Pacific Coast is mild and generally pleasant throughout the year. The annual variation in rainfall is far more important than that of temperature. On the whole, the climate is stimulating, and the levels of health and per capita output are about as high as in the Northeastern states. Most of the health resorts are in the south. The damp and cool air on the coast (and the night fogs associated with it) does not penetrate far inland, nor does it reach high up in the hills. The hilly back country and the sheltered parts of the coast are excellent resort places for patients with a large variety of troubles. Winter and spring are the favored seasons, for the vegetation is then in its full glory. In many respects the climate resembles that of the French Riviera, and the landscapes are equally attractive.

19

From Weather Lore to Forecasting

It should be mentioned at the outset that the theories and techniques which form the basis of weather forecasting are highly varied. Even a short account would have to include rather involved mathematical derivations, as well as a summary of a vast volume of experience and operational practice. On the whole, weather forecasting represents an application of advanced meteorology, and it cannot be described in a short chapter. All we can do here is to give a bird's-eye view of the field as a whole and bring to the fore the lines along which forecasting has developed.

Weather Lore. Long before science, as we know it, began to take form, men watched the sky, noted the characteristics of the seasons, and tried to arrange their activities as well as they could according to the changing weather. Undoubtedly, many astute observers were able to gain some knowledge of the more typical weather sequences and to formulate rules which were useful on occasions. For example, it is known that the vikings (about A.D. 1000) were able to choose the "right weather" for their spring journey to Iceland, which took several days to accomplish. In the light of modern knowledge, it seems probable that the signs they looked for were the drift of cirrus clouds. Normally, these clouds drift from the west or northwest and are then associated with traveling storms. However, cirrus drifting from south or east (in Norway) is often indicative of persistent anticyclonic conditions with favorable southeasterly winds toward Iceland. Such situations are particularly frequent in spring, and the meteorologists call them *blocking situations*, because the eastward passage of the Atlantic storms is blocked.

In the far more ancient cultures of the Near East, the weather was believed to be controlled by the gods and the stars. In the Babylonian writings, the idea of an astral control was prominent, while the Hebrews expressed strong religious convictions. The thought of extraneous control weakened under the influence of the Greeks and the Romans, and though religious undertones have been strong even up to modern times, there are few reflections of them in the large volume of weather lore and proverbs which we find in the writings of the Western world.

The desire for order and for linking what takes place to some kind of cause has always been stronger than our ability to discover true relationships. While some of our proverbs reflect sound principles, many of them are void of scientific substance. With considerable simplification, our weather lore and proverbs may be divided into four groups.

1. *The Phases of the Moon.* As examples of weather lore related to the phases of the moon, we may quote:

> Snow coming two or three days after new moon will remain on the ground some time, but that falling just after new moon will soon go off.

> A general mist before the sun rises near the fall moon presages fair weather.

> In the decay of the moon
> A cloudy morning bodes a fair afternoon.

> When the moon lies on her back,
> Then the sou'west wind will crack;
> When she rises up the nods,
> Then northeasters dry the sods.

> If the moon on a Saturday be new or full
> There always *was* rain, and there always *wull.*

It suffices to say that analyses of observations have failed to uncover any relation between the weather and the phases of the moon, and there is no theory to suggest that any such relation should exist.

2. *People and Animals.* The belief that the reactions of humans and animals foretell the weather has always been strong. For example:

> A coming storm your shooting corns presage,
> And aches will throb, your hollow tooth will rage.

> Ringing in the ears at night indicates a change of wind.

> Hark, I hear the asses bray;
> We shall have some rain today.

> When black snails on the road you see,
> Then on the morrow rain will be.

> When the locks of the Navahos turn damp in the scalp house, surely it will rain.

While it is certain that people and animals react to the existing weather, there is nothing to suggest that they can indicate what is coming, except to the extent that a coming change is often related to what exists. For example, the reference to the dampness of the locks of the Navahos can readily be explained, for human hair absorbs moisture (see page 25), and rain is often preceded by moist air.

3. *Optical Signs.* Many proverbs relate to the rainbow, and some of these are easy to explain. For example:

> A rainbow in the morning, is the shepherd's warning;
> A rainbow at night is the shepherd's delight.

> Rainbow to the windward, foul fall the day;
> Rainbow to the leeward, damp runs away.

Both of these reflect sound experience from Western Europe and other parts of the belt of prevailing westerly winds. A rainbow is seen in the direction opposite to the sun, so that a morning rainbow is to the west (or windward), and the chances are that rain is approaching. On the other hand, a rainbow in the evening would indicate that the rain has passed.

Other proverbs are related to such rings around the sun or the moon as are called *halos.* For example:

> When the sun is in its house (halo), it will rain soon.

Halos occur as a result of refraction of light through ice crystals, and they are seen when a canopy of cirrostratus (see page 42) covers the sun or the moon. Cirrostratus are often the first sign of an approaching warm front, and, more likely than not, rain or snow will follow. The presence of ice crystals at high levels is favorable for release of precipitation (see page 66).

The customary halo (the small one) has an angular radius of 22°. On occasion, a larger and fainter halo, with a radius of 46°, is seen, but it is seldom complete. The weather proverbs refer to the small halo, and it is remarkable that reference to it as a sign of rain is found in ancient Babylonian writings.

4. *Weather Sequences.* There is a large group of proverbs which refer to sequences of events, and some of these can be supported on scientific grounds. For example:

> Thunder in spring, cold will bring.

> At sunset with a cloud so black,
> A westerly wind you shall not lack.

> If the sky is of a deep, clear blue or a sea-green color near the horizon, rain will follow.

The first proverb reflects the observation that spring thunderstorms are often associated with cold fronts, while the summer thunderstorms occur often within warm air masses.

The second proverb refers to a dark cloud in the western sky; in the belt of westerly winds (where the storms move eastward) this might well indicate an advancing storm.

The meaning of the third proverb is perhaps not so obvious. The color of the sky suggests clean polar air. When such an air mass arrives in mid-latitudes, it is usually unstable, and showery rain is common.

The following had wide circulation in the days of sailing ships:

> Mackerel sky and mare's-tails
> Make tall ships carry low sails.

Here, mare's-tails are tufted and streaky cirrus clouds which drift with the winds aloft. In mid-latitudes, such clouds drifting from the west or northwest are often a sign of an advancing cyclone.

Under the headings of *optical signs* and *weather sequences*, we have quoted only proverbs which can be supported on scientific grounds. In both groups, there are many which have little or no meaning.

Most of the proverbs reflect a desire to produce a cute rhyme or a piece of witty prose rather than sound information. The rule that the best way of sailing from Boston to Cuba is to sail south until the butter melts and then turn east was not meant as practical advice, and the same is true of many of the proverbs. On the whole, the substance of the weather proverbs falls far short of the very considerable weather wisdom possessed by mariners, particularly during the time of sailing ships. By reading the ship's barometer, by watching the changing sky, wind, swell, etc., and by keeping neat logs, these men accumulated much valuable knowledge of the weather sequences and used their knowledge to avoid disasters. Unfortunately, knowledge gained from experience alone cannot readily be recorded and passed on to others.

Some Technological Milestones. Though meteorology is as old as other branches of the physical sciences, weather forecasting, as a public service, is only about 100 years old. It was only after Morse's invention of the telegraph (about 1840) that it became possible to establish a communication system suitable for rapid collection of meteorological reports. The first systematic experiments in weather telegraphy and forecasting began in England and France about 1860, and a decade later, forecasting services had been established in many capitals.

To begin with, the meteorologists were concerned mainly with the forecasting of major storms. Since so many of these came from the oceans, the forecasting services were hampered by lack of observations from the high seas. The next milestone was Marconi's invention of radio (about

1900). As radio became standard equipment in ships, it became possible to collect reports also from the ocean areas. After about 1920, ocean weather reports began to become available in fair numbers, and soon thereafter, aircraft equipped with instruments came into use. Although the observation flights were few and far between, much useful knowledge was gained. In later years, the aviation industry has created new and fascinating problems for the forecasters to solve. On the whole, aviation and forecasting have developed hand in hand.

The next milestone came about 1930. By this time, the Russian meteorologist Moltchanoff had invented his radiosonde, and Bureau (in France) and Väisälä (in Finland) had succeeded in developing instruments which could be attached to small balloons, thus providing soundings of temperature, pressure, and humidity through the troposphere and lower stratosphere. In later years, these instruments have been extended to provide measurements of the winds. At the same time, the balloons have been improved, so that heights of 15 to 20 miles are now reached routinely. On the whole, the impact of the radiosonde in meteorology may be compared to that of X-ray equipment in medicine. This is even more true of radar, which was developed during the Second World War. In later years, radar has been added to the long list of meteorological equipment. It provides an easy means of locating the radiosonde balloons and is much used in tracking thunderstorms, tornadoes, and hurricanes.

A very recent landmark is the electronic computer, pioneered by von Neumann. It has revolutionized the processing of data and made it possible to solve many problems which cannot readily be tackled by customary mathematical techniques.

Finally, instrumented rockets and space vehicles should be mentioned. It is probable that rockets will soon be used to obtain routine soundings through the uppermost layers, while satellites transmit photographs of the ever-changing cloud systems and measure the radiant energy that goes in and out of the atmosphere.

The early weather charts rarely contained more than 30 observations. At the present time there are about 10,000 ordinary land stations scattered over all continents and many islands. In addition, there are about 1,000 stations sending up balloons to measure the conditions of the free atmosphere. About 3,000 commercial ships and about 50 specially equipped weather ships provide observations; several squadrons of aircraft are engaged in meteorological reconnaissance, including the spotting of hurricanes, and commercial aircraft provide much useful information.

In spite of these imposing figures, it should be remembered that the atmosphere fills a vast space, that observations are still sparse from the equatorial belt and the polar regions, and that these are the sources and sinks of the heat that drives the atmospheric machinery. Observations are sparse also from the ocean areas, and these areas supply most of the moisture to the atmosphere.

Observations and Analyses. In a manner of speaking, we may say that the meteorological observations make up the raw material which, through several processings, comes out as the end product which is known as a forecast. This processing of the data is what we call analysis. In many respects analysis can hardly be separated from forecasting, for it is through a series of analyses that we build a bridge from what has happened to what will happen.

In its strict meaning, the word *analysis* means a separation into component parts. In a wider sense, it may be taken to mean an examination of the component parts separately as well as in their relation to the whole, and it is in this meaning that the word will be used here. What is typical of weather analysis is that the component parts and the systems are extraordinarily complex and the observations far from ideal.

The observing stations are widely scattered in space and time, and many aspects of the weather processes may not be evident in the reports. In particular, this is true of the smaller-scale systems, such as thunderstorms, squall lines, tornadoes, etc. Many stations suffer from poor exposures, with the result that it is difficult to distinguish between local and general conditions. While skill in the reading of instruments is readily acquired, it is far more difficult to obtain reliable visual observations (for example, of the various forms of clouds, snow, rain, etc.), particularly during hours of darkness.

After the observations have been recorded, the observer has to make certain reductions and conversions. The observations are then translated into coded messages and transmitted to the receiving centers, where they are decoded and plotted. Through these manipulations, errors occur, and these must be weeded out in the analysis. Furthermore, the replacement of visual observations, first by code numbers and then by such plotting symbols as were shown in Fig. 43, results in loss of detail.

The first aim of the analysis is to eliminate the effects of faulty and unrepresentative observations, to separate local from general effects, to fill in gaps, and to restore lost details. When this has been done, the forecaster has a picture of the weather situation which, as far as possible, approximates what the observations *ideally* ought to have provided.

The second aim of the analysis is to bring to light the component parts of the weather systems at work and to identify these with the underlying physical processes. By component parts are here meant the entities discussed in Chaps. 7 to 15, such as air masses and fronts, cyclones and anticyclones, systems of clouds and precipitation, upper waves, and so on. The analysis is complete when the components have been explained and organized as working systems. Throughout, the analyst strives to establish continuity in time so that the current weather chart follows logically from the foregoing ones. The explanatory and evolutionary aspects of the analysis are important, for they provide the link that enables the forecaster to go from the past to the future. In the field of weather analysis, we find that scientific knowledge and long experience are equally important.

Forecasting. If we consider our activities in daily life, we shall find that we are very often engaged in some kind of forecasting. Most of what we do is done because we predict, rightly or wrongly, that certain results will follow. What guides us in these predictions is past experience, our own as well as that of others. All we know about nature comes from past experience, and this projects itself into forecasts for the future. However, the methods which we use in forecasting are highly varied and depend very much on how precisely our experience can be formulated. What is typical of present-day weather forecasting is that the methods vary over a very wide range. At the one end of the scale, we use mathematical and statistical operations which are so complex that high-capacity electronic computers are needed. At the other end, we have to rely on experience which is so vaguely formulated that we may speak of *wisdom*, rather than *knowledge*. The width of this range is an indication of the complexity of the systems with which the weather forecaster has to deal.

In broad outline we may distinguish between three approaches to the forecasting problem.

1. *Forecasts Based on the Equations of Physics.* In certain fields, our knowledge appears to be so complete that we are able to generalize and formulate certain laws of nature. In most cases, this results in mathematical equations, and these establish some kind of relation between an *existing state* and the *rate at which the state changes*. In principle, these laws make it possible to compute a future state from an existing one. Examples of such laws are Newton's laws of motion (page 147) and the first law of thermodynamics (page 75). If the equations are sufficiently simple, so that we can solve them, the problem of forecasting is very simple. All we have to do is to observe the initial state accurately and compute what will happen thereafter. Examples of such forecasts are numerous. For example, all the astronomical information in the almanac represents such forecasts.

Within the last few years, forecasts of this type have been produced also in meteorology, but here we encounter severe difficulties. Some of these are due to lack of suitable observations, but the main difficulty is due to the fact that the equations that govern the processes in the atmosphere are so complex that they cannot be solved. The remedy here is to simplify the equations by retaining only those terms which are of vital importance. These stripped-down equations are then solved by numerical processes, using electronic computers. Forecasts of this type are generally known as numerical forecasts, and numerical-forecasting centers are now established in several countries.

In any type of forecasting, the large-scale circulation patterns (such as cyclones, anticyclones, upper waves, etc.) are of primary importance. Since the motion is very nearly geostrophic (see page 152), the large-scale motion systems are well represented by the pressure distribution, and the greatest success has been achieved in the forecasting of such large-scale pressure systems. The problem of forecasting clouds and precipitation is far more complex, but here, too, some progress has been made.

2. *Forecasts Based on Statistics.* In certain areas, our knowledge of individual events is incomplete, while past data and experience have provided much information on the behavior of certain groups of events. Our experience can then best be formulated in a statistical manner.

We have already seen that the equations that govern the processes in the atmosphere are so complex that complete solutions are not obtainable. However, the atmosphere goes from one state to another in complete obedience to these equations. In fact, the weather charts that we draw several times a day represent graphical pictures of the solutions which the atmosphere actually provides. The thought then occurs to try to organize these solutions into statistical collectives so that some relationship between the past and the future becomes established. The connecting link between what happened yesterday and today and what will happen tomorrow is obtained from a statistical treatment of a large number of similar cases in the past. There are, of course, practical limits to the amount of data that can be used. So, again, we have to simplify and let the complex processes in the vast space of the atmosphere be represented by a fairly small number of parameters.

At first glance, it appears as if the physical and the statistical approaches to the problem of weather forecasting are totally different. But this is not so. The parameters that enter into any statistical scheme must be chosen so as to represent the physical processes as well as our experience allows. In both schemes, the complex processes of the atmosphere are represented by their bare essentials. The forecasts obtained from the equations of physics give a definite result, which may be more or less satisfactory. Conversely, the forecasts obtained by statistical techniques express a probability. A forecast of the latter type may read: The most probable maximum temperature tomorrow is 84°F, and there is a 90 per cent chance that the actual maximum temperature will be between 80 and 88°F. In all forecasts a certain tolerance must be accepted, and only experience can tell how many parameters are needed to stay within the acceptable tolerance.

Statistics, in one way or another, has always proved useful in weather forecasting, and some very simple schemes have been tried extensively. However, it is only after electronic computers became available that statistical forecasting could be attempted on a large scale.

3. *Forecasts Based on Experience.* The forecaster in meteorology has much in common with the general practitioner in medicine. Both are well grounded in their sciences, but the knowledge gained from books, laboratory exercises, and clinical research does not suffice when it comes to the handling of complex cases. And in both fields, complex cases are frequent.

In the atmosphere, we find large and small systems of different life spans superimposed upon one another, and each cannot be treated separately. While it is easy to describe the ideal cyclone, the ideal thunderstorm, the ideal fog, and so on, the forecaster has to deal with interwoven processes, and there is no way of assigning values to each. Local sources of pollution and moisture enter into the considerations, and the effects of land and sea, mountain ranges, lakes, etc., must be taken into account. From long experience, the forecaster has learned to assess the importance of these influences. Though his knowledge is not so precise that he can express it in standard formulas or statistical regressions, it is, nevertheless, extremely useful, for it adds much to the general features that can be forecast by more rigorous techniques.

In the course of time, much of the knowledge gained through experience becomes crystallized in the research crucibles, and each time a new theory is developed, it becomes easier for the practitioner to accumulate and organize new experience. Through these interactions, the spiral of progress continues.

If we look back over the last 100 years, we find that weather forecasting was based almost exclusively on experience up to about 1920. At this time, the concepts of air masses, fronts, and cyclone development began to make their influence felt and resulted in greatly improved analyses. After 1930, certain formulas were developed which could be used to compute the rate of movement of well-defined pressure systems. At the same time, simple statistical schemes were developed, particularly for forecasting local weather conditions. About 1950, electronic computers came into being, and it is only since then that it has been possible to attempt physical and statistical forecasting on a broad basis.

Explanation of Technical Terms

The meanings given here are those which the words have acquired in meteorological and related uses. The origins are given or indicated by the letters G—Greek, L—Latin, and S—Spanish.

Adiabatic process: a process in which no heat passes into or out of the substance. G. *a* (not, without) + *dia* (through, across) + *batos* (passable). If heat is involved, the process is said (somewhat illogically) to be nonadiabatic. An adiabatic chart is a diagram used in describing adiabatic processes.

Advection: transportation of any property by the horizontal movement of air. L. *ad* (to, toward) + *vehere* (to carry). Thus, advection fog is a fog caused by warm air being carried to a colder place.

Albedo: a measure of the part of the incoming solar radiation which is reflected from the earth and the atmosphere. L. *albus* (white), the thought being that a white surface reflects the radiation.

Anemometer: an instrument for measuring the force or the speed of the wind. G. *anemos* (wind) + *metron* (measure).

Aneroid barometer: a barometer in which the change of pressure is indicated by the motion of the elastic top of a box from which the air has been partly exhausted. In contrast to the mercury barometer, the aneroid contains no liquid. G. *a* (not, without) + *neros* (liquid) + *oid*, from *eidos* (in the form of, like).

Anticyclone: system of winds blowing around a center of high pressure. G. *anti* (opposite, against) + *kuklos* (circle).

Argon: an inert gas; one of the constituents of the atmosphere. G. *argos* (idle).

Atmosphere: the gaseous envelope surrounding any heavenly body, especially the earth. G. *atmos* (vapor or breath) + *sphaira* (sphere, or ball).

Atmospherics: interfering sounds in aerial communication due to electric disturbances in the atmosphere.

Baric: pertaining to pressure (see barometer).

Barograph: a self-recording barometer, usually of the aneroid type. G. *baros* (weight) + *graphos* (writing, writer).

Barometer: an instrument for measuring atmospheric pressure. G. *baros* (weight) + *metron* (measure). The pressure is determined by the weight of the air column. See also aneroid barometer.

Bora: a cold winter wind from a northerly direction blowing over the shores of the northern Adriatic. G. *boreas* (north wind).

Cirrus: a form of high cloud having diverging filaments like locks of hair or wool. L. *cirrus* (curl). *Cirrostratus* (layer or sheet of cirrus), *cirro-cumulus* (cirrus forming a pattern of heap-shaped clouds).

Climate: the weather conditions which, in combination, characterize a region or a place. G. *klima*, from *klino* (slope).

Convection: transportation of heat (or other properties) by movement of air, usually along the vertical. L. *cum* (with, together) + *vehere* (to carry).

Cumulus: heap-shaped cloud or set of rounded masses of cloud heaped on each other. L. *cumulus* (heap). *Cumulus humilis* (humble, small); *cumulus congestus* (heaped to excess); *cumulonimbus* (with rain or other forms of precipitation).

Cyclone: system of winds blowing around a center of low pressure. G. *kuklos* (circle).

Doldrums: region of calms and light baffling winds near the equator. Origin obscure.

Exosphere: the outermost layer of the atmosphere. G. *exo* (outside) + *sphaira* (sphere, or ball).

Front: a sloping boundary between two air masses of different temperature. L. *frons, frontis* (forehead, foremost part of anything). Originally, the term *polar front* was used to indicate the forward side of an advancing mass of polar air.

Geostrophic: pertaining to the deflective force due to the rotation of the earth. G. *geo* (earth) + *strophikos*, from *strephen* (turn). Hence, geostrophic wind, balance, etc.

Hydrometeor: any form of precipitation (rain, snow, hail, etc.). G. *hudor* (water) + *meteoros* (lofty).

Hydrostatic: pertaining to the equilibrium of, and the pressure exerted by, liquids or gases at rest. G. *hudrostates* (hydrostatic balance), from *hudor* (water) + *statikos* (stand).

Hygroscope: an instrument which indicates (by the aid of which one can see) changes of moisture. G. *hugros* (wet) + *skopein* (to see). Hence, *hygroscopic* (having ability to absorb or condense moisture from the air).

Ion: a particle of moving matter carrying an electric charge. G. from *eimi* (go). *Ionosphere* [a layer in the upper atmosphere in which ionization processes are of particular interest (see Chap. 1)].

Iso-: G. *isos* (equal). Thus, *isobar* (line on chart connecting places of equal pressure), isotherm, etc.

Katabatic wind: a drainage wind caused by gravitation of cold air off high ground. G. *kata* (down) + *batos* (passable).

Meniscus: the convex top of mercury (or other liquid) in a glass tube (e.g., barometer). G. *meniskos* (crescent), from *mene* (moon).

Mephitic: noxious, poisoning, etc. L. *mephistis* (noxious emanation). *Mephitic air,* an early name for nitrogen.

Mesosphere: a warm layer above the stratosphere and below the ionosphere. G. *mesos* (middle) + *sphaira* (sphere, or ball).

Meteorology: study of the state and processes of the atmosphere. G. *meteorologia,* from *meteoros* (lofty) + *logos* (discourse).

Nimbus: cloud from which rain falls. L. *nimbus* (cloud). *Fracto-nimbus* (broken nimbus, or scud), *nimbostratus* (layer of nimbus).

Occlusion: a complex front which forms when a cold front overtakes a warm front; also, a cyclone having such a front. L. *oc* (from *ob,* in the way of) + *cludere* (to shut, to close).

Pause: the boundary between two layers, or, more specifically, a change in the thermal structure (e.g., tropopause, stratopause, etc.). L. *pausa,* G. *pausis* (stop or break).

Pluviograph: a self-recording rain gage. L. *pluvia* (rain) + G. *graphos* (writing, writer).

Psychrometer: an instrument for measuring the moisture content of the air by use of a dry- and a wet-bulb thermometer. When water evaporates from the wet bulb, the thermometer cools. G. *psukhros* (cold) + *metron* (measure).

Savanna: a type of warm climate with a wet and dry season (see Chap. 18). S. *zavana.*

Stratosphere: the second lowest of the main layers of the atmosphere (see Chap. 1); it is characterized by more or less isothermal conditions and a highly stable stratification. L. *strato-,* from *sternere* (to strew, to spread out) + G. *sphaira* (sphere, or ball). The term is more meaningful when considered in contrast to troposphere.

Stratus: continuous horizontal layer of cloud. L. from *sternere* (to strew, to spread out). *Stratocumulus* (layer of cumuliform clouds), *alto-stratus* (high stratus), etc.

Tornado: a violent and destructive storm of very small horizontal extent. Probably from S. *tronado* (thunderstorm).

Tropopause: the upper limit of the troposphere. G. *pausis* (stop). See troposphere.

Troposphere: the lowest main layer of the atmosphere (see Chap. 1); it is characterized by a steep lapse rate, a low degree of hydrostatic stability, and, as a result, overturnings occur frequently. G. *tropos,* from *trepein* (to turn) + *sphaira* (sphere, or ball). See stratosphere.

Turbulence: irregular air motion caused by eddies superimposed upon a general flow. L. *turbulentus,* from *turba* (disorder) + suffix *lent* (full of).

Typhoon: violent hurricane in the China seas. Arabic *tufan,* from G. *tuphon* (whirlwind), Chinese *tai fung* (big wind).

Virgae: streaks of precipitation falling from clouds but not reaching the ground. L. *virga* (rod, twig).

Recommended Reading

Books marked by one asterisk require a fair knowledge of mathematics and physics to be read with advantage; those with two asterisks may be said to be more demanding.

Brooks, C. P. E.: "Climate in Everyday Life," Philosophical Library, Inc., New York, 1951.

———: "Climate through the Ages," McGraw-Hill Book Company, Inc., New York, 1949.

Byers, H. R.: "General Meteorology," McGraw-Hill Book Company, Inc., New York, 1944.

——— and R. T. Braham: "The Thunderstorm," U.S. Department of Commerce, Washington, 1949.

Flora, S. D.: "Hailstorms in the United States," University of Oklahoma Press, Norman, Okla., 1956.

Geiger, R.: "The Climate near the Ground," Harvard University Press, Cambridge, Mass., 1950.

Godske, C. L., T. Bergeron, J. Bjerknes, and R. C. Bundgaard: "Dynamic Meteorology and Weather Forecasting," American Meteorological Society and Carnegie Institution of Washington, 1957.**

Goody, R. M.: "The Physics of the Stratosphere," Cambridge University Press, New York, 1954.*

Haurwitz, B.: "Dynamic Meteorology," McGraw-Hill Book Company, Inc., New York, 1941.*

——— and J. M. Austin: "Climatology," McGraw-Hill Book Company, Inc., New York, 1944.

Holmboe, J., G. E. Forsythe, and W. Gustin: "Dynamic Meteorology," John Wiley & Sons, Inc., New York, 1945.**

Humphreys, W. J.: "The Ways of the Weather," Jaques Cattell Press, Lancaster, Pa., 1942.

Inwards, R.: "Weather Lore," Rider and Company, London, 1950.

Johnson, J. C.: "Physical Meteorology," John Wiley & Sons, Inc., New York, 1954.**

Kendrew, W. G.: "The Climates of the Continents," Oxford University Press, London, 1942.

Kimble, G.: "Our American Weather," McGraw-Hill Book Company, Inc., New York, 1956.

Landsberg, H.: "Physical Climatology," Pennsylvania State College, State College, Pa., 1941.

Ludlam, F. H. and R. S. Scorer: *Cloud Study*, John Murray, London, 1957.

Malone, T. F.: "Compendium of Meteorology," American Meteorological Society, Boston, 1951.

Markham, S. F.: "Climate and the Energy of Nations," Oxford University Press, London, 1947.

Middleton, W. E. K.: "Vision through the Atmosphere," University of Toronto Press, Toronto, 1942.**

——— and A. F. Spilhaus: "Meteorological Instruments," University of Toronto Press, Toronto, 1953.*

Namias, J.: "Thirty-day Forecasting," American Meteorological Society, Boston, 1953.

Petterssen, S.: "Weather Analysis and Forecasting," 2d ed., vols. I and II, McGraw-Hill Book Company, Inc., New York, 1956.*

Riehl, H.: "Tropical Meteorology," McGraw-Hill Book Company, Inc., New York, 1954.

——— and Collaborators: "The Jet Stream," American Meteorological Society, Boston, 1954.

Schneider-Carius, K.: "Wetterkunde Wetterforschung," Verlag Karl Alber, Freiburg/München, 1955.

Tannehill, I. R.: "Hurricanes: Their Nature and History," Princeton University Press, Princeton, N.J., 1944.

Thornthwaite, C. W., and Collaborators: "Recent Studies in Bioclimatology," American Meteorological Society, Boston, 1954.

Trewartha, G. T.: "An Introduction to Climate," McGraw-Hill Book Company, Inc., New York, 1954.

Störmer, C.: "The Polar Aurora," Clarendon Press, Oxford, 1956.

Sutton, O. G.: "Micrometeorology," McGraw-Hill Book Company, Inc., New York, 1953.**

Visher, S. S.: "Climatic Atlas of the United States," Harvard University Press, Cambridge, Mass., 1954.

Weber, F. P., and G. Hinsdale: "Climatology and Principles of Climatotherapy," Philadelphia, 1901.

Willet, H. C.: "Descriptive Meteorology," Academic Press, Inc., New York, 1944.

World Meteorological Organization: *International Cloud Atlas*, vols. I and II, Geneva, 1956.

Conversion Factors and Tables

Conversion Factors

1 foot = 0.3048 meter
1 meter = 39.37 inches = 3.2808 feet
1 mile = 1.6093 kilometers
1 kilometer = 3,280.8 feet = 0.62137 mile

1 inch mercury = 25.4 millimeters = 33.8640 millibars
1 millimeter mercury = 0.03937 inch = 1.3332 millibars
1 millibar = 0.02953 inch = 0.75006 millimeter

1 mile per hour = 1.467 feet per second = 0.447 meter per second =
  1.610 kilometers per hour = 0.868 knot
1 meter per second = 3.600 kilometers per hour = 1.940 knots
1 knot = 1.152 miles per hour = 1.854 kilometers per hour = 0.515
  meter per second

Degrees Fahrenheit = $\frac{9}{5}$ degrees centigrade + 32
Degrees centigrade = $\frac{5}{9}$ (degrees Fahrenheit − 32)

TABLE I.—CONVERSION OF INCHES OF MERCURY TO MILLIBARS

In.	.00	.01	.02	.03	.04	.05	.06	.07	.08	.09
0.00	0.00	0.34	0.68	1.02	1.35	1.69	2.03	2.37	2.71	3.05
0.10	3.39	3.73	4.06	4.40	4.74	5.08	5.42	5.76	6.10	6.43
0.20	6.77	7.11	7.45	7.79	8.13	8.47	8.80	9.14	9.48	9.82
0.30	10.16	10.50	10.84	11.18	11.51	11.85	12.19	12.53	12.87	13.21
0.40	13.55	13.88	14.22	14.56	14.90	15.24	15.58	15.92	16.25	16.59
0.50	16.93	17.27	17.61	17.95	18.29	18.63	18.96	19.30	19.64	19.98
0.60	20.32	20.66	21.00	21.33	21.67	22.01	22.35	22.69	23.03	23.37
0.70	23.70	24.04	24.38	24.72	25.06	25.40	25.74	26.08	26.41	26.75
0.80	27.09	27.43	27.77	28.11	28.45	28.78	29.12	29.46	29.80	30.14
0.90	30.48	30.82	31.15	31.49	31.83	32.17	32.51	32.85	33.19	33.53
1.00	33.86	34.20	34.54	34.88	35.22	35.56	35.90	36.23	36.57	36.91
1.10	37.25	37.59	37.93	38.27	38.60	38.94	39.28	39.62	39.96	40.30
1.20	40.64	40.98	41.31	41.65	41.99	42.33	42.67	43.01	43.35	43.68
1.30	44.02	44.36	44.70	45.04	45.38	45.72	46.05	46.39	46.73	47.07
1.40	47.41	47.75	48.09	48.43	48.76	49.10	49.44	49.78	50.12	50.46
1.50	50.80	51.13	51.47	51.81	52.15	52.49	52.83	53.17	53.51	53.84
1.60	54.18	54.52	54.86	55.20	55.54	55.88	56.21	56.55	56.89	57.23
1.70	57.57	57.91	58.25	58.58	58.92	59.26	59.60	59.94	60.28	60.62
1.80	60.96	61.29	61.63	61.97	62.31	62.65	62.99	63.33	63.66	64.00
1.90	64.34	64.68	65.02	65.36	65.70	66.03	66.37	66.71	67.05	67.39
2.00	67.73	68.07	68.41	68.74	69.08	69.42	69.76	70.10	70.44	70.78
2.10	71.11	71.45	71.79	72.13	72.47	72.81	73.15	73.48	73.82	74.16
2.20	74.50	74.84	75.18	75.52	75.86	76.19	76.53	76.87	77.21	77.55
2.30	77.89	78.23	78.56	78.90	79.24	79.58	79.92	80.26	80.60	80.93
2.40	81.27	81.81	81.95	82.29	82.63	82.97	83.31	83.64	83.98	84.32
25.00	846.6	846.9	847.3	847.6	848.0	848.3	848.6	849.0	849.3	849.6
25.10	850.0	850.3	850.7	851.0	851.3	851.7	852.0	852.4	852.7	853.0
25.20	853.4	853.7	854.0	854.4	854.7	855.1	855.4	855.7	856.1	856.4
25.30	856.8	857.1	857.4	857.8	858.1	858.5	858.8	859.1	859.5	859.8
25.40	860.1	860.5	860.8	861.2	861.5	861.8	862.2	862.5	862.9	863.2
25.50	863.5	863.9	864.2	864.5	864.9	865.2	865.6	865.9	866.2	866.6
25.60	866.9	867.3	867.6	867.9	868.3	868.6	868.9	869.3	869.6	870.0
25.70	870.3	870.6	871.0	871.3	871.7	872.0	872.3	872.7	873.0	873.4
25.80	873.7	874.0	874.4	874.7	875.0	875.4	875.7	876.1	876.4	876.7
25.90	877.1	877.4	877.8	878.1	878.4	878.8	879.1	879.4	879.8	880.1

TABLE I.—CONVERSION OF INCHES OF MERCURY TO MILLIBARS—
(*Continued*)

In.	.00	.01	.02	.03	.04	.05	.06	.07	.08	.09
26.00	880.5	880.8	881.1	881.5	881.8	882.2	882.5	882.8	883.2	883.5
26.10	883.8	884.2	884.5	884.9	885.2	885.5	885.9	886.2	886.6	886.9
26.20	887.2	887.6	887.9	888.3	888.6	888.9	889.3	889.6	889.9	890.3
26.30	890.6	891.0	891.3	891.6	892.0	892.3	892.7	893.0	893.3	893.7
26.40	894.0	894.3	894.7	895.0	895.4	895.7	896.0	896.4	896.7	897.1
26.50	897.4	897.7	898.1	898.4	898.7	899.1	899.4	899.8	900.1	900.4
26.60	900.8	901.1	901.5	901.8	902.1	902.5	902.8	903.2	903.5	903.8
26.70	904.2	904.5	904.8	905.2	905.5	905.9	906.2	906.5	906.9	907.2
26.80	907.6	907.9	908.2	908.6	908.9	909.2	909.6	909.9	910.3	910.6
26.90	910.9	911.3	911.6	912.0	912.3	912.6	913.0	913.3	913.6	914.0
27.00	914.3	914.7	915.0	915.3	915.7	916.0	916.4	916.7	917.0	917.4
27.10	917.7	918.1	918.4	918.7	919.1	919.4	919.7	920.1	920.4	920.8
27.20	921.1	921.4	921.8	922.1	922.5	922.8	923.1	923.5	923.8	924.1
27.30	924.5	924.8	925.2	925.5	925.8	926.2	926.5	926.9	927.2	927.5
27.40	927.9	928.2	928.5	928.9	929.2	929.6	929.9	930.2	930.6	930.9
27.50	931.3	931.6	931.9	932.3	932.6	933.0	933.3	933.6	934.0	934.3
27.60	934.6	935.0	935.3	935.7	936.0	936.3	936.7	937.0	937.4	937.7
27.70	938.0	938.4	938.7	939.0	939.4	939.7	940.1	940.4	940.7	941.1
27.80	941.4	941.8	942.1	942.4	942.8	943.1	943.4	943.8	944.1	944.5
27.90	944.8	945.1	945.5	945.8	946.2	946.5	946.8	947.2	947.5	947.9
28.00	948.2	948.5	948.9	949.2	949.5	949.9	950.2	950.6	950.9	951.2
28.10	951.6	951.9	952.3	952.6	952.9	953.3	953.6	953.9	954.3	954.6
28.20	955.0	955.3	955.6	956.0	956.3	956.7	957.0	957.3	957.7	958.0
28.30	958.3	958.7	959.0	959.4	959.7	960.0	960.4	960.7	961.1	961.4
28.40	961.7	962.1	962.4	962.8	963.1	963.4	963.8	964.1	964.4	964.8
28.50	965.1	965.5	965.8	966.1	966.5	966.8	967.2	967.5	967.8	968.2
28.60	968.5	968.8	969.2	969.5	969.9	970.2	970.5	970.9	971.2	971.6
28.70	971.9	972.2	972.6	972.9	973.2	973.6	973.9	974.3	974.6	974.9
28.80	975.3	975.6	976.0	976.3	976.6	977.0	977.3	977.7	978.0	978.3
28.90	978.7	979.0	979.3	979.7	980.0	980.4	980.7	981.0	981.4	981.7
29.00	982.1	982.4	982.7	983.1	983.4	983.7	984.1	984.4	984.8	985.1
29.10	985.4	985.8	986.1	986.5	986.8	987.1	987.5	987.8	988.2	988.5
29.20	988.8	989.2	989.5	989.8	990.2	990.5	990.9	991.2	991.5	991.9
29.30	992.2	992.6	992.9	993.2	993.6	993.9	994.2	994.6	994.9	995.3
29.40	995.6	995.9	996.3	996.6	997.0	997.3	997.6	998.0	998.3	998.6
29.50	999.0	999.3	999.7	1000.0	1000.3	1000.7	1001.0	1001.4	1001.7	1002.0
29.60	1002.4	1002.7	1003.1	1003.4	1003.7	1004.1	1004.4	1004.7	1005.1	1005.4
29.70	1005.8	1006.1	1006.4	1006.8	1007.1	1007.5	1007.8	1008.1	1008.5	1008.8
29.80	1009.1	1009.5	1009.8	1010.2	1010.5	1010.8	1011.2	1011.5	1011.9	1012.2
29.90	1012.5	1012.9	1013.2	1013.5	1013.9	1014.2	1014.6	1014.9	1015.2	1015.6
30.00	1015.9	1016.3	1016.6	1016.9	1017.3	1017.6	1018.0	1018.3	1018.6	1019.0
30.10	1019.3	1019.6	1020.0	1020.3	1020.7	1021.0	1021.3	1021.7	1022.0	1022.4
30.20	1022.7	1023.0	1023.4	1023.7	1024.0	1024.4	1024.7	1025.1	1025.4	1025.7
30.30	1026.1	1026.4	1026.8	1027.1	1027.4	1027.8	1028.1	1028.4	1028.8	1029.1
30.40	1029.5	1029.8	1030.1	1030.5	1030.8	1031.2	1031.5	1031.8	1032.2	1032.5
30.50	1032.9	1033.2	1033.5	1033.9	1034.2	1034.5	1034.9	1035.2	1035.6	1035.9
30.60	1036.2	1036.6	1036.9	1037.3	1037.6	1037.9	1038.3	1038.6	1038.9	1039.3
30.70	1039.6	1040.0	1040.3	1040.6	1041.0	1041.3	1041.7	1042.0	1042.3	1042.7
30.80	1043.0	1043.3	1043.7	1044.0	1044.4	1044.7	1045.0	1045.4	1045.7	1046.1
30.90	1046.4	1046.7	1047.1	1047.4	1047.8	1048.1	1048.4	1048.8	1049.1	1049.5

TABLE II.—CONVERSION FROM CENTIGRADE TO FAHRENHEIT

°C	0	1	2	3	4	5	6	7	8	9
+40	104.0	105.8	107.6	109.4	111.2	113.0	114.8	116.6	118.4	120.2
+30	86.0	87.8	89.6	91.4	93.2	95.0	96.8	98.6	100.4	102.2
+20	68.0	69.8	71.6	73.4	75.2	77.0	78.8	80.6	82.4	84.2
+10	50.0	51.8	53.6	55.4	57.2	59.0	60.8	62.6	64.4	66.2
+ 0	32.0	33.8	35.6	37.4	39.2	41.0	42.8	44.6	46.4	48.2
− 0	32.0	30.2	28.4	26.6	24.8	23.0	21.2	19.4	17.6	15.8
−10	14.0	12.2	10.4	8.6	6.8	5.0	3.2	1.4	− 0.4	− 2.2
−20	− 4.0	− 5.8	− 7.6	− 9.4	−11.2	−13.0	−14.8	−16.6	−18.4	−20.2
−30	−22.0	−23.8	−25.6	−27.4	−29.2	−31.0	−32.8	−34.6	−36.4	−38.2
−40	−40.0	−41.8	−43.6	−45.4	−47.2	−49.0	−50.8	−52.6	−54.4	−56.2

TABLE III.—CONVERSION OF METERS PER SECOND TO KILOMETERS PER HOUR TO MILES PER HOUR TO KNOTS

m/sec	km/hr	mph	Knots
1	3.6	2.2	1.9
2	7.2	4.5	3.9
3	10.8	6.7	5.8
4	14.4	8.9	7.8
5	18.0	11.2	9.7
6	21.6	13.4	11.7
7	25.2	15.7	13.6
8	28.8	17.9	15.6
9	32.4	20.1	17.5
10	36.0	22.4	19.4
11	39.6	24.6	21.4
12	43.2	26.8	23.3
13	46.8	29.1	25.3
14	50.4	31.3	27.2
15	54.0	33.6	29.1
16	57.6	35.8	31.1
17	61.2	38.0	33.0
18	64.8	40.3	35.0
19	68.4	42.5	36.9
20	72.0	44.7	38.9
21	75.6	47.0	40.8
22	79.2	49.2	42.7
23	82.8	51.4	44.7
24	86.4	53.7	46.6
25	90.0	55.9	48.6
26	93.6	58.2	50.5
27	97.2	60.4	52.5
28	100.8	62.6	54.4
29	104.4	64.9	56.3
30	108.0	67.1	58.3
31	111.6	69.3	60.2
32	115.2	71.6	62.2
33	118.8	73.8	64.1
34	122.4	76.1	66.0
35	126.0	78.3	68.0
36	129.6	80.5	69.9
37	133.2	82.8	71.9
38	136.8	85.0	73.8
39	140.4	87.2	75.8
40	144.0	89.5	77.7
41	147.6	91.7	79.6
42	151.2	94.0	81.6
43	154.8	96.2	83.5
44	158.4	98.4	85.5
45	162.0	100.7	87.4
46	165.6	102.9	89.4
47	169.2	105.1	91.3
48	172.8	107.4	93.2
49	176.4	109.6	95.2
50	180.0	111.8	97.1

TABLE IV.—STANDARD ATMOSPHERE EQUIVALENTS

Height, km	Temperature, °C	Pressure, mb	Height, km	Temperature, °C	Pressure, mb
0	15	1,013.25	10.769	−55	234.53
2	2	794.90	12	−55	193.38
4	−11	616.29	14	−55	141.35
6	−24	471.65	16	−55	103.30
8	−37	355.82	18	−55	75.53
10	−50	264.19	20	−55	55.21

Index